MODERN ARBORICULTURE

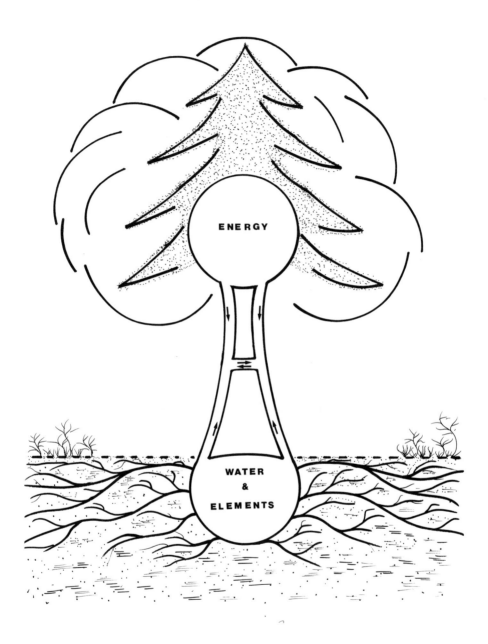

FRONTISPIECE: Trees are like large living pumps. A continuing supply of energy is required to maintain high order in the pumps. High order means health.

MODERN ARBORICULTURE

A SYSTEMS APPROACH TO THE CARE
OF TREES AND THEIR ASSOCIATES

By

ALEX L. SHIGO

Shigo and Trees, Associates
4 Denbow Road
Durham, NH 03824-3105 U.S.A.

DEDICATION

TO

ALL PEOPLE WHO

TOUCH TREES

I thank our daughter, Judy Ruth Smith, for typing the long list of references,
and
I thank my wife Marilyn for all the rest of the typing,
and for many helpful comments.

The Author: Alex L. Shigo was born in Duquesne, Pennsylvania on May 8, 1930. He received his Bachelor of Science degree in Biology from Waynesburg College in 1956 and his Master of Science degree in Plant Pathology from West Virginia University in 1958. In 1960 he received the degree of Doctor of Philosophy in Plant Pathology from West Virginia University. From 1959 to 1985 he was employed by the U.S. Forest Service as chief scientist and Project Leader of a Pioneering Project on Discoloration and Decay in Forest Trees. He has dissected over 15,000 trees with a chainsaw. He has studied trees in many countries. His research yielded 270 publications and he has received many honors and awards. He believes that we must help trees by helping the people who work with trees by providing sound educational programs based on research.

Shigo, Alex L., 1930–
    Modern Arboriculture: a systems approach to the care of trees and their associates / by Alex L. Shigo.
    p.   cm.
    Includes bibliographical references and index.

    ISBN 0-943563-09-7

    1. Arboriculture—Handbooks, manuals, etc.   2. Trees, Care of—Handbooks, manuals, etc.   I. Title.
SB435.S454   1991
635.9'77—dc20   90-28411
                                                            CIP

MODERN ARBORICULTURE

MODERN ABORICULTURE IS ABOUT NEW AND BETTER WAYS TO HELP TREES STAY HEALTHY, SAFE, AND ATTRACTIVE.

MODERN ARBORICULTURE IS ABOUT THE TREE SYSTEM; HOW IT GROWS, HOW IT DEFENDS ITSELF, AND HOW IT EVENTUALLY DIES.

MODERN ARBORICULTURE IS ABOUT USING YOUR MIND AS WELL AS YOUR MUSCLES.

Many old treatments have hurt the tree system. Many adjustments to old practices must be made now.

I hope you will give trees and their associates — tree system — a fair chance. Learn about them. Touch them.

To the professor:

President Abraham Lincoln said, *"Excuse this long letter. I did not have time to write a short one."* Callimachus the Alexandrian poet said, *"A big book is a big evil"* (299). I have kept these points in mind as I wrote this book. I believe a professor should use a book as a guide; not as **THE** course. The book should be as short as possible.

There is room everywhere in this guide for you to teach the course the way you think best.

To the self-study student:

I know you need this information but you have to be out working to pay the bills! Take the book with you and go through a few diagrams each day. Start discussions about the diagrams with your fellow workers; your foreman, supervisor, and customers. As you have take-downs, make a few extra cuts to expose the wood behind old pruning cuts and wounds. Do this for a short time and you will understand more about your trees than any book can teach you.

CORE BOOKS

If you are teaching Modern Arboriculture, or if you are a person who wants to know more about the many tree subjects discussed here, I suggest that you have several general college textbooks at your side: chemistry, biochemistry, physics, botany, and molecular biology. There are many fine books available. I used 60, 106,123,292, and 353. Of course I also suggest that you have my other books, A New Tree Biology, A New Tree Biology Dictionary, and Tree Pruning at your side.

REFERENCES

I have tried to concentrate on scientific papers published in international journals. The papers are those I have read, and they serve as the basis for the concepts in this book.

Some of these papers are highly technical. I hope researchers and professors who are teaching modern arboriculture will study them. The references are there also for the students who will go on to become researchers.

I have tried to minimize citing newsletters, notes, and leaflets. Arborists in all countries have easy access to their regional journals that give details on their trees and their problems and treatments. To summarize the contents of these journals would add little to what is now known.

I have tried to give you a book with some new ideas and concepts. I ask the question; if the old information was or is so good, why do we have trees that received these treatments in such a poor state? Why do many trees planted in cities in the United States live for only 7 to 10 years? Apparently, the correct information is not getting out to the people who need it. Survival of any system depends on adjustments and changes. I believe we need some adjustments and changes in the way information is presented.

REFERENCES CODES

To make reading easier, I have included few references in the text for the diagrams. More references are listed at the end of most diagrams. I have listed many references at the end of major subjects.

References to research I published alone or with colleagues are preceded by a "S", A New Tree Biology by an "A", A New Tree Biology Dictionary by a "B", and Tree Pruning by an "H". Please check "B" for details on many terms used in this book. "A" and "H" contain many photographs that can be compared with the diagrams in this book. All other references have numbers only. All references are listed in the back of the book.

SCOPE—TREES

Black walnut, sugar maple, cherry, apple. Are they: Shade trees? Ornamental trees? Food trees? Timber trees? Amenity trees? They are trees!

While rereading many of the papers for references, it was clear to me that people who work with and write about forest trees rarely cite the work of people who work with fruit trees, and vice versa. Every group has selected its type of tree, and all the other "types of trees" do not fit with theirs.

Arboriculture means the care of trees.

Forestry, urban forestry, fruit production and even bonsai, all belong *under* the heading of arboriculture. They all deal with trees. The care of trees.

The scope of this book deals with trees and their associates throughout the world. The information is applicable to the arborist, landscape architect, nursery person, forester, urban forester, fruit grower, bonsai enthusiast, and all other people who care about trees.

BACKGROUND

Tree workers have told me they need better information to help them help trees.

The best way to learn about trees is to dissect them and to study them. This is what we do in workshops. In the appendix I give the outline we used in workshops.

The next best way to learn about trees is to use clear, simple, diagrams. Diagrams send messages in all languages. Diagrams do not focus on any one species.

This book is based on questions, concerns, and discussions that have come from the many workshops and seminars I have had from October 1985 to January 1991. In this book I try to answer your questions and concerns. Still, I do not have all the answers. I repeat; I believe that once you begin to understand how the tree system works, you will have answers that are much better than I can give you.

MY AIM

To give you what you need in the way you want it; clear, simple, brief, and practical.

MY GUIDES

Here are some famous quotations that have helped to guide me as I wrote this book.

Einstein said, *"All explanations should be made as simple as possible, but no simpler."* Also, he said, *"If it appears very complex, it is probably wrong!"*

Kant said, *"I do not fear being refuted as much as I fear being misunderstood."*

Galileo said, *"My critics will not look through my telescope."*

Tolstoy said, *"I know that most men, including those at ease with problems of the greatest complexity, can seldom accept even the simplest and most obvious truth if it be such as would obligate them to admit the falsity of conclusions which they have delighted in explaining to colleagues, which they have proudly taught to others, and which they have woven, thread by thread, into the fabric of their lives."*

ON CHAINSAWS, MICROSCOPES, MAN AND THE MEDIA

Trees are the biggest organisms on earth. Yet minute microorganisms are major causes for their breakdown (12,16,98,171,285,293). Man and his actions also are major causes of tree problems. To study big trees, small microbes, and misdoings by man, special tools and procedures are needed (5:12). For over 30 years I used large chainsaws to dissect thousands of trees (A,H). Many nutrient media were used to grow hundreds of thousands of microbes in the laboratory. Microscopes were used to view the inner beauty of trees and the wonderful and fascinating micro world.

To reach man I used beautiful paintings by David Carroll, and wood samples that had a beautiful finish. It has not been easy to "sell" concepts of decay, disease, and death. I did not do it alone. I was surrounded by many hard-working assistants and colleagues. Many people gave freely of their time, muscles, and ideas. I listened carefully to the people who worked with trees. **I have always had the highest respect for tree workers.** They have taught me so much about trees. Now it is my turn to give it back.

In this book I discuss subjects I have touched and studied (A,B,H). I have read the literature and listened when others discussed their research, experiences, and ideas. We never go this way alone. I have tried to incorporate all of these ingredients in this book. Still, I cannot give you all the answers, or even most of them. I keep reaching for 100%. However, if I can give you 90%, or in some cases, only 70%, that is the best I can do. People who want and expect 100% from natural systems do not understand how they work. Nature also "reaches" for 100%, but seldom does it operate beyond the limits of 80 + or – 10%.

If I can help you with 70%, or maybe 90%, I know you will fill in the rest to serve your specific needs. That is the way this educational system should work. It is with this spirit and hope that I write this book.

ACKNOWLEDGEMENTS

The concepts presented in this book came primarily from the 27 3½-day workshops given since 1986. Many people spent long days preparing for the workshops. They made it possible for the participants and me to learn about their trees; from the root tips to the buds. The dissections and discussions set the stage for this book.

I thank them, and I am sure the trees would thank them. Here are the workshops and their sponsors.

1. Portsmouth, New Hampshire, October 1986, 2 workshops sponsored by the National Arborist Association; Robert Felix and Peter Gerstenberger, with help from Mary Reynolds. A third workshop was held in October 1987, also in Portsmouth.

2. Walla Walla, Washington, Whitman College, Timothy Werner.

3. Boone, North Carolina, Appalachian State University, Jim Rice with help from Cindy Rice. Five workshops so far, and 2 per year scheduled for as long as I can do it.

4. Baltimore, Maryland, A and A Tree Experts, Ronald Orem.

5. Orlando, Florida, Disney World, Sponsored by the American Society of Consulting Arborists; Jack Siebenthaler and Charles Bingaman, with lots of help from Way Hoyt and Katy Moss Warner.

6. Portland, Oregon, Rock Creek Community College, sponsored by the National Arborist Association members in Oregon; Tom Shotzbarger, William Owen, and Richard Proudfoot; two workshops.

7. Duluth, Minnesota, Dept. of Natural Resources, Jana Campbell.

8. Tomahawk, Wisconsin, International Society of Arboriculture, Wisconsin Chapter. Robert Skiera and Kenneth Ottman.

9. Auckland, New Zealand, Auckland University, Treescape, Ltd., Edward and Helen Chignell, with lots of help from James Perks.

10. Lancaster, England, Lancashire College. Dr. Dealga O'Callaghan and Jeremy Barrell, sponsored by the Arboricultural Association with help from Ms. Jean Berry; two workshops.

11. Badenweiler, West Germany, Badenweiler Park, David MacIntyre and Ulrich Pfefferer with help from the Park Director Herrn Dipl. Ing. Woelke, sponsored by the South Germany Association for Natural Tree Care. (Süddeutscher Baumpfleger)

12. Minneapolis, Minnesota, Rainbow Tree Care, Thomas Prosser.

13. Tempe, Arizona, University of Arizona, Artistic Arborists, Inc., Tim Johnson and Karen Waller.

14. Varese, Italy, Villa Ponti, Fito Consult, Dr. Daniele Zanzi.

15. Olds, Alberta, Canada, Olds College, Ms. Anita Schill and Ms. Geraldine Byrne.

16. Dublin, Ireland, University College Dublin, The Tree Council of Ireland, John McCullen, Noel O'Shea, and Dr. David Robinson.

17. Vught, The Netherlands, Pius Floris Boomverzorging, Castle Maurick, and, lots of help from Marleen Floris.

18. Winterthur, Switzerland, Reto Rutishauser, with help from Klaus Woodtli.

19. Omaha, Nebraska, Nebraska Arborists Association, Philip Pierce, with help from Tom Wiems and David Mooter.

REVIEWERS

I thank the many reviewers who took a great amount of time to read the manuscript, and to make corrections, and to offer valuable suggestions for improvements:

Dr. Richard Churchill, Horticulturist, Teacher, and Chairman, Plant and Soils Department, Southern Maine Technical College, South Portland, Maine.

Dr. Kim D. Coder, Plant Pathologist and Extension Specialist in Arboriculture, Extension Forest Resources, University of Georgia, Athens, Georgia.

Kenneth R. Dudzik, Forester, Northeastern Forest Experiment Station, Durham, New Hampshire.

H. Sharon Ossenbruggen, Technology Transfer Specialist, Northeastern Forest Experiment Station, Durham, New Hampshire.

Dr. Charles W. Owens, Physical Chemist, Professor, and Vice President for Academic Affairs, Radford University, Radford, Virginia.

Mary Reynolds, Urban Forester, New Hampshire Division of Forests and Lands, Portsmouth, New Hampshire.

Thomas Shotzbarger, Arborist and Teacher of Arboriculture, McFarland Landscape Services, Philadelphia, Pennsylvania.

Dr. Desmond E. Smith, Technical Director, and Tree Anatomist, Acrowood, Inc., Everett, Washington.

Dr. Kevin Smith, Plant Physiologist, Northeastern Forest Experiment Station, Durham, New Hampshire.

Klaus Vollbrecht, Landscape Architect, Swedish Agricultural College, Alnarp, Sweden.

Dr. Daniele Zanzi, Plant Pathologist and President of Fito Consult, Varese, Italy.

Contents

MODERN ARBORICULTURE MEANS:

1. The right tree in the right place.
2. Building designs that give trees space to grow.
3. Beautiful trees growing in clusters.
4. Healthy trees growing below grade.
5. Young trees with space to grow and with proper early pruning.
6. The target is removed, not the tree.
7. No sprouts from a correct pruning cut.
8. Early training regulates size and shape of trees.
9. The sidewalk is cut, not the tree or its roots.
10. Proper care for old trees, and respect for their dignity.
11. Planting trees at the proper depth.
12. People touching trees and learning how they work, before they work on them.
13. Treatments that destroy defense systems must be stopped.
14. Treatments that cause serious internal injuries must be stopped.
15. Treatments that start other problems must be stopped.
16. Treatments that injure and kill transplanted trees must be stopped.

GERMANY
1. The right tree in the right place.

NEW ZEALAND
2. Building designs that give trees space to grow.

ARIZONA
3. Beautiful trees growing in clusters.

FLORIDA
4. Healthy trees growing below grade.

NEW YORK
5. Young trees with space to grow and with proper early pruning.

SPAIN
6. The target is removed, not the tree.

NORTH CAROLINA
7. No sprouts from a correct pruning cut.

CALIFORNIA
8. Early training regulates size and shape of trees.

HAWAII

9. The sidewalk is cut, not the tree or its roots.

DENMARK
10. Proper care for old trees, and respect for their dignity.

AUSTRALIA
11. Planting trees at the proper depth.

ITALY

12. People touching trees and learning how they work, before they work on them.

(Photo by Paulo Contini, courtesy of Dr. Daniele Zanzi, Fito-Consult)

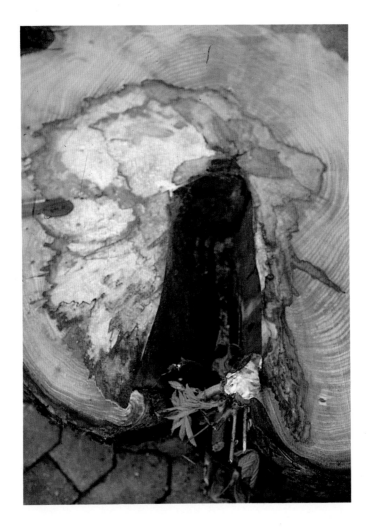

13. Treatments that destroy defense systems must be stopped.

14. Treatments that cause serious internal injuries must be stopped. (A single injection treatment with a growth regulator.)

14

15. Treatments that start other problems must be stopped. (The sun was important, but it acted after the tissues were weakened by the flush cut. In cold areas frost gets the blame for cracks that are started by flush cuts.)

16. Treatments that injure and kill transplanted trees must be
stopped. (The wrapper hid serious basal wounds. Note the
high green grass, indicating over-fertilization at planting
time.)

A BRIEF HISTORY OF TREES
AND THEIR TREATMENTS

Man and trees always have been close associates (61,62,63,80,143,214,400). Trees, *were* here first. The association was not always beneficial for trees (400). Man has had a taking association with trees. The trees were there to be taken, stripped of their fruit, burned for cropland, and cut for buildings and for firewood.

We often dwell on the old parks and gardens, and some few city sites where trees did get some respect. But, sad to say, these situations were in the minority. However, arboriculture did emerge from these attempts to grow trees (80).

Many of the tree care practices that were developed centuries ago have changed little over the years (61,62,63,118,130,144,282,336). Trees were wanted for their amenity values. The tree had to be kept in its place, and it had to constantly yield to the powers of man.

As I go around the world I ask people why they have treated their trees the way they have. The answers are as many as the people who are asked. Through all of the answers, some similar threads appear. Man has always respected the majesty of trees. At the same time, man believed that the world centered about man (299, 354). Everything revolved around the earth that revolved around man. Man had to show his power. The trees had to yield to this power. Trees were topped and mutilated for the benefits of man.

Practices are deep-rooted in attitudes. Attitudes grow within people as survival factors. Attitudes are closely attached to rationalization. Something is done because it assures survival. When what is done is not the most pleasing to see, rationalization steps in. In time the attitude becomes fixed. Here is an example. Early civilizations developed in close groups. Buildings were close together, streets were narrow, and garden spaces had to have sun. People wanted shade for animals, wood for fires, and sprouts for weaving baskets. The answer was simple; cut the top off a tree and you get everything you want!

When I stare into some of the paintings of Vincent van Gogh, I see the same feelings within the faces of his people as I see in the trees painted in the background. The mutilated willows did give shade, they provided firewood, and they yielded many supple sprouts for baskets. After growing up with such trees near them, they felt that is the way trees should look. When they emigrated to another country, they treated the trees the same way as they did in their old home.

Many people want to treat trees as people. They want to dress the wounds, cut out rot until only clear wood shows and fill cavities with concrete to stop rot (61, 62,63). Trying to change these treatments has not been easy, even with all kinds of scientific information that shows that the treatments do more harm than good (A,B,H).

Beginning to emerge from this was commercial arboriculture. Most of the treatments came from those done by the gardeners for the kings (80) and ultra-rich, and from the farmers who planted and pruned trees for fruit (355,390). We must not forget the impact of the forester who wanted to grow trees fast and straight for timber (214). However, timber was the second priority for many of the foresters. They were more interested in managing forests for wildlife. The Kings' gardens and forests were for hunting.

As the knowledge of these practices began to spread beyond the salaried gardeners and foresters and the self-employed farmers, the commercial arborist began to emerge. This was good, because the arborist could extend services to the middle class. Cavity filling for the rich was the beginning of arboriculture (61,62,63). Slowly the services were extended to others. The practices changed very little.

Old arboriculture was based on three treatments: cutting branches flush to the stem, painting wounds, and filling cavities. Spraying came later. Now spraying has become a difficult treatment because of many regulations. Flush cutting is beginning to fade (96,192,197,198,336,373,402,403), as is the use of wound dressings. In the U.S.A., cavity filling is no longer a major treatment. In Europe and some other countries the major treatments are being adjusted (22,23,336,373), but it will take some time before they are erased.

At the turn of the century many world events had a strong impact on tree care practices. In the U.S.A. the first telegraph poles were set at the end of the 19th century. Line clearance became a new job for the tree workers. It has developed, in the U.S.A., as one of the major jobs for tree workers. Many adjustments are being made in these practices.

After the first world war jobs were difficult to find. Some people, tough in body, mind and spirit, set out to start tree care as a commercial business in the U.S.A. They had their small trucks and saws, and traveled from town to town doing tree work.

After the second world war new tools began to appear. The heavy chainsaws available in the late 1930's became available in the 1940's at a reasonable weight. Spraying became king. Many small companies became big companies on the basis of spraying. Then came the chipper and the aerial lift. These tools set the stage for a new age in arboriculture. The middle class was increasing. More people could afford tree care. Husbands and wives were working. To have a lawn with trees became important. City decay was being replaced with malls and parks. People wanted green (21,231,235)!

In October 1957 Sputnik was placed in orbit. This was the beginning of the science "revolution". The science race was on. The physicists had the stage with atomic bombs and atomic power (123). The chemists previously had the stage with DDT, and the many agricultural chemicals able to kill anything or to make anything grow (106). The clarification of the DNA molecule started molecular biology (60), and then the focus was on man and the environment (396). The events came rapidly.

The stage is now set for the biologist. People are concerned for this planet. Sputnik has landed — crashed? Engineers and computer people are common. People want to help the earth. The spotlight is now on us. This is the first time in our history that the world has a common concern; our environment.

The responsibilites are awesome. After centuries of mistreatments, it is time to stand up and aim for something better.

HOW MANY TEETH IN A HORSE'S OR BEAR'S MOUTH?

In a dank, candlelit room, with large wet stones for walls, the great society of elitists were discussing the question of how many teeth there are in a horse's mouth.

A small child wandered to the dimly lit doorway, and listened. Then ran. Found a horse. Opened its mouth and counted its teeth. Then ran back to the doorway. Burst into the room and shouted the answer.

He was whipped and thrown out of the room into the dark street, because the elitists really did not want the answer, they wanted the long discussion.

If helping trees depends on counting teeth in a horse's or bear's mouth, then let's get out there and start counting teeth! We do not have time for long discussions.

(Story from old records in philosophy)

This black bear made of wood was coated with wound dressing every year. It was on the campus of the University of Maine in Orono. The right paw was so decayed that it fell off. The author is using a drill to test for decay in the head. The Shigometer helped to detect decay throughout the bear. It was dismantled for the sake of safety. The wound dressing provided perfect conditions for rot to develop rapidly. (Photo courtesy of Dr. Richard Campana, and the University of Maine.)

21

INTRODUCTION

Think of the diagrams as maps for buried treasures. The maps will never give you the treasures. But the maps can lead you to the treasures. You must go outside. You must do some digging. You must touch trees.

The first series of diagrams set the stage. Then the parts and processes of the tree system are discussed. From there we go to a systems approach for treatments based on energy flow to maintain high order.

It is extremely important to know that most of the concepts and treatments given in this book have come to me from tree people who are using them effectively now in their businesses.

The parts and processes of the tree system do not come in neat packages. Every part and process overlaps with other parts and processes. Because this is so, I could not design this book in a way that put every subject in a neat package or chapter. There are many repeats and overlaps. Often the subject is introduced, but details on the subject are not given until later when the subject overlaps or relates to another subject. In the end, this is the way natural systems work. It is not always a smooth ride. If we are going to work with natural systems, we must do it nature's way.

Now we are ready to start our journey into the tree.

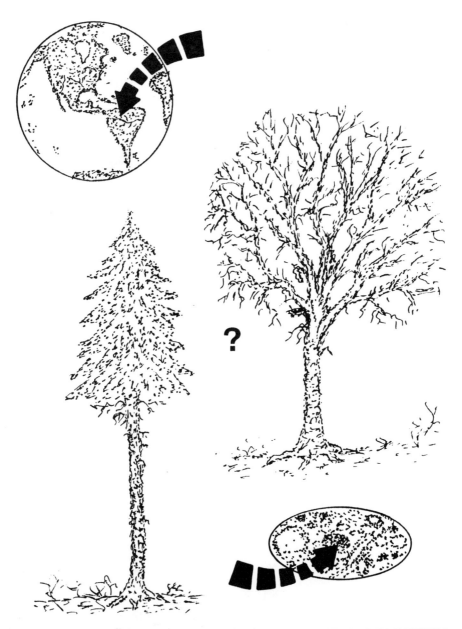

OUR ENVIRONMENT IS A WORLDWIDE CONCERN

1. TREE BIOLOGY IN A WORLD OF EXTREMES

World environmental problems (396) and genetic engineering (60) are focal points for biology today (292). Tree biology is left out (A). Modern Arboriculture focuses on the tree as a major part of our environmental systems.

This is the first time in the history of man that there is a common worldwide concern: our environment (149,155).

23

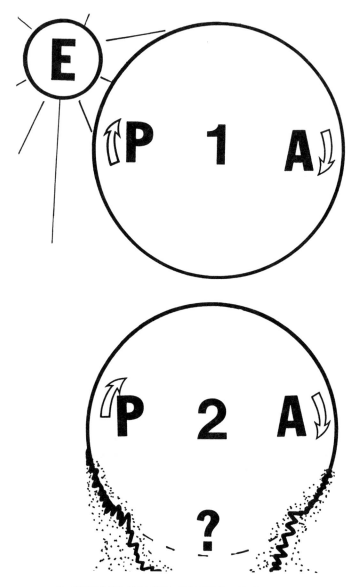

2. CIRCLES OF LIFE, DEATH, AND REBIRTH

Natural systems have developed as processes of buildup and breakdown [1] by plants (P) and animals [A]. Man's actions have disrupted many of these processes [2](396). [E is energy.]

Our responsibility is to mend the torn pieces of our natural system and to develop new and better practices that will assure its survival.

Adjustments must come to many practices. But first, adjustment must come to the attitudes of people. As tree professionals, this means that we must find new and better ways to communicate with lay people about our natural systems (S: 81,89,102,128).

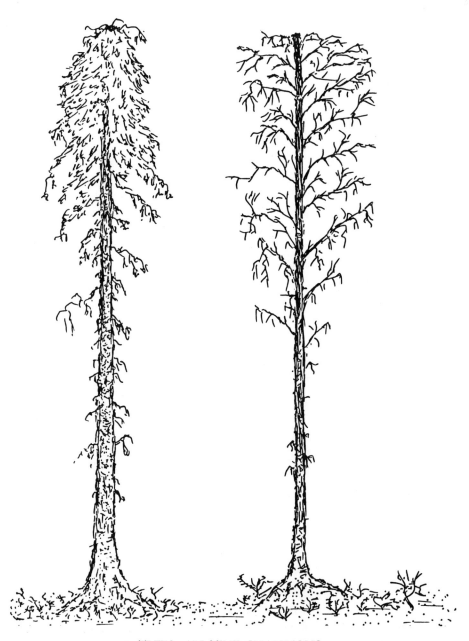

3. TREES, ALL-TIME CHAMPIONS

Trees are and always have been the largest organisms on earth. Trees in cities and forests are dying from injuries and abuses caused by man and machines. Yes, trees are tough, but only as long as they have a fair chance for survival. It is our job to see that they get that fair chance.

General tree care: 21,38,57,92,94,162,192,227,235,240,247,250,311,313,314,334, 403.

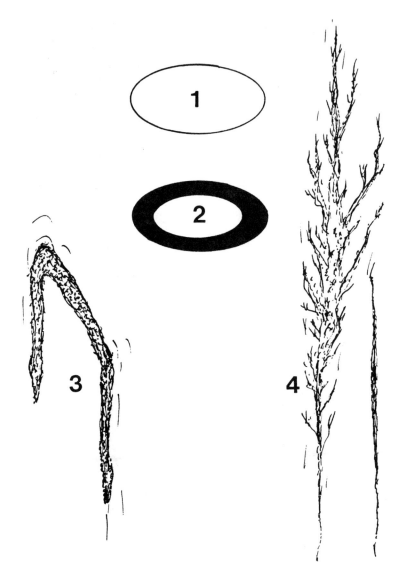

4. TREES AND PEOPLE ARE SIMILAR IN MANY WAYS,
YET DIFFERENT IN OTHER WAYS

Animal cells have thin boundaries [1]. Tree wood cells have thick, tough boundaries or walls [2]. Animal tissue will not support itself [3]. Animals require skin and bones to keep the cells in place. Every splinter of wood [4] is self-supporting (139,146). Cell walls of wood are made of cellulose, lignin, and hemicelluloses (73,159).

Thin boundaries on animal cells allow them to move. Animals move away from agents and situations that threaten their survival. Trees cannot move. Trees grow where they find themselves, adapt, or die. Trees planted incorrectly in the wrong places are committed to an early death at the time of planting (156,317).

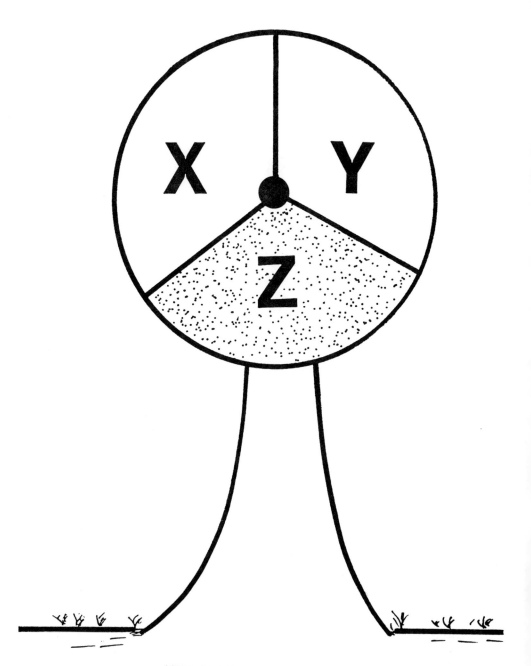

5. TREE PEOPLE AND PART THREE

Tree people touch trees. Tree touchers have an innate understanding about natural systems [X](155). Tree people understand the basics of business [Y]. I am trying to add the third part to complete the circle [Z]. Once tree people begin to understand how the tree system works, they will be the ones who develop the best practices for working on the trees (A,B,H).

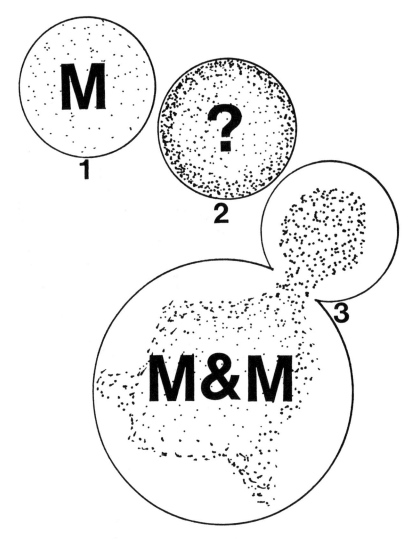

6. TIME FOR THE M & M TREE PERSON

Tree people are tough [1]. But, tough is not enough. We must add *mind* to the *muscles*. We must become M & M people. As the M & M concept takes hold [2], a larger circle will be needed in which to operate [3]. That larger circle is *Modern Arboriculture*.

Arboriculture more than any other profession demands an equal amount of physical and mental work. This is a unique feature of arboriculture. Playing a musical instrument comes close to arboriculture in this way because playing an instrument demands a keen union of mind and muscle. And, again, like playing a musical instrument, arboriculture cannot be learned from a book. You must touch the instrument. You must touch the tree. Both professions take a great amount of study. People who play a musical instrument without ever having professional lessons seldom reach the positions gained by those who do. So it is with arboriculture. Bad habits — music, arboriculture — are very difficult to change, but not impossible.

28

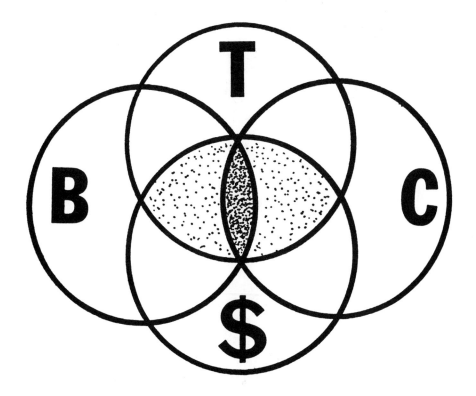

7. TREES AND YOUR BODY, CAR, AND BUSINESS

Trees [T] are different from your body [B], car [C], and business [$] in many ways. However, there are basic threads that go through all four. They all require some type of fuel for survival. There are other threads that we will discuss later. Progress starts when we can discriminate between similarities and differences among many items in a group (146,188,299,354).

Most people know much more about their bodies, cars or businesses than they know about trees. We must transfer what you already know about your body, car, and business to trees.

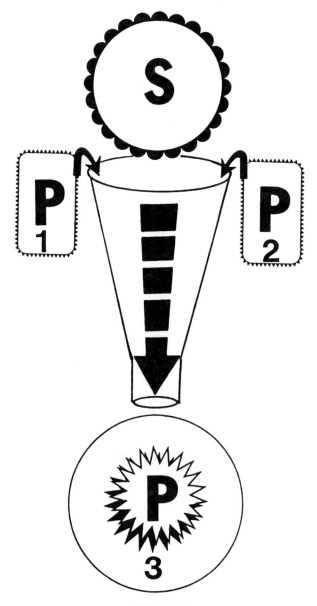

8. THE SYSTEM

A system [S] is an orderly collection or parts [P 1] and processes [P 2] that produce a predetermined product or service [3]. The tree and its associates are a living
system. Survival of any living system depends on 8 factors (see page 209). One
of the factors is a constant supply of fuel to maintain order. When energy becomes
limiting, a system goes from order to disorder (123). No system can increase in
mass beyond the energy available to power it (123). Many of the concepts of physics
and chemistry (106,123,292,353) fit the tree system, your car system, your body
system, and your business system.

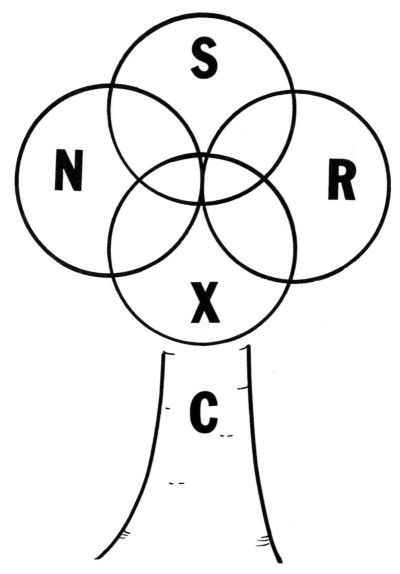

9. MAINTAINING ORDER IN A SYSTEM

The more orderly a system, the more stable or healthy it is and the more energy required to maintain it. Health is the ability to resist strain. Strain is a nonreversible condition resulting from excess stress (123). Stress is a reversible condition. The system begins to operate *near* the limits for which it was designed. The system starts to wobble. When wobble continues, a part or even the whole system breaks. Stress goes to strain. There are 5 ways to resist stress and strain in a living system: 1. Sanitation [S]; 2. Proper nutrition [N]; 3. Rest [R]; 4. Motion or Exercise [X]; and 5. Regular checkups [C].

31

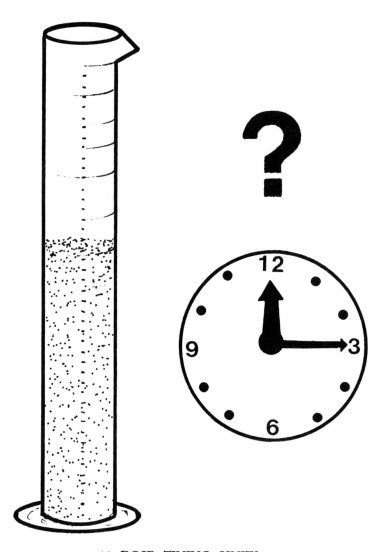

10. DOSE, TIMING, LIMITS

A professional knows...dose (how much), timing (when), and the limits of the system. Not an easy task.

We can help the system or obtain many benefits from the system if we understand dose, timing, and the limits of the system.

Dose means not only what we may add, but what we may take from the system. Timing means not only when we should treat but when we should harvest.

Limits mean that point in dose and timing where additional actions will cause the system to go from order to disorder.

Limits mean we can add or take only so much, and we can repeat these actions only so often. When we exceed the limits of the system, it will not return to its original state.

32

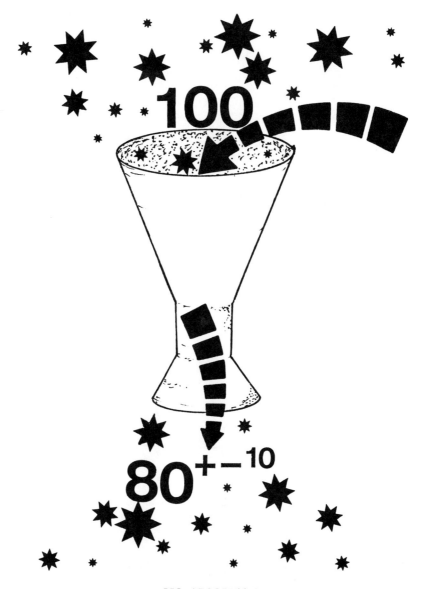

11. NO ABSOLUTES

There is no machine, including our life "machine" that will yield as many units out as are put in. Energy must constantly come into a system to maintain order (123). The efficiency of the system is all important. Reach for 100% every time; but when you can get 90%, I say grab it and run with it! This is the tactic of natural systems for survival. Many enter the race, but few finish. Knowing the limits of any system is very important. Know where the curve bends. Know where added energy buys very little. Know when to cull a tree. To cull is one of the best treatments we can use for sick or defective young trees. It is more economically sound to cull and start over again, than to keep a sick tree that has had its dignity destroyed.

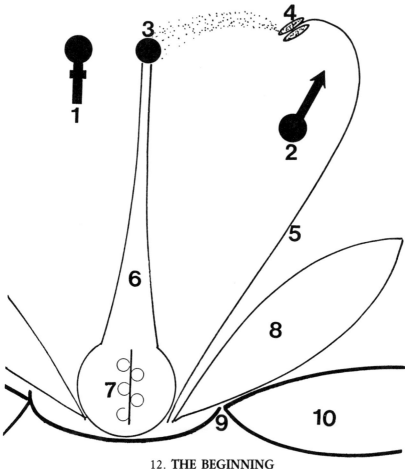

12. THE BEGINNING

Tree life starts with a seed. The female [1] and male [2] parts come together to start new life. The receptive stigma [3] receives the pollen from the anther [4] at the end of the filament [5]. The pollen grows down the pistil [6], meets the female eggs and a tree seed begins [7]. A seed is a ripened ovule [7]. A fruit is a ripened ovary and its attached parts. Most tree flowers have petals [8], and bracts [10]. The ovary sits in a receptacle [9]. Some trees have only male flowers, while others have only female flowers. The male and female flowers may be on the same tree—oak, poplar, pine—or on separate trees—ash, holly, ginkgo. Many trees have perfect flowers—male and female parts in the same flower—elms (292), magnolia, California laurel, citrus, and most species in the rose family.

Chemicals such as NAA—naphthalene acetic acid—have been used to prevent flowering (49). The fruit on some trees—olives, ginkgo—cause problems on streets. Ginkgo fruit has a foul odor. Deblossoming chemicals or chemicals that cause early fruit abscission could be used to conserve energy in stressed plants. American elm produces a seed crop every year. The seeds mature before the leaves form. Prevention of reproduction could conserve energy in an infected tree.

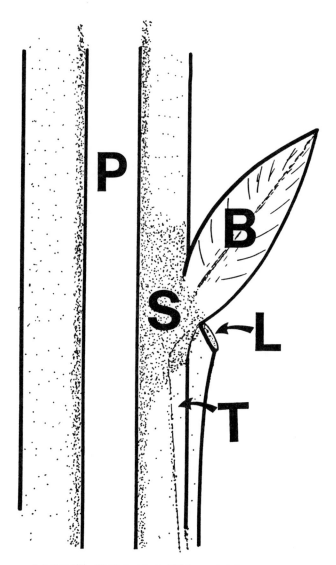

13. BACK TO BUDS AND THE BEGINNING

As new leaves form, buds form in the axils at the base of the petiole. Not all of the buds grow the next season. If the tree is stressed, the buds at the twig tips do not grow. Buds will grow farther back on the twig where there is enough water and energy reserve to start growth. Here is a fall dissection of a bud [B]. The old leaf scar [L], pith [P], twig cortex [T] and starch-rich zone are shown [S]. The bud does not store starch. The starch at the bud base provides the energy to start growth. Note that the bud does not connect with the pith of the twig [P]. As a stem bud grows it will form its own pith. The pith of branches does not connect with the pith of the joining stem (S: 186). Some buds squeeze against the twig and a type of included tissue forms similar to included bark (see diagrams 89 and 91). Some buds form only flowers, or only stems. Some buds contain both.

14. BUDS AND PRUNING

Learn the bud patterns of the trees you are treating (129). Learn to tell the flower buds from the leaf and stem buds. Pruning to regulate growth is best after the leaves form and the buds are obvious. Make cuts close to the buds. Some people still believe that roots send up food for buds to open. Roots send water and elements, but little or no energy substances. An easy way to prove this is to cut a tree or branch in early winter. Put the cut end of the branch or trunk into a stream or pond. Next year the leaves will grow and flower buds will bloom. An interesting point about this simple experiment is that usually not all the twigs or branches on the tree will grow. I have done this experiment many times and it always amazes me to see the growth in spring. And, for certain, the roots had nothing to do with it! I wish I could tell before spring which twigs and branches will die. I wonder if some recycling of energy is in order so that some of the buds grow. There is so much we don't know! I suspect turgor pressure is a major factor involved in this story.

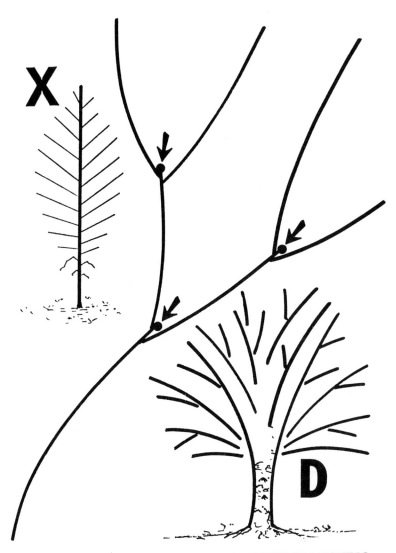

15. EXCURRENT AND DECURRENT BRANCHING

Excurrent [X] and decurrent [D] are types of branching. Excurrent branching results from apical dominance and decurrent branching results from apical control. Excurrent is weak apical control and strong apical dominance, and decurrent is strong apical control and weak apical dominance. Regardless of the terms, some trees have a strong single stem because the apical bud does grow every year—conifers mostly. Other trees have apical buds that often abort. In the natural forest, most trees start life with strong leader growth. Then when the trees grow to the canopy height, the apical buds abort (arrows). This happens with conifers and other trees. The tree architecture becomes a series of codominant stems. The top becomes rounded. This is a sign of maturity in the natural forest. Trees that grow in hot, dry, climates often develop wide rounded crowns early in life.

37

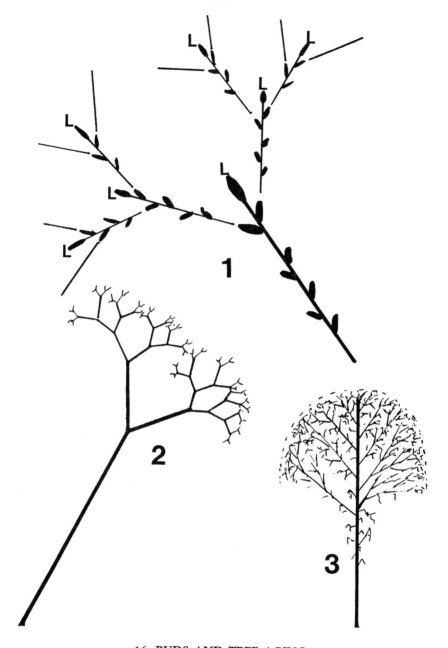

16. BUDS AND TREE AGING

As trees age, branching becomes more codominant [1]. The leader buds on opposite and alternate branched trees act the same; they begin to abort as trees age. Many understory trees, such as dogwood and hawthorn, start codominant branching early [2]. Even strongly excurrent trees developed rounded crowns with many codominant branches [3]. Foresters use height growth on a site as a major factor indicating whether the site is poor or good. Early training of young trees can bring on codominant branching and limit the height growth.

38

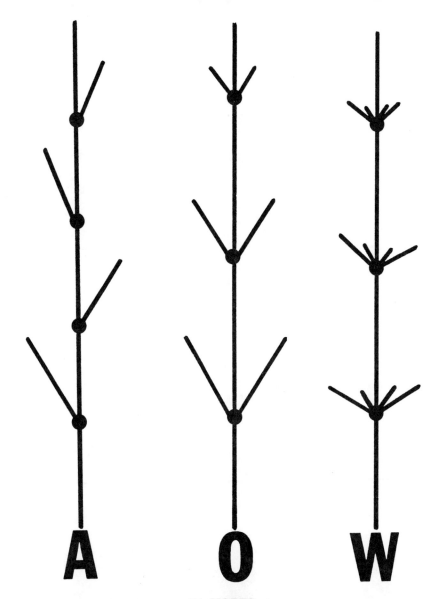

17. NODES

Nodes are positions on a stem where leaves form. There are 3 basic nodal patterns and positions of buds and leaves: A, alternate; O, opposite; W, whorled. The nodes are meristematic points. Buds formed at the base of leaves are at nodes. The buds may not grow the year after they are formed. Instead, they may remain, not as fully-formed buds, but as points of meristematic activity. They are called dormant or sleeping buds. On many tropical trees the dormant buds or stem buds form flowers and fruit. This is called cauliflorae — stem flowers. Once the buds begin to grow they usually form new buds. In some trees the dormant buds may form so many new buds that large burl-like growths form. These are wood carvers delights. As branches grow, the branch connections are often called branch nodes.

39

18. FOREST TREE GROWTH PATTERNS

Trees growing in natural forests usually start life with excurrent branching. Lower branches die when they are small. When the tree grows to the height of the canopy for its area, condominant branching starts. In dry, hot climates, trees usually start life with more codominant stems. Most pioneer tree species—those that grow first on open land—grow very fast when young. They usually require full sunlight. Birch, cherry, and sweetgum are good examples. When birch or cherry are shaded, problems start. Pioneer species usually have very shallow, fine roots. They are facultative for mycorrhizae when young. This means they can grow for several years with or without mycorrhizae. This is why some trees—*Populus* species—can grow on strip mine spoils.

19. CITY TREE GROWTH PATTERNS

Lower branches on city trees may persist throughout the life of the tree. Most city trees develop many codominant stems early in life. In a sense, the city tree ages faster that its forest relatives. I have been surprised many times to see very large city trees that were not very old. We seem to connect age with size. Yet, many forest trees are not as massive yet are much older. Large low branches on a city tree are not hazardous just because they are large and low. However, if they have included bark, they are very hazardous. When a large horizontal low branch has included bark, the scene is set for fracture. Forest trees seldom have large low branches. Forest trees "squeeze off" branches with included bark while the branch is small. And, if included bark persists, the stems are usually vertical and less prone to fracture.

41

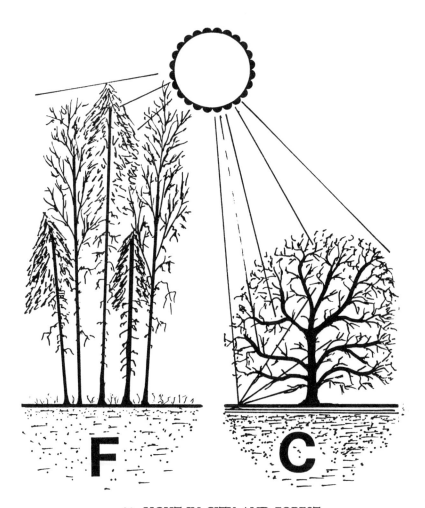

20. LIGHT IN CITY AND FOREST

In the natural forest, trees receive light only from one direction—straight downward [F]. In the urban forest, trees receive light from all directions; downward, from the sides, and bounced upward from the pavement [C]. The quick thought is that light is energy, so the city tree gets more energy. In a way this is true. Then we come back to city tree architecture, size, and aging.

We must remember that trees became trees in the natural forests. Their genetic programs come from the forest. Yes, we have domesticated cats and dogs. We have not domesticated lions and wolves. There is no doubt that some trees grow better in our cities than others. WE have had to learn the hard way that some trees such as American and English elms find it difficult to leave the forest. They are group trees. Yes, they survive planting for over a hundred years, which is a very short time in the generation time of a tree. Some trees "resist" being planted "off site", such as conifers on hardwood sites, where it may take a few generations—hundreds of years—before the effects are seen. The trees become weakened and any stress agent can take over.

42

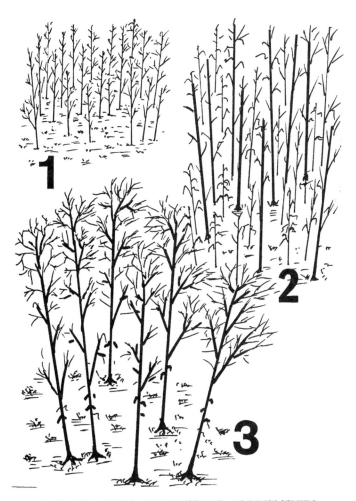

21. WHY WE MUST UNDERSTAND FOREST TREES

Trees in the natural forest adapted to their sites over many years. Those that did not adapt to a site, died, or grew on other sites. My point, over and over again, is that we must understand the tree as it grows in its natural site first [young 1, mature 2, over mature 3]. To try to treat a city tree without understanding the tree as it grows in its natural site is like drawing a data curve with only a y axis; and no base line! When we plant a tree so far removed from its natural site, the tree will have problems. Yes, the tree may tolerate the site, but it will exist in a weakened state. The microorganisms will do their naturally assigned duty; take it away! When we plant shade trees in the sun, sun trees in the shade, low pH trees in high pH soil, group trees as individuals, and the list goes on; it is a wonder we have any trees growing in our cities. Once we understand the tree in its natural site, our job as professionals should be to put the right tree on the right site! I wonder how much longer so many people will show their lack of professionalism by planting birches in the shade, dogwoods in full sunlight, and the poor pin oak in high pH soils! Then they drill them full of holes to insert magic cures.

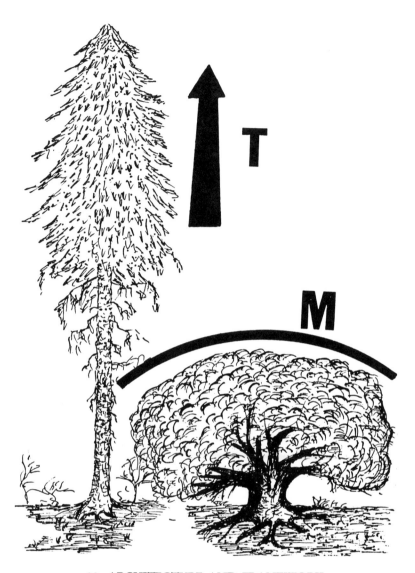

22. ARCHITECTURE AND FRAMEWORK

Framework is the basic structural design of a system. Architecture is the complete design of a system. The trunk and major branches determine the tree framework. The leaves, twigs, and the overall shape of the tree determines its architecture. Some trees are so strongly programmed for their framework and architecture that they will grow the same way in the open as in the natural forest. A giant sequoia will grow straight up out in the open[T]. Many tropical trees or trees from the hot dry regions [M] will form codominant stems very early in life whether planted in the open or if crowded with other trees. My point again; if this feature is under such strong control, just think how many unseen features must also be under strong control.

44

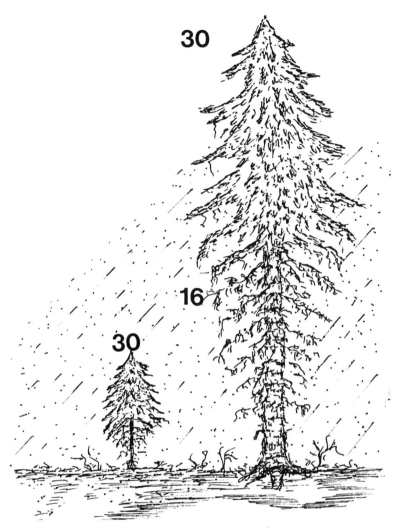

23. WHY DO BRANCHES DIE?

Branches die when they are shaded; everybody knows that! If this is so, why do you commonly see branches dead on large forest trees while smaller trees of the same species are alive and growing in deeper shade than the branch? I diagram a common forest scene. A white pine is 30 years old and the branches are dying at about age 16. Yet under the large pine, are smaller pine trees that are also 30 years old. There are many dwarf trees in the forest. When a branch on a large tree can no longer provide enough energy for roots, trunk, and woody parts of its branch, it dies. Yes, shade is part of the answer. But shade is not the complete answer or the dwarf would not be alive in deeper shade. The dwarf usually does not reproduce. It is small, and it has small energy requirements. So the little light it gets is enough. You can start with a small tree and keep it small. You cannot make a big tree a small healthy tree no matter what you do.

45

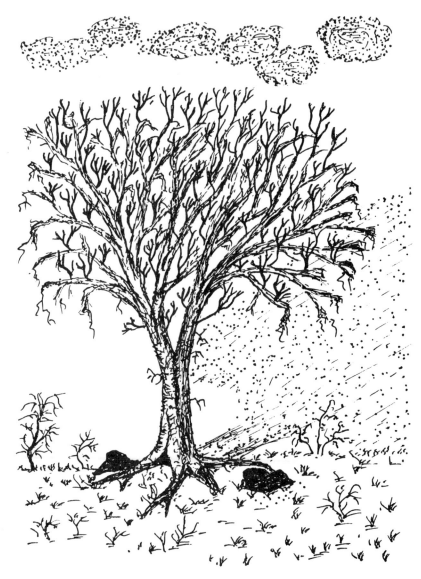

24. OLD TREES AND SPROUTS

The last stage of growth of old trees in the natural forest is shown by the death of most twigs; but the leaves grow on sprouts from dormant buds. A close look at very old trees in a natural forest will reveal a great number of sprouts. The dormant buds are the trees "old age pension". When trees are topped, or when flush cuts are made, the tree sprouts. In a sense, the tree is using its old age reserves, or emergency energy system. With the old tree in the natural forest there is sunlight for the sprouts. And, they grow. When a sprout begins to grow after a topping job, many of the sprouts are in the shade. The sprouts use energy to grow out, and when they are in the shade no energy is returned (401). Yes, some species can tolerate this treatment, but most cannot.

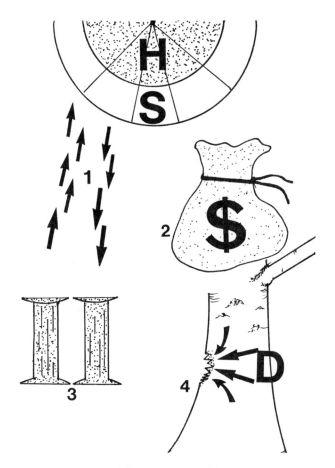

25. SAPWOOD, HEARTWOOD

Wood is a highly ordered arrangement of cells that have walls of cellulose and lignin in all gradations from living, to dying, to dead. Sapwood [S] contains living cells; heartwood [H] does not. But, there is more to sapwood and heartwood. Sapwood has 4 major functions: 1. transport from root to shoot and radially into and out of wood; 2. storage of energy reserves in living parenchyma cells, axial and radial; 3. mechanical support cells with strong walls of cellulose and lignin; 4. defense by conversion of energy reserves to chemicals that resist the spread of pathogens. Heartwood [H] is age-altered protection wood. As the inner sapwood parenchyma cells die, their walls and sometimes their cell contents are filled with chemicals that resist decay. Because these chemicals can be extracted in other chemicals, the protection substances are called extractives. Heartwood formation is genetically controlled. Energy is required to form the extractives. Energy is required to transport nitrogen-based chemicals out of the dying cells. The extractives usually impart a color darker than sapwood to the heartwood. Heartwood maintains a mechanical support function as the core of static mass and it reacts when injured to form boundaries. Heartwood will discolor.

Heartwood: 68,74,89,108,126,131,146,166,322,333;S:54.

47

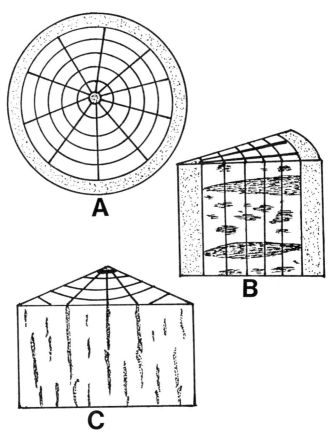

26. THREE VIEWS OF WOOD; TRANSVERSE,
RADIAL, AND TANGENTIAL

Transverse sections are cross sections through a stem, root, or branch [A]. Radial sections are longitudinal cuts through the radii of a stem, root, or branch [B]. Tangential sections are straight cuts at a tangent to the growth increments [C]. Almost all tree biology came from experiments on seedlings or small trees, and from transverse cuts on larger trees. This is understandable because it was very difficult to dissect trees longitudinally before the powerful, lightweight chainsaws began to be manufactured after 1950. Yes, there were power chainsaws before 1950 all the way back to the late 1920's; but they were very heavy and often required two strong bodies to operate them. In 1959 I started longitudinal radial dissections of beech, birch, and maple in the northeastern United States. These trees have bright white wood and no heartwood. I had an endless supply of trees to cut. I had a powerful, relatively lightweight saw (40 pounds) and lots of strong, enthusiastic assistants. Because the trees did not have a history of fire or insect wounds, it was very easy to see every small defect. I had the help of many U.S. Forest Service foresters who showed me the best places to cut and gave me the cutting histories of the areas. Thousands and thousands of trees were dissected and studied. Hundreds and hundreds of isolations were made for microorganisms. I had lots and lots of good help from every direction (A,H).

48

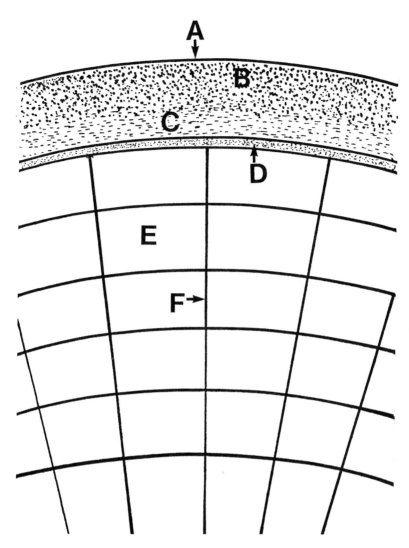

27. YOUNG STEM ANATOMY

The basic design of all woody young stems is similar: A, epidermis; B, cortex; C, phloem; D, cambial zone; E, compartment within growth increments and radial sheets of parenchyma cells; F, radial sheets of parenchyma cells. Conifers and hardwoods have these same features in young stems. The epidermis contains waxy substances and suberin. The cortex contains mostly parenchyma cells that have chlorophyll. Parenchyma cells have relatively thin walls and a great amount of living substance — protoplasm. Cortex with chlorophyll is an energy trapping tissue. Young trees are like large annual plants. The young twigs on mature trees also have a similar anatomy. Sprouts, and especially suppressed sprouts, from dormant buds often have a thinner layer of cortex. This means that epicormic sprouts (see diagrams 76, 83, and 84) are not as efficient as healthy young twigs for trapping energy.

49

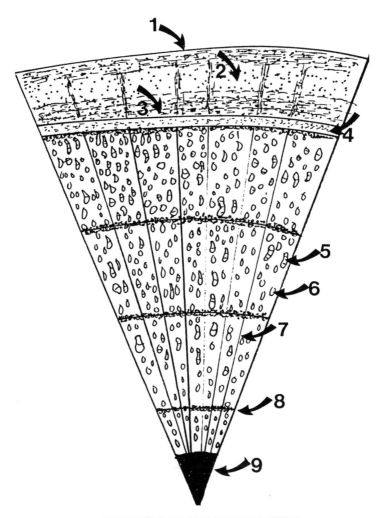

28. DIFFUSE POROUS YOUNG STEM

Angiosperms—covered seeds—have 2 basic types of wood anatomy: ring porous and diffuse porous. Diffuse porous wood—maple, birch, poplar—has vessels of about equal size and diameter arranged at about equal distances from each other throughout the growth increment (115). Here are the major anatomical features of a young hardwood stem: 1, epidermis; 2, cortex; 3, phloem; 4, cambial zone; 5, transverse section through several contiguous vessels; 6, transverse section through a single vessel; 7, radial sheet of parenchyma, a ray; 8, marginal axial parenchyma that forms at the end of the growth increment; 9, pith (The open spaces in the wood contain fibers). Vessels do end. When several vessels abut each other and a transverse cut is made, the vessels will look like item 5 in the diagram. The cambial zone begins to form phloem and xylem at the time leaves begin to form. The first xylem cells lack lignin, and they have the consistency of jelly. Peel the bark off a stem in spring and run your fingernail along the wood. The new cambium and xylem will collect on your nail as a white jelly. When the cells are lignified, then they are wood.

50

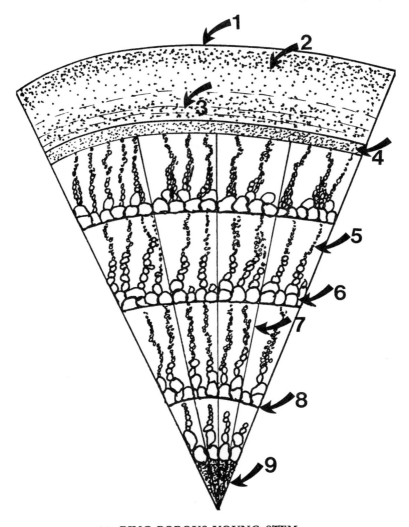

29. RING POROUS YOUNG STEM

Ring porous wood has large diameter vessels in the first portion of the growth increment and vessels of smaller diameter later in the growth increment. Here are typical features of young ring porous stems: 1, epidermis; 2, cortex; 3, phloem; 4, cambial zone; 5, latewood small diameter vessels; 6, earlywood or springwood large-diameter vessels; 7, ray of radial parenchyma; 8, thin band of axial parenchyma as marginal parenchyma; 9, pith (The open spaces in the wood contain fibers). Some ring porous trees—oak, elm, chestnut—have very thick rays made up of many radial parenchyma cells. It is easy to count the growth increments in ring porous wood because each new growing season starts with large-diameter vessels. Many trees have wood anatomy that graduates between diffuse and ring porous (86,407). Ash is a good example of a wood type that is not strongly diffuse or ring porous. Many tropical trees are extremely diffuse porous and it is difficult or impossible to count the growth increments.

51

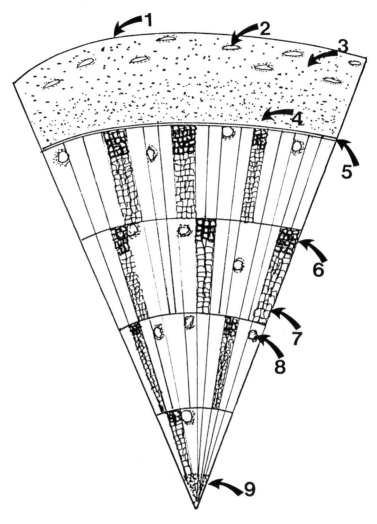

30. CONIFER WOOD ANATOMY

Conifers are gymnosperms — naked seeds. Conifers do not have vessels. They have tracheids. There are two types of conifer wood: resinous and nonresinous. Nonresinous wood has few or no resin ducts in the wood. The diagram shows the features of a young resinous conifer: 1, epidermis; 2, resin duct in bark; 3, cortex; 4, phloem; 5, cambial zone; 6, latewood tracheids or fiber tracheids; 7, earlywood tracheids, (Tracheids are throughout the wood. They are drawn only in a few compartments here.); 8, resin duct in wood; 9, pith. Resin ducts are enlarged parenchyma cells. The ducts may form from radial parenchyma; but most ducts form from axial parenchyma. Normal-sized axial parenchyma cells surround the duct. Ducts are more common in the latewood. Some trees such as true firs (*Abies*) have ducts in bark but none in wood. Spruce has very few ducts. Some conifers produce many ducts after injury. These ducts are called traumatic resin ducts.

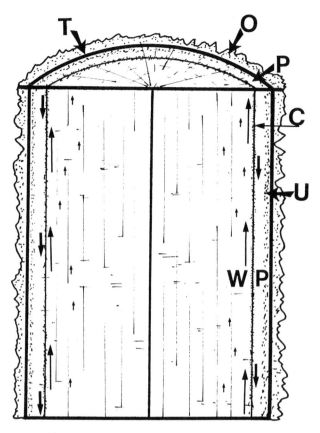

31. **TRANSVERSE AND RADIAL VIEW**
OF A MATURE TRUNK

Mature trees have an outer bark that contains suberin—cork [0]. A cork cambium or phellogen [T] produces the outer bark or phellem [0]. A thin layer on the inner side of the phellogen is called the phelloderm. Collectively the 3 bark tissues are called the periderm (119,349). Phloem [P] is on the inner side of the periderm. Phloem transports photosynthates from source—cells with chlorophyll—to sink—living cells in branches, trunk, and roots (408). Phloem transport is basipetal—toward the base. It is not entirely correct to say phloem transports downward, because the photosynthate must move up many hanging branches before it goes down the trunk. The cambial zone is on the inner side of the phloem [C]. As bark matures, the older phloem is crushed against the periderm [U]. It is only the young, inner phloem that is active in transport. On the inner side of the cambial zone is the wood. Wood means cellulose and lignin in the cell walls. Hemicellulose, a polysaccharide, is also a part of cell walls. Vessels in wood [W] transport water and elements, mostly, from root—source—to sinks—living cells in trunk, branches, and leaves. Vessel transport is acropetal—toward the top. The connection of living cells in wood and bark is the symplast. The symplast is active in radial and axial transport of nutrients and other substances (115).

53

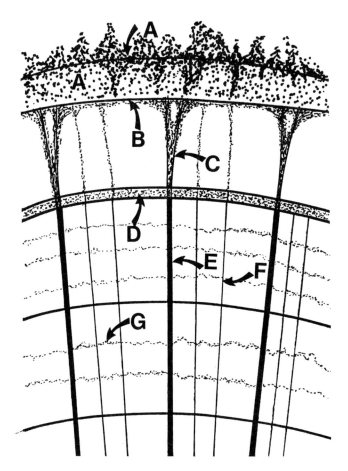

32. SYMPLAST AND APOPLAST

The symplast is the network of living cells in wood and bark (115). The outer periderm is A in the diagram. The cambial zone [D] is the center of the network made up of the phellogen [B], phloem rays [C], large wood rays [E], very small rays [F] and bands of connecting axial parenchyma [G]. Strands of living material called plasmodesmata connect the protoplasm in the cells as a network of living material. The vessels, fibers, cell walls, and open spaces make up the apoplast. Water can be absorbed in the apoplast. Movement of materials in the apoplast is not directly associated with an energy requirement. I say directly, because transpiration involves guard cell movement which requires energy. As water leaves the leaves, the water and some dissolved solutes move in the apoplast. Movement in the symplast requires a high amount of energy. Substances are moved against concentration gradients. It is as moving water uphill. The symplast also moves nutrients to the cambial zone. The cells in the cambial zone do not store energy reserves. The cambial zone is a cell generator. The energy to keep the generator going comes from other cells in the symplast. After wounding, electrical voltage changes occur rapidly in the symplast (237).

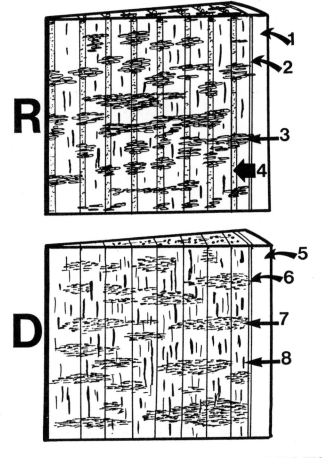

33. RADIAL VIEWS OF RING AND DIFFUSE POROUS WOOD

A radial view of a ring porous [R] wood shows: 1, bark; 2, cambial zone; 3, sheets of radial parenchyma; 4, large springwood vessels. A radial view of a diffuse porous [D] wood shows: 5, bark; 6, cambial zone; 7, sheets of small radial parenchyma cells; 8, vessels. Vessels are made up of many individual cells. The individual cells are like barrels stacked one on top of the other. The tops and bottoms of the barrels often have pointed ends. When the partitions between all the barrels break, then the vessel becomes functional. All vessel cells are alive when formed by the cambial zone. The cells grow rapidly and the cell contents break away from the vessel walls. Then the cell dies. This may take a week or a few weeks. The vessel does not become functional until it is dead. The vessel is rarely perfectly straight in an axial direction. This is why only portions of vessels are seen in the radial view. Tracheids in conifers start life as living single cells. They grow and their protoplasm breaks away from their walls. The tracheids remain as single transport cells. The vessels in angiosperms are like long tracheids. Fibers are thick-walled cells that serve a mechanical support function. Fibers may live for months, or in a few species, for years.

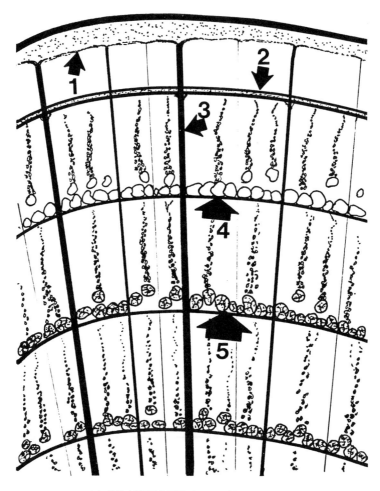

34. TRANSPORT AND STORAGE

Transport can be a dynamic process through the living cells of the symplast or an absorptive process through the dead parts, or apoplast. Energy storage can only be in living cells. In most ring porous trees, transport of water and elements is primarily through the 2 or 3 most recently formed growth increments. Storage can be in 8 or more growth increments. The diagram shows a ring porous transverse section: 1, phellogen; 2, cambial zone; 3, ray; 4, open large springwood vessels; 5, large springwood vessels plugged by tyloses. In many ring porous species — white oak, black locust, American elm — tyloses begin to form in the two-year-old growth increment. Vessels in diffuse porous trees are plugged by gums, granular materials, and varnish-like materials. Vessels in diffuse porous trees do not form tyloses. Tyloses do form in ring porous trees. Tracheids in conifers have openings called pits between the tracheids. The pits close and block transport after 10 to 20 years. The time varies greatly for different species. In some diffuse porous trees transport and storage may remain active in 50 or more growth increments.

56

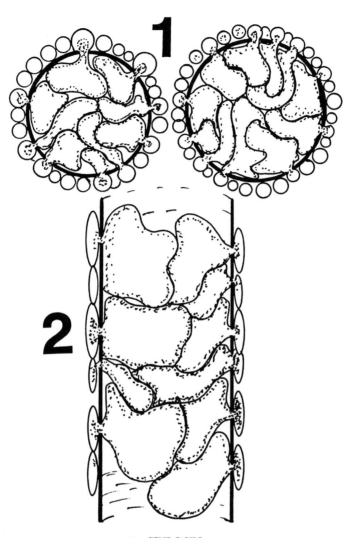

35. **TYLOSES**

Tyloses are balloon-like protrusions from axial parenchyma cells into vessels (1 and 2). Axial parenchyma cells may surround vessels [1], or contact the vessels only partially about their circumference. The parenchyma that surround the vessels are called paratracheal parenchyma. The axial parenchyma cell is alive. It has a pit connection with the dead vessel. As wood ages, the contents of the axial parenchyma cell balloons out into the vessel [2]. There are slight variations on the type of tylosis formed. Some have a distinct membrane boundary; and others have only a thin membrane-like boundary. The tyloses plug the vessels. Tyloses form in large earlywood vessels and in smaller latewood vessels. The parenchyma cell dies after it forms the tylosis. White oak, *Quercus alba*, is used for whiskey barrels because the tree forms abundant tyloses in the second and third youngest growth increment. Deep injection holes into trees that form tyloses makes no sense.

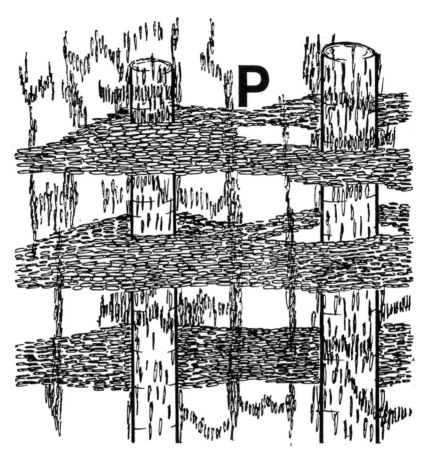

36. RAYS IN RING POROUS WOOD

Oaks and many other ring porous species often have very thick bands of radial parenchyma. The thick bands are obvious when transverse sections are made. The radial parenchyma contact the axial parenchyma that are in contact with the vessels [P]. The axial parenchyma that are in contact with both the vessel and radial parenchyma are called contact parenchyma. The contact parenchyma play key roles in the symplast (325). When contact parenchyma are killed, plugs will not form. In some diffuse porous woods such as sugar maple, *Acer saccharum*, that is tapped for sap to make syrup (378,379,S: 35,111). Chemicals are added to the tap hole to prolong the flow of sap. Paraformaldehyde in pill form is often put into the tap holes (S:35,111,117). The chemical kills the contact parenchyma and the vessels become plugged with gums or granular materials. The tap holes produce more sap. The treatment leads to early decay because vessel plugging is a first line defense against vertical spread of pathogens. Heavy use of paraformaldehyde, overtapping, high vacuum tensions, cutting of all trees other than maples in a maple bush, and the great number of roads and machine travel have drastically changed the maple syrup industry. The trees are so weakened that minor stresses now become major ones. Acid rain is blamed. The real pathogens are called greed and ignorance of tree systems!

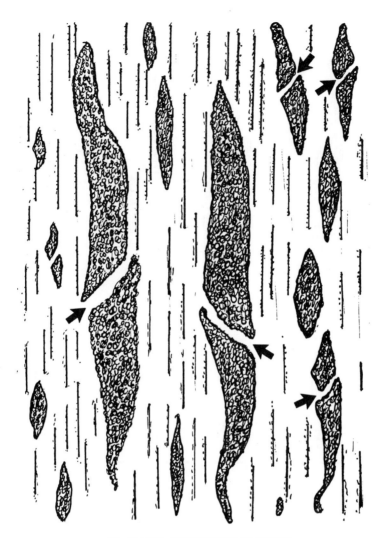

37. RAYS, TANGENTIAL VIEW

Radial sheets of radial parenchyma are called wood rays, or sometimes medullary rays. As the girth of the tree increases, new rays are formed. A tangential view of rays is shown in the diagram. Note that no two rays touch (arrows). This feature is protective because if a microorganism infects one sheet of radial cells, the microorganism will not have easy access to another ray. Tree wood is constructed like a basket. Axial cells weave in and out of radial sheets of cells. And, the sheets of cells are separated by spaces occupied by fibers with thick walls. This arrangement of cells makes it very difficult for pathogens to invade. The pattern of wood cells, strange as it seems, also benefits the wood-rotting pathogens. If the pathogens digested all the cells, the trunk would collapse and there would be no structure to hold the fungus fruit body. It is amazing when you see how natural systems work. My hope is that as you learn more about how the systems work, you will be in the best position to determine the best treatments to work on the trees.

59

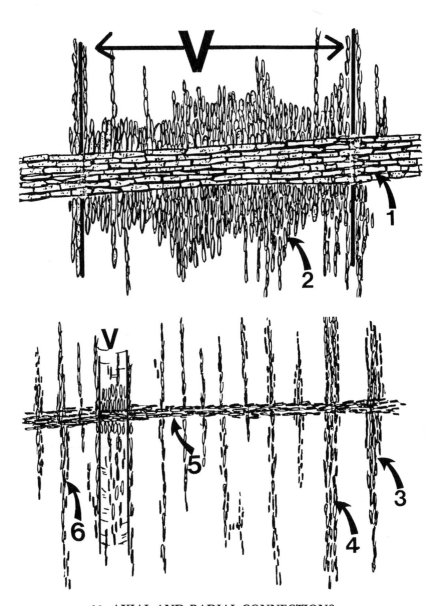

38. AXIAL AND RADIAL CONNECTIONS

The cambial zone is made up of axial and radial cells. The axial cells are called fusiform initials and the radial cells are ray initials. An enlargement of a vessel [V, above] shows the relative size of the vessel [V] to the radial [1] and axial [2] parenchyma. In the lower diagram, the enlargement is not as great as above. The features are: 3, phellogen; 4, cambial zone; 5, ray; 6, axial parenchyma. The axial parenchyma also contact the vessel [V]. The living connection — symplast — and the nonliving connection — apoplast — twine together as a close knit fabric. Now you see why wood cannot be called dead.

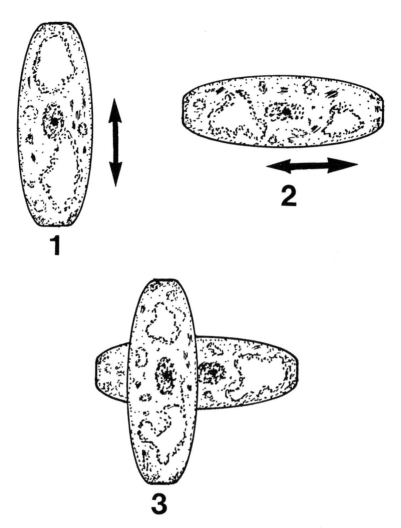

1

2

3

39. AXIAL AND RADIAL PARENCHYMA CELLS

Parenchyma cells in the cambial zone have their long axis parallel to the trunk—axial [1]—or perpendicular to the trunk—radial [2]. The cambial zone is made up of axial and radial cells [3]. Each mother cell divides to form two daughter cells. They mature to become two new mother cells that divide again. As the cells divide and mature, and divide and mature, the cambial zone gets thicker. Then the cells on the outside and inner side of the zone begin to differentialte. Differentiation marks the end of the division processes. The axial cells or fusiform initials differentiate to form vessels, fibers, or axial parenchyma in angiosperms; and tracheids, fiber tracheids, and axial parenchyma in conifers. The radial initials form radial parenchyma. The parenchyma, as living cells, still have the capacity to divide. However, they are locked in place by other cells, so division could occur but the cells would be half their size. When wounds break away wood cells, the still living parenchyma along with the still living cambial cells divide to form callus. In tropical trees a new bark may form over the surface of shallow wounds.

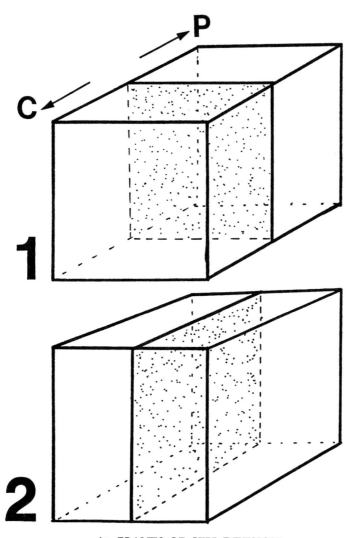

40. PLANES OF CELL DIVISION

The cambial cells may divide in a periclinal plane (shaded area, 1) where C is toward the bark and P is toward the pith, or in an anticlinal plane (shaded area,2). By dividing in these two directions, the cells keep pace with increase in girth and circumference. In phellogen cells, periclinal divisions are more frequent than anticlinal divisions. The increase in circumference leads to the breaking of the phellogen. A new layer of phellogen starts again. This pattern of phellogen disruption leads to the pattern of outer bark plates and fissures. In birch and beech, the phellogen divisions keep pace with the increase in girth and circumference, thus the bark is smooth and remains on the tree. Other bark patterns form on trees such as *Platanus* species, and the smooth bark *Eucalyptus* species. In these species the outer bark sloughs off.

Anatomy: 86,95,115,116,117,119,139,157,177,178,180,199,222,277,279,284, 312,315,349,358,362,405,406,407,408.

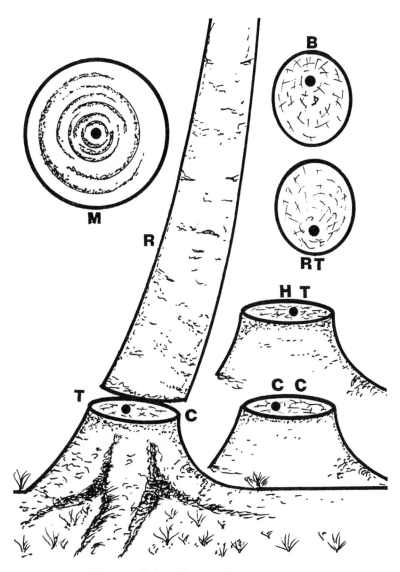

41. REACTION WOOD

Reaction wood [R] is wood altered as a response to lean. In conifers, thicker growth rings with thicker cell walls and more resin-type substances form on the down side of the lean. Conifers form compression wood as a type of reaction wood [C]. In hardwoods, cell walls thicken on the upside of the lean; hardwoods have tension wood as a type of reaction wood [T]. Transverse sections through the trunk base show how a hardwood would appear [HT] and a conifer [cc]. A transverse section through large branches on most trees will look like B; while a transverse section of most large roots will look like RT. The dot in RT shows the center of the root, not the pith. Roots do not have a pith. In conifers, a spiral-type pattern may form as the tree leans in different directions as it grows [M].

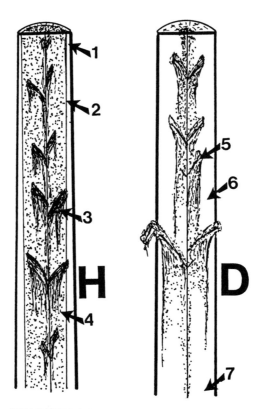

42. HEARTWOOD AND DISCOLORED WOOD

Heartwood [H] is age-altered wood. Discolored wood [D] is injury-altered wood. Heartwood is a protection wood. As the wood ages, extractives are impregnated into the cell walls and, in some cases, the cell lumens. In H:1, Sapwood; 2, Sapwood-heartwood border; 3, Discolored heartwood associated with an old branch core; 4, Sound heartwood. In D:5 is an old branch core with associated discolored wood, 6 and 7 are sound, clear wood. When trees are dissected longitudinally, heartwood-forming trees will have a fairly uniform inner core of wood darker than the sapwood. The electric resistance of heartwood is higher than that of the sapwood. Sound heartwood contains extractives that are only slightly soluble in water. Note that heartwood will discolor when wounded (S: 126) or when branch corewood is infected. Discolored wood in its early stages is a protection wood. As microorganisms invade wounds and branch stubs, they break down the protective discolored wood, and defective discolored wood results. All discolored wood does not develop into decayed wood. Some discolored wood and the pioneer microorganisms that may infect it may stall the invasion by decay-causing fungi. When holes are drilled into trees, and elements essential for the growth of microorganisms are introduced, the column of defective discolored wood will develop rapidly. Discolored wood is dead wood.

Discoloration: 15,75,108,131,148,195,196,327,328,330,332,375;
S: 6,16,20,21,22,25,27,29,34,42,66.

64

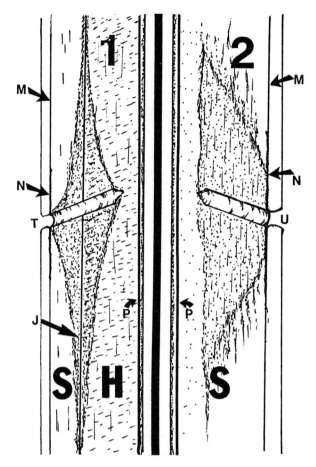

43. WOUNDS IN SAPWOOD AND HEARTWOOD

Longitudinal radial sections from 2 trees show wounds in a heartwood-forming tree [SH] and in a tree that does not form heartwood [S]. Even in the heartwood-forming trees the wound must penetrate the sapwood [S] first (S: 68). A barrier zone will form [N] to separate the wood present at the time of wounding [M] from the new wood that will continue to form. Note the different shapes of the columns associated with the wounds in the two trees. In tree SH, the wound T penetrates the heartwood H at point J, the sapwood-heartwood boundary. The column of discolored wood develops farthest along the sapwood-heartwood boundary present at the time of wounding (S: 27). In the sapwood tree, wound U penetrates sap-wood that has cells in greater stages of aging as the pith [P] is approached (S: 32). When sugar maple trees are tapped for sap, and no chemicals are added to stimulate sap flow, most columns of discolored wood will be small (S: 35,111,117). When paraformaldehyde pills are inserted into the tap hole, the axial parenchyma surrounding the vessels are killed and no vessel plugs form (S: 35). Then more sap flows, but at the expense of larger columns of decayed wood. There is always a price to pay.

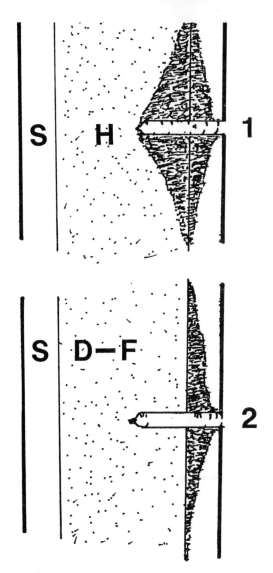

44. WOUNDS IN FALSE HEARTWOOD AND HEARTWOOD

Wounds in heartwood [1] and false heartwood [2]. False heartwood is wood altered to a protection state higher that the sapwood in the species as a result of depletion of energy reserves. (See summary of tree defense in appendix for more details.) Diagram 1 is a repeat of the pattern shown for a wound in a heartwood forming tree as shown in diagram 43. When a drill wound penetrates false heartwood [D-F] as shown in 2, note that the new column of discolored wood forms only in the sapwood and not in the column of false heartwood (S: 27). These experiments showed that heartwood did react to wounds, but false heartwood did not. Heartwood apparently still contains some chemicals that will react when oxygen becomes available (S: 126). Some potential energy must still remain in heartwood. False heartwood gains its protective characteristics by exhausting all its energy reserves, and then it is truly in balance with the environment, dead.

66

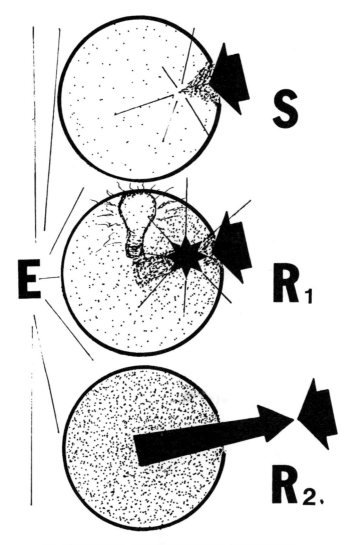

45. STIMULUS, RECOGNITION, RESPONSE

Stimulus [S], Recognition [R] and Response [R2]. Survival of any system depends on its ability to recognize [R] a stimulus [S] that threatens it, and then respond rapidly and effectively [R2] (S: 178,187).

How rapid and effective the response will be depends greatly on the availability of reserve energy [E] (384). Reserve energy is used to mount a quick and effective block to any agent that threatens survival (385). How fast the stimulus is recognized and how fast the response is developed are also key elements for survival. The best way to determine, or to test, the vigor of a system is to stimulate it with a wound. Vigor is the capacity to resist strain. Vigor is a genetic feature. It is often confused with vitality (B). Vitality is the ability to grow under the condition the system finds itself.

Wound response: 319,320,321;
S: 61,63,78,107,108,137,143,158,171,178,188.

67

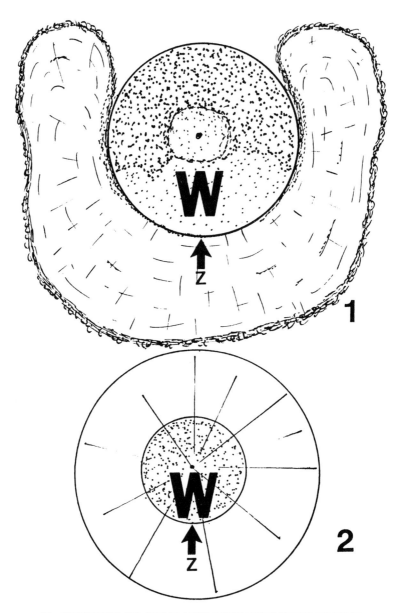

46. CONCEPT OF COMPARTMENTALIZATION BEGINS

Dissections of thousands of trees in the field with a chainsaw (S: 12), starting in 1959, began to reveal basic patterns of columns of discolored and decayed wood in trees (S: 16,17,18,20,23,25,27,29,31,32). The diameter of the tree at the time of wounding [W] was the greatest diameter of the column. Diagram 1 shows a transverse cut through the wound and diagram 2 show a transverse cut several meters above the wound. In many samples a distinct boundary (Z) separated the wood present at the time of wounding from wood that formed later.

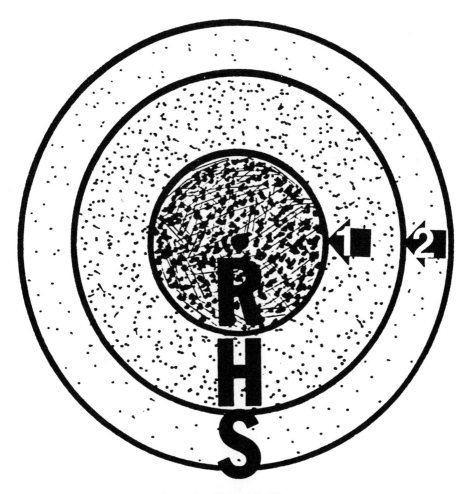

47. HEARTROT

Dissections of trees that had a heartwood core showed similar patterns. It was not uncommon to find hollows or columns of discolored or decayed heartwood [R] surrounded by sound cores of heartwood [H] and sapwood [S] (S: 42,45,49,68,126). Again, there was a distinct boundary [1] between the decayed heartwood [R] and the sound heartwood [H]. This boundary was different from the sapwood-heartwood boundary [2]. **It was time to question the heartrot concept.** If heartwood-rotting fungi decay heartwood, as stated in many textbooks, why did the rot confine itself to the wood present at the time of wounding?

Decay: 1,16,18,24,33,53,69,70,110,111,112,113,114,133,134,140,159,195,211, 328,332; S: 16,17,20,21,22,25,27,29,34,42,65,66,75,77,83,154,164,192.

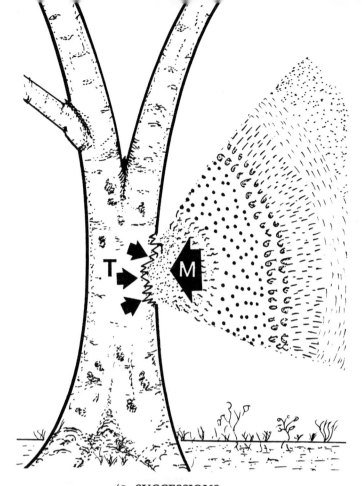

48. SUCCESSIONS

Succession is an orderly sequence of microorganisms [M] that invade a tree [T]. There are no set patterns for successions. Many factors will affect successional patterns: tree species, wound type, wound position, wound treatment, time of year of wounding, species of microorganisms in the area and their numbers, temperature, and many other environmental factors.

Succession means that many microorganisms are associated in discoloration and decay of wood. Some pioneers may speed invasion, while others may slow its development. Microorganisms do not prepare a place for others. When they are able to colonize an area, they usually alter it to suit their survival. A habitat is where you can live and survive. A niche is the habitat, or portion of it, that has been altered as a result of an organism or organisms living in it. The alterations usually enhance the protection of the organisms, thus increasing the chances for continual survival. Purposefully altering successional patterns may be a way to slow the development of defects in trees. Experiments with inoculation of the fungus, *Trichoderma harzianum* showed that under some conditons, the decay process could be temporarily stalled.

Successions: 110,111,112,113,114, S: 1,6,7,13,24,44,45, S: 69,95,113.

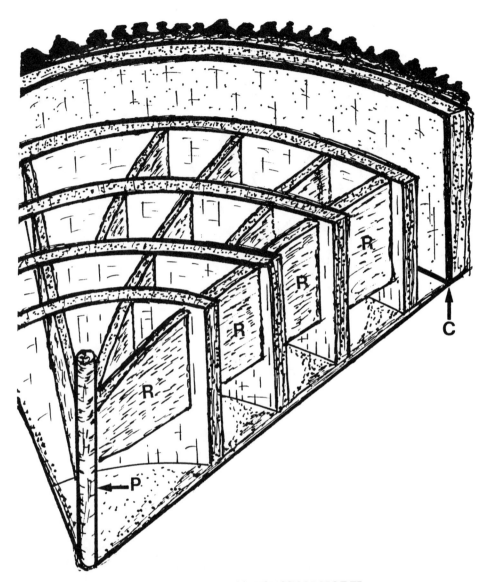

49. COMPARTMENTALIZATION MODEL

It was time to revisit and re-examine the tree. Organisms develop in ways that suit their survival. Maybe the tree has some different ways for survival after injury and infection? Maybe the tree is not just a large core of dead wood surrounded by a single layer of living cells, the cambium? Can trees heal? Healing was the crucial question. From all of these questions a "new" type of tree began to emerge, the compartmented tree. The tree was seen as a highly compartmented system (S: 101,109,119). Each growth ring was a compartment, and each growth ring was divided into smaller compartments by radial sheets of parenchyma cells [R]. The cambium was not a single layer but a cambial zone [C]. P is the Pith.

71

50. A MULTIPLE PLANT

Every growth period a "new" tree grows over the older trees; 1,2,3,& 4. H is heartwood, and S is sapwood.

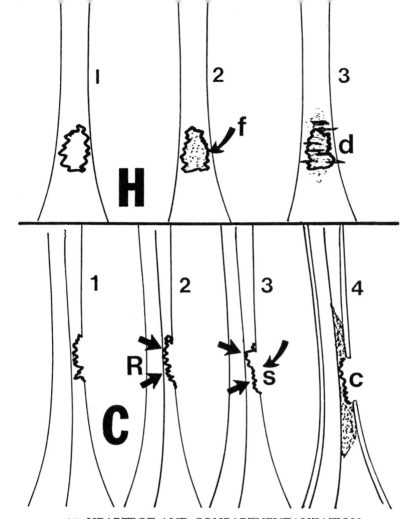

51. HEARTROT AND COMPARTMENTALIZATION

The heartrot concept [H] was a wonderful concept that got tree pathology started as a science (133). The concept was built about three major events: 1, Wounds; 2, Infection of exposed heartwood by a decay-causing fungus; 3, The breakdown of the heartwood. Heartrot was not considered a disease because the breakdown of a dead tissue, the heartwood, did not fulfill the commonly used definition of a disease. The concept did not consider the response of the living tree. The heartrot concept was a decomposition concept. The compartmentalization concept [C] has four major events: 1, Wound; 2, Response of the compartmented tree to compartmentalize the injured and infected wood; 3, Succession of microorganisms as a force against the survival force of the tree; 4, Development of discolored or decayed wood within compartments. The compartmentalization concept has two major parts: Part 1 includes events in the wood present at the time of wounding, Part 2 includes events that take place after wounding.

Wounds: 52,61,63,76,77,78,108,189,191,192,193,238,241,261,302,303,325,327, 328,384,393,395; A,H.

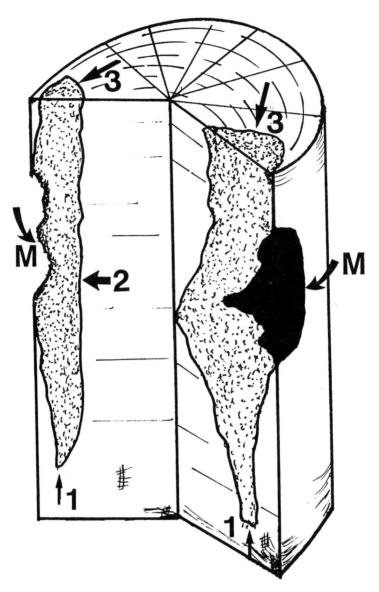

52. CODIT, PART 1

Just as compartmentalization has two parts, so does CODIT. CODIT is a model of compartmentalization. CODIT is an acronym for Compartmentalization Of Decay In Trees. Do not mix the model with the biological process (S: 174,185). Part 1 of CODIT consists of three walls that give model designations to the reaction zone. Wall 1 resists vertical spread of decay. Wall 2 resists inward spread. Wall 3 resists lateral spread. Part 1 is in the wood present at the time of wounding [M]. Again, walls 1,2 and 3 are model terms. They are not biological features. Note that wall 2 no longer exists once the defect reaches the pith. (The D in CODIT could also mean defects. It is the model rather than the specifics of the acronym that is important.)

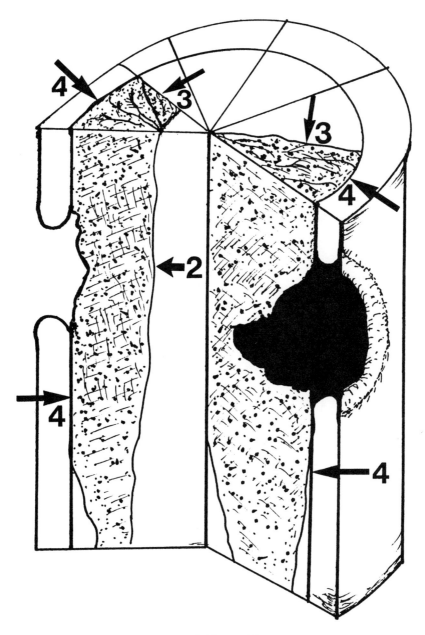

53. CODIT, PART 2

After wounding, the still living cambial zone about the wound begins to form a new boundary, the barrier zone. The model representation of this zone is wall 4. Wall 4 is a boundary that separates the wood present at the time of wounding from the new wood that continues to form. Wall 4 is a very strong protection boundary. As we will see later, cracks often start along wall 4 (S: 14,148,176,183,200). Here is another example of a tradeoff for the tree. A strong boundary walls off the pathogens, but the boundary may become the site of an internal crack.

75

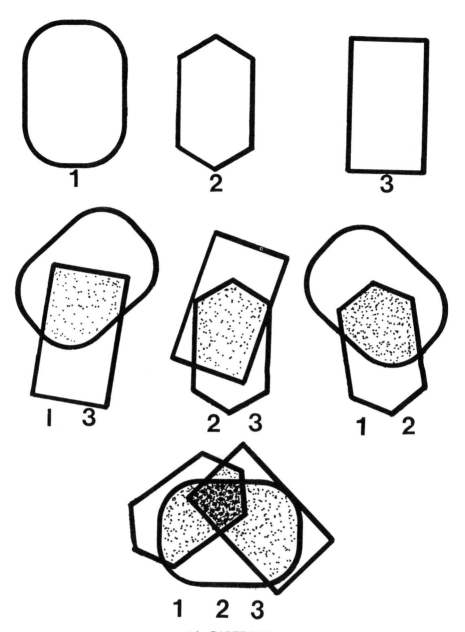

54. CAUTION!

Natural systems do not come in discrete little units. We present a concept in its most simple form only to start our thinking about it. Natural systems are usually mixtures and blends of the major ingredients. We usually see them not as 1, or a 2, or a 3 or even as a 1,3 or 2,3 or 1,1; but as 1 and 2 and 3, and often the units are very numerous. So it is with the compartmented tree and the concept of compartmentalization. A model was needed to help us understand the great mix of many unit parts. It was time for CODIT (S: 101).

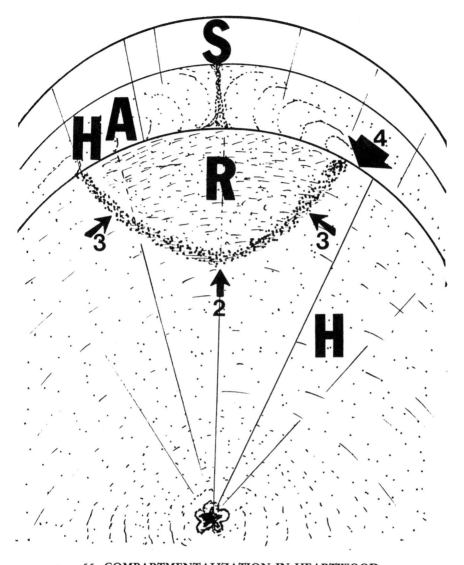

55. COMPARTMENTALIZATION IN HEARTWOOD

Compartmentalization is a boundary-setting defense process. Examine the diagram and the infected heartwood [R] within the heartwood [H]. The size of the tree at the time of wounding is shown by the arrow and wall 4. Heartwood is a protection wood, but when it is wounded a reaction takes place that forms a boundary [CODIT 2 and 3] about the injured and infected wood (S: 126). The boundary may be in response to enzymes activated by oxygen, or in response to chemicals given off by the invading microorganism. If heartwood did not have some extra protection, decay-causing fungi would grow at will in the heartwood. They don't! S is sapwood and HA is heartwood that formed after wounding.

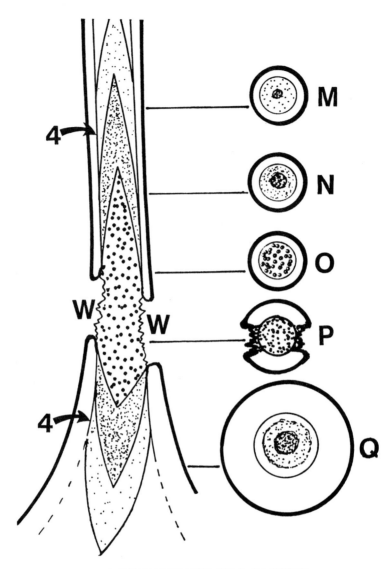

56. DEVELOPMENT OF A COLUMN

Longitudinal dissections clarify patterns that are often confusing when viewed on the transverse surface. The diagrammed tree was wounded on opposite sides [W,P] when it was the diameter shown by the arrows and 4. Transverse sections at points M,N,O,P, and Q show the defect patterns. In M it appears that the central column of defective discolored wood is spreading out at will. The same is shown at point Q. The barrier zone, 4, shows the diameter limits of the columns of discolored wood, defective discolored wood, and decayed wood. The columns of defective and decaying wood develop as cones through the cylinder of wood present at the time of wounding. Many artifacts have been studied from transverse sections. (An artifact is a structure or substance not present, but made to appear present as a result of some action.)

78

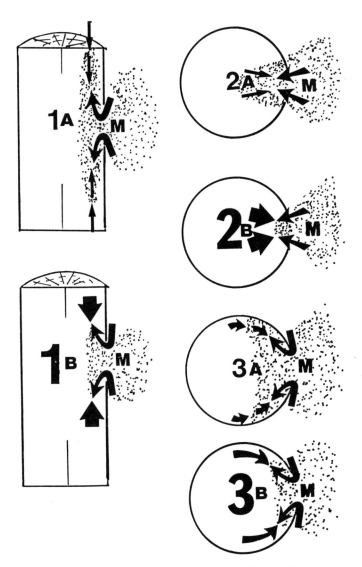

57. CODIT WALLS, WEAK OR STRONG

Diagram 1A shows weak walls 1 and strong invasion force by microorganisms through a wound [M]. A long defect column will form. 1B shows strong walls 1 against the microorganisms [M]. A short column will form. 2A shows weak walls 2 against the invasion force of the microorganisms [M]. A deep defect column will form. 2B shows a strong wall 2. A shallow column will form. 3A shows weak walls 3. The defect will spread inward and laterally to the sides of the wound. 3B shows equal forces between walls 3 and the invading microorganisms [M]. A moderate-sized column will form. It is apparent that many combinations of resisting forces or CODIT walls and invading forces by microorganisms can result in a great variety of shapes and sizes of defect columns.

79

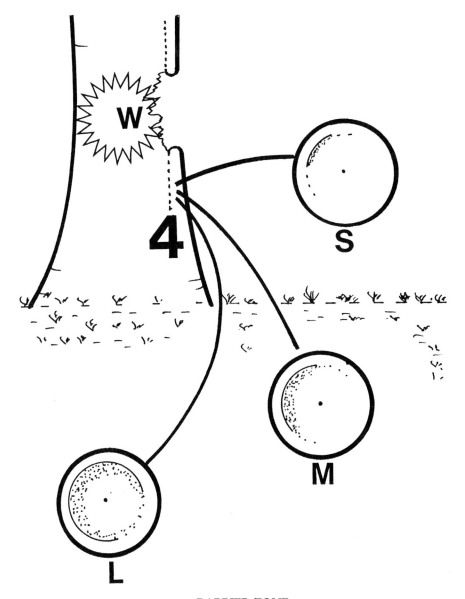

58. BARRIER ZONE

The barrier zone, or wall 4, is a separating boundary between wood present at the time of wounding [W] and wood that continues to form after wounding. Many factors, still poorly understood, regulate the size of the barrier zone. It may be small [S], moderate [M] or large [L] both in the longitudinal and circumferential direction. The severity of the wound, time of wounding, and the type of pioneer microorganisms that infect play a major role in the process. Some tree species form small barrier zones but very strong walls 2 and 3. Other species form strong walls 4 but weak walls 1,2,and 3. Eventually, the wood behind wall 4 will no longer store energy reserves.

Barrier zone: 191,193,263,264,265,324,335,358; S: 121,131,142,149,

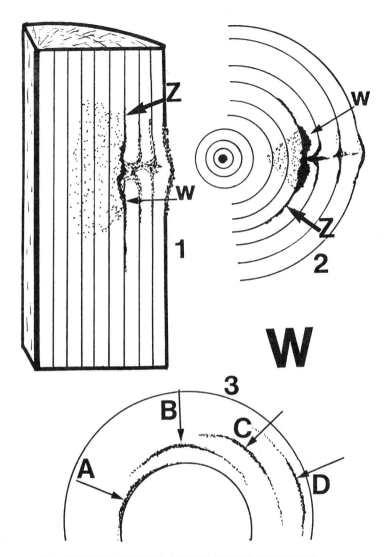

59. BARRIER ZONES AND DATING WOUNDS

Because trees do not heal, the wounded wood and the barrier zone will remain in the wood. In 1 and 2 the wound was infected during the dormant period 3 years before the trunk was cut. It is always best to make your observation of the position of the barrier zone [Z] as far away from the wound [W] as possible. Old bark and rotted wood near the wound could complicate your observation. When the barrier zone is within the growth increment [3] the position in the increment can make it possible to date a wound within 5 to 10 days of when it was inflicted. In A, immediately after leaves began to form; B, a third of the growth period; C a half, and D near the end of the growth period. To be accurate you must know the development of the growth ring of the species you are dating (53). In most species, the growth increment starts to form as leaves start to form, and about 90% of the increment will be completed within 6 to 8 weeks later.

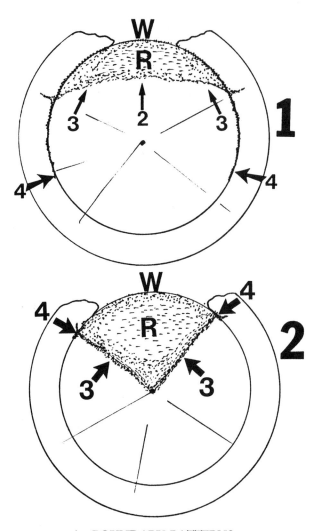

60. BOUNDARY PATTERNS

Shape and size of defect columns [R] vary greatly. Boundaries also vary greatly. So much depends on tree species, genetics, type and severity of the wound, time of wounding, and no doubt, many other factors that we do not understand. Diagram 1 shows walls 2 and 3 of about equal force but a very extended 4. This pattern can be found in maples and birches. In diagram 2, wall 2 was weak, but 3's were very strong. Wall 4 did not extend beyond the wound (W is wound; R is rot). This pattern is common in oaks and conifers. Note that in both diagrams no other columns of defect were present. It is important to learn the basic types of columns and boundaries in the trees you treat (53). About 90% of the trees you work with will be 10 species. Autopsy of wounded trees will help you learn the boundary patterns. Then you will be able to assess the potential hazards from wounds.

82

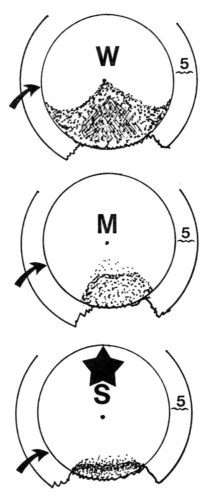

61. GENETICS OF COMPARTMENTALIZATION

Studies by geneticists have shown that boundary setting or compartmentalization is under moderate to strong genetic control (196,300,302,303,323). When wounds were inflicted at the same time on the same species of trees, different patterns and sizes of defect columns resulted. The studies were done on many trees in the same area (S: 86,92,93,97,112,116,122,123,124,155,165). Statistics were used to analyze the results. The experiments showed that microorganisms alone were not the reasons for the different patterns. Some trees were weak [W], some moderate [M] and some strong [S] compartmentalizers. (Diagrams show 5 growth increments after wounding; arrows.) Recent research has shown biochemical differences between weak and strong compartmentalizers in the species *Populus tremuloides,* aspen (323). Some researchers feel that people who graft have unknowingly selected for strong compartmentalization because strong compartmentalizers graft easier than poor compartmentalizers (302,303). It is time to start selecting more individuals for strong compartmentalization and to start planting them in our cities and forests. It can be done.

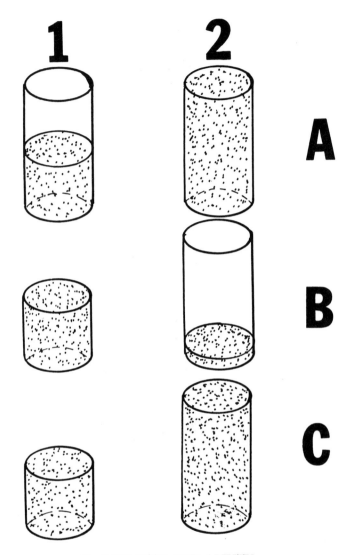

62. CAPACITY AND ABILITY

Time to look again at vigor and vitality, and genetics and environment. Capacity is what you have. Ability is what you do with what you have. Vigor is a genetic feature. It deals with what you have. Vitality is an environmental factor. It deals with how well you can grow and survive under the environmental conditions you find yourself (B). Here are three simple diagrammatic examples: 1A and 2A have the same capacity; but 2A has twice the ability of 1A. 1B has half the capacity of 2B, but 1B has four times the ability of 2B. 1C has half the capacity of 2C, and half the ability. What this means is that if we provide a proper environment for our agricultural crops (294) and our trees, we can help them to be healthy, even if they have a few genetic problems.

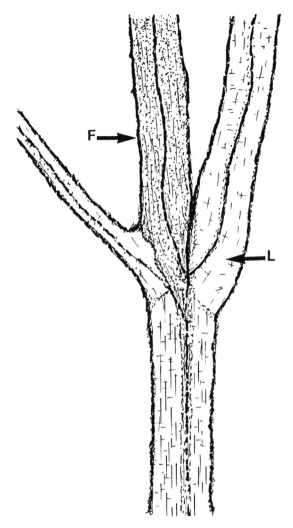

63. FIRE BLIGHT AND COMPARTMENTALIZATION

Fire blight is a serious disease of many plants in the rose family (310,371,372). Fire blight was the first plant disease shown to be caused by a bacterium. The bacterium infects natural openings in the flower, the nectararies. In trees the bacterium spreads rapidly in the flower parts and in the current annual growth tissues of the plant. The leaves die and wrinkle as if burned, thus the name for the blight. The bacteria fall into the natural openings within the branch crotches, and spread to form cankers (S: 186). When many cankers come together, the stem dies [F]. However, the dead leader will remain separate from living codominant stems [L] or branches. If many cankers form on the trunk, the tree will be killed. I use this example to introduce branches and natural openings in trees. There are many "easy" ways for pathogens to grow into trees. The tree forms boundaries to block the spread of the pathogens. Now it is time to examine how branches are attached to trunks.

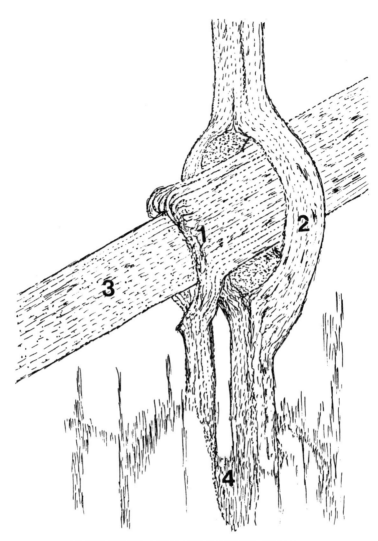

64. BRANCH ATTACHMENT TO TRUNK

Branch tissues usually begin to form before trunk tissues do. As the branch tissues develop toward the base of the branch, the tissues turn to form a collar [1]. The trunk tissues begin to form later, and they circle the branch collar with a trunk collar [2]. The new branch collar fits over the shaft of the tissues in the existing branch [3]. The branch and trunk tissues develop connections below the collars [4]. The branch collar and trunk collar are collectively called the branch collar (S: 186,A,H), Please note that this is a diagrammatic view. Many times the collar-forming tissues mix with each other and the collars are not distinct. Collars may also form in an orderly way on one side and not so orderly on the other side. On some trees, the trunk collar does not meet until far below the branch collar. A sunken spot identifies the situation. When such branches are cut, a dead spot will form under the branch (see diagram 78).

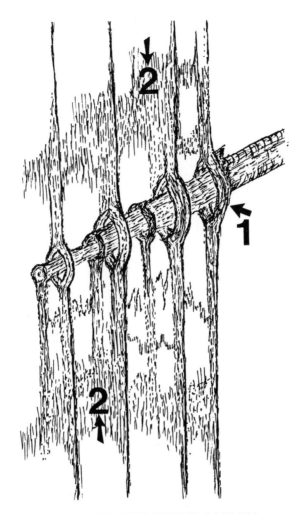

65. BRANCH AND TRUNK COLLARS

The water and elements for the branch move in the branch tissues. Water and elements for wood above the branch move upward through the trunk collar(405,406,407). The collars are switching zones for transport. In the bark, or phloem, similar switching zones [arrow 1] direct photosynthate from the branch downward and around the base of the branch, and photosynthate from the trunk above the branch also moves downward and around the branch in the same pattern. There are lateral connections above and below the branch [arrows 2]. Again, how distinct the branch tissues are from the trunk tissues within the trunk vary greatly for different species. It appears that in some species, some roots and branches have strong connections. Branch roots have similar connections with larger roots, except the direction of the collars are reversed, or upside down. *Just as branches are really not structurally attached to trunks, neither are roots structurally attached to the tree base.* The small strip of branch tissue below the branch cannot be considered a structural attachement. The holding power of roots and branches lies in the series of collars.

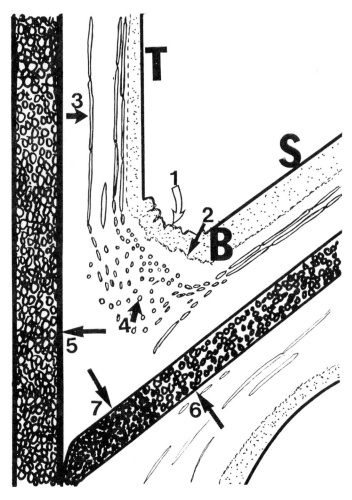

66. BRANCH CROTCH

When a saw cut is made longitudinally through a branch crotch, it will appear as if the trunk tissues [T] and branch tissues [S] are continuous. This cutting artifact appears in hundreds of textbooks. When a branch trunk union or crotch [B] is split with an axe or knife, a different view becomes apparent. A closer view of a small branch-trunk union shows the following: 1, Wrinkled bark that later forms the branch bark ridge. 2, Wrinkled cambial zone that often ruptures and reaches the surface within the branch crotch. When this happens, and potential pathogens are there, cankers can start. It is the major starting point for a great number of cankers. 3, Vessels are like tubes in the trunk, but in the crotch area [4] the vessels are circles. A longitudinal cut through the crotch appears like a transverse cut because the cells have changed their orientation about the collar. 5, The pith with a sheath, and the same in the branch [6]. The branch pith does not connect directly with the trunk pith. A pith protection zone (S: 186) may form at the base of the branch pith [7], or sheaths of the branch pith and trunk pith separate the two tissues. [See diagram 13 for more details on how the bud begins to form and grow.]

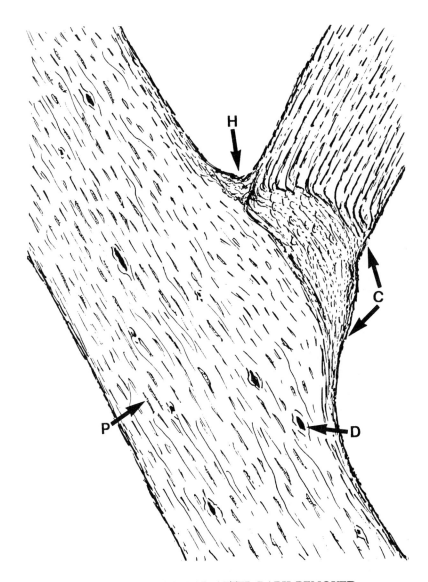

67. BRANCH COLLAR AFTER BARK REMOVED

When leaves are forming, the bark can be removed easily and the pattern of tissues can be seen clearly, especially on ring porous trees such as elms and northern oaks. The reason the bark peels so easily at that time is because the first xylem to form has little or no lignin. The first xylem is like jelly. The branch crotch [H] may have a gap where the tissues part or go one way or another. This area is an Achilles' heel, or vulnerable spot, that can be easily infected by pathogens. Living cells may be at or near the surface for a short period. The collar [C] shows the turning of the branch tissues. Other features you may see are tips of ray sheets [P]. They are very obvious on oaks. Dormant buds [D] or points of meristematic tissues, appear as dense lenticular spots.

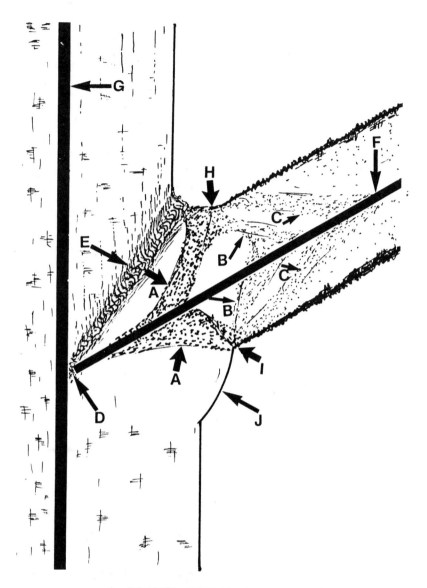

68. BRANCH COLLAR, INSIDE VIEW

Longitudinal dissection of a branch collar after a branch dies, reveals the following: A, the branch protection zone (374) made up of phenol-based substances in hardwoods and terpene-based substances in conifers (76,79,193,214). B and C show first positions of the branch protection zone. On many species the zones form outward into the branch first. In most conifers the zone is well-formed before the branch dies. D is the gap where the branch pith [F] approaches the trunk pith [G]. E is called compacted xylem. It follows the angle of the branch bark ridge. H is the upper limit of the branch protection zone and I is the lower limit. A correct cut would be from H to I. J is the swollen collar below the branch.

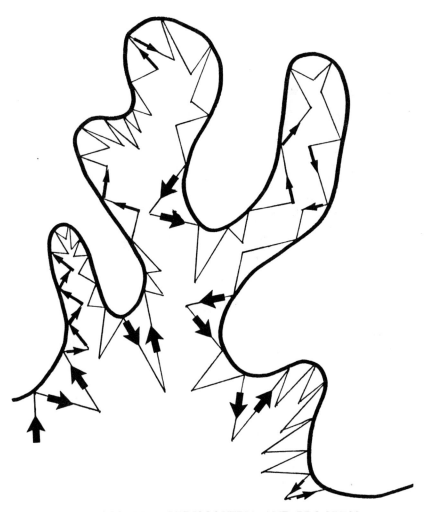

69. DISCOVERY, REDISCOVERY, AND PROGRESS

Advances in science come not so much from discovery as they do from rediscovery. Much of what we think is new was known many years ago (305). In 1754 researchers knew that the collar should not be removed or decay would develop rapidly (214). The protection zone on the branch collar was well understood over a century ago. Then why did the flush cut persist? Mainly because of one word — *healing*. Everybody thought that the large ribs of "callus" meant strong "healing". Now we know, that what they called callus (393) was really woundwood (explained in detail in 1903 by Ernst Küster) (180) and what they called "healing" was not healing. We seem to bounce around in science as shown in the diagram. The first few "hits" or discoveries never seem to be accepted. Yet when we view the process over time, we see that the constant hitting and bouncing against the wall does begin to outline the true shape of things. And, even when this is all done, it still does not mean that it will be accepted.

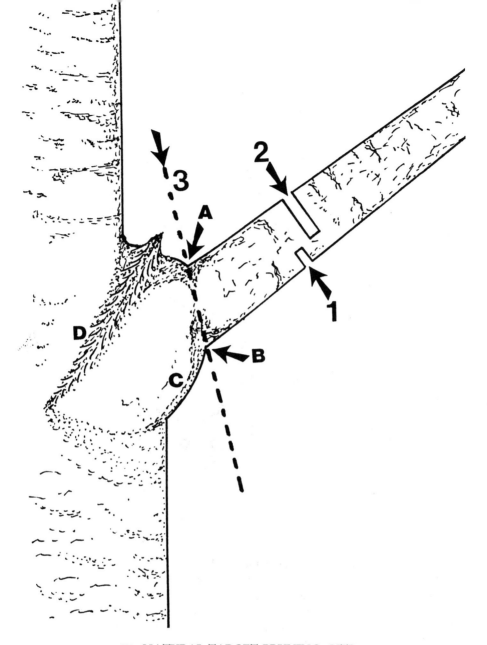

70. NATURAL TARGET PRUNING, NTP

Correct pruning cuts should be made as close as possible to the branch collar [C]. Start by removing the branch [1 and 2] to prevent tearing the bark, and then make the final cut [3] from A to B. Do not leave a stub. Do not injure or remove the collar [C]. Do not cut behind the branch bark ridge [D] where it may protrude within the branch crotch. Do not paint the wound.

Pruning: 29,36,67,71,74,76,79,132,154,214,229,242,355,388,390,391; S: 100, 118,141,169,186.

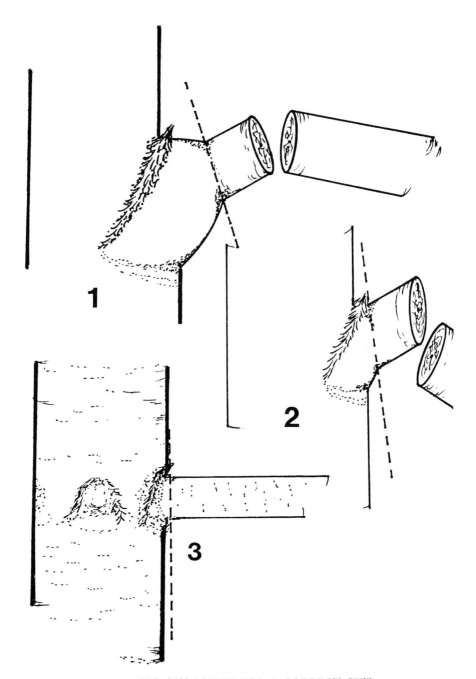

71. NO SET ANGLE FOR A CORRECT CUT

The size of the collar determines the correct position of the pruning cut. The collar may be large [1], medium [2], or flat [3]. There is no set angle for a correct cut. All cuts shown in the diagrams are correct cuts.

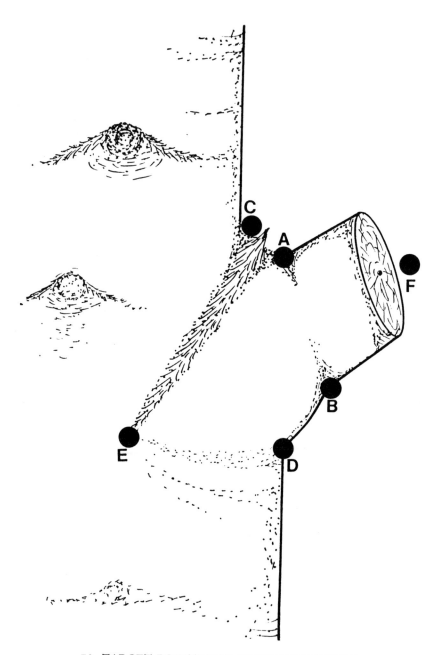

72. TARGET POINTS FOR CORRECT PRUNING

A correct cut is from A to B. Do not put a pruning tool behind the branch bark ridge where it protrudes in the crotch [C]. Point D is where the collar joins the trunk. Point E is the lower end of the branch bark ridge. Always stub cut the branch first [F]. These targets can be seen on most branches, but not all branches. Targets A and B may require adjusting on some branches.

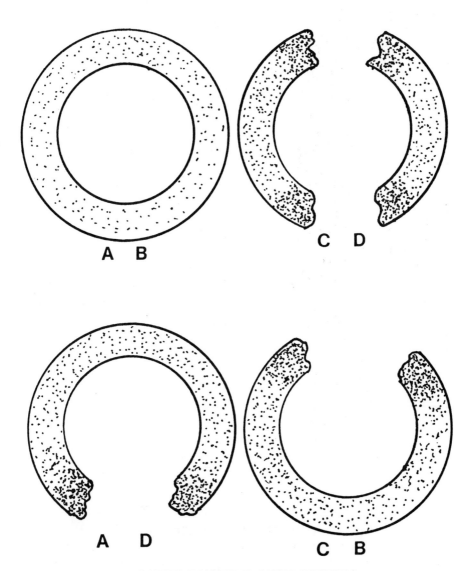

73. CALLUS PATTERNS AFTER PRUNING

When correct cuts are made [A to B], (see diagram 72) a complete circle or "doughnut" of callus will form about the cut the next growing season. When cuts remove the collar [C to D], callus forms only to the sides. When cuts are too close below, [A to D] or too close above, [C to B] broken rings of callus will form. (If cavities are wanted for birds or small animals (47), make cuts from A to D. A cavity will form rapidly below the cut. This treatment is good for wildlife, but harmful for trees.

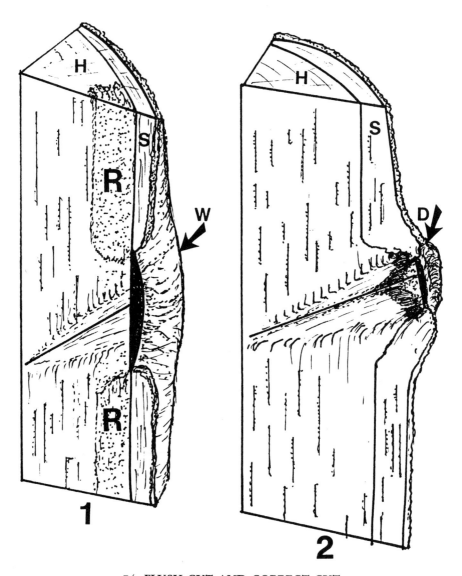

74. FLUSH CUT AND CORRECT CUT

Flush cuts are injurious because they remove the tree's protection boundary (374) that forms within the branch collar [1]. Large ribs of woundwood [W] (180) will form, and large columns of rot [R]. When correct cuts are made [2], a ring of wound-wood will form [D] and the protection boundary will form within the collar. These diagrams are from a red oak, 6 years after similar sized branches were pruned correctly [2] and incorrectly [1]. S is sapwood and H is heartwood. The large ribs of woundwood about the flush cut were considered a sign of strong healing for centuries (214). The rot that formed within was then dug out to sound wood, and the cavity was filled. And, while the worker was there, more flush cuts were made. What a way to stay in business!

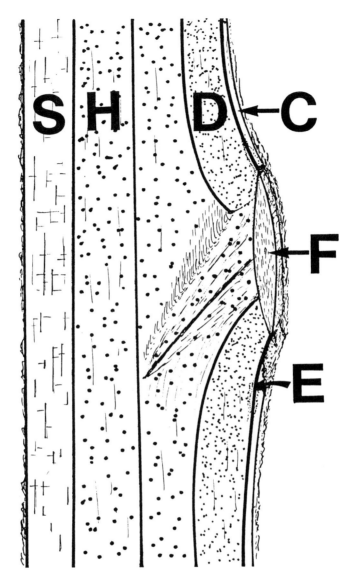

75. FLUSH CUT AND INFECTION

Flush cuts [F] not only destroy a tree's major defense process by removing the tissues that produce the branch protection zone, but the flush cut leads to a reduction of energy reserves in the tissues about the wound. H is heartwood, S is sound sapwood, D is discolored and dead sapwood, C is the single growth increment that formed after the cut, and E is the barrier zone that separates D from C. The current growth increment [C] is taking energy, not storing energy, leaving the new wood about the wound defenseless. This is why large cankers often form about flush cuts. Insects may also infest the defenseless new growth. Cracks and dead spots may develop when the defenseless new growth is exposed to sudden extremes in temperature.

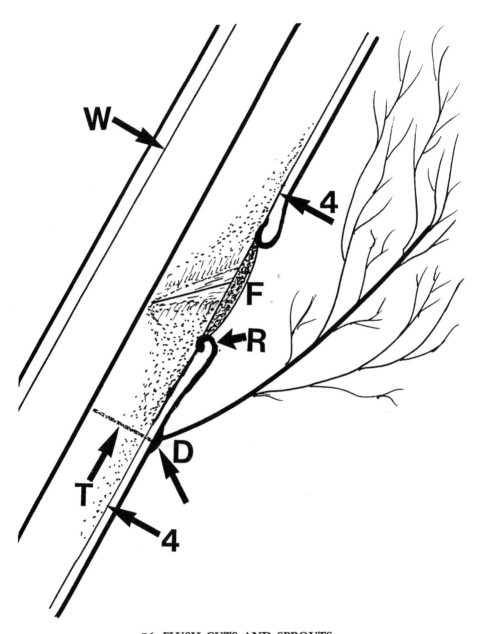

76. FLUSH CUTS AND SPROUTS

Flush cuts [F] lead to excessive sprouting [D]. Barrier zones [4] separate the infected wood from the thin layer of sound but defenseless wood. Any dormant bud (D) from an internal bud trace [T] will be stimulated to grow when energy reserves decrease suddenly near the bud. Sapwood on the opposite side [W] will be thick and it will have stored energy. The thin layer of wood near the flush cut will have little or no stored energy. Sprouts from callus [R] may also form.

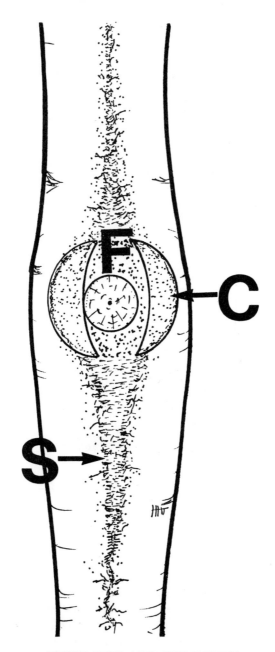

77. FLUSH CUTS AND SUN INJURY

The thin layer of defenseless wood above and below a flush cut [F] may crack or be killed when it is exposed to extremes in temperature. The likelihood of this happening increases as the flush cuts are made on the southwestern side of the tree. C is the callus. In cold climates "frost cracks" may form and in warm climates "sun injury" may occur. The heat and cold are important, but they rarely *start* the processes that lead to the injuries. (See diagrams on included bark (154) and self-wounding for more on the subject.)

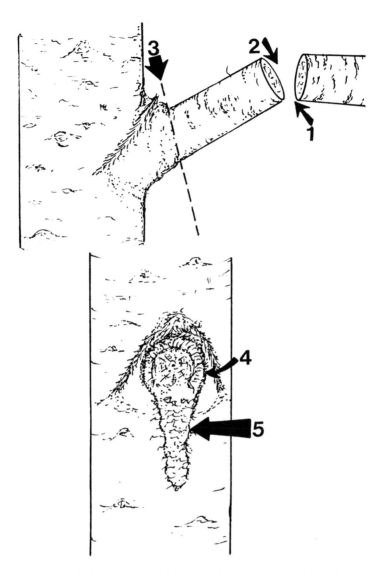

78. CAMBIAL DIEBACK UNDER CORRECT CUTS

On some trees, the cambium may dieback under the pruning cut even when the cut is made correctly [1,2, and 3]. Callus [4] will form partially about the cut; but the dieback will spread beneath the wound. A common cause of this is that the trunk collar does not join the branch collar beneath the branch. On some branches a sunken spot under the branch is a sign of this problem. Or cuts made in winter may lead to this problem. When the dead spot forms, cut away the dead bark with great care. Do not enlarge the dead spot. Cut as shallow as possible. Do not try to anticipate the dead spot by scribing immediately after the cut is made. If possible, wait until the callus-woundwood tissues show exactly the margin of the dead spot. Then remove the bark with great care. This dieback problem increases with the size of the branches that are removed.

100

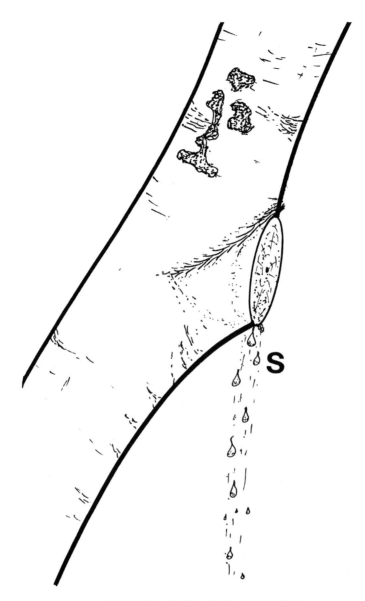

79 . CORRECT CUTS AND SAP FLOW

When correct pruning cuts are made during late winter or early spring on some tree species—maples, birches—sap will flow from the wounds [S]. This is a normal wound response in these species. The sap will flow for a few days to a few weeks and then stop (379). Our studies (S: 35,11,117) showed no injury as a result of the sap flow. If the flow is considered unsightly, or if there is concern because of the sap flow, pruning can be done immediately after the leaves have expanded fully. Do not confuse the flow of sap, which is normal, with the flow of wetwood fluids that are associated with infections by bacteria. (For more, see diagrams and discussion on wetwood.)

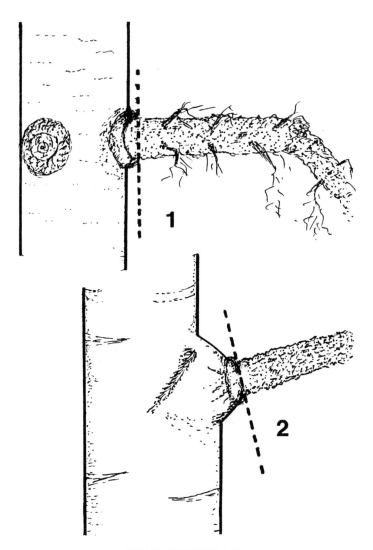

80. DEAD BRANCH REMOVAL

Cut dead branches as close as possible to the ring of sound, healthy wood that surrounds the base of the branch. Do not injure or remove the base of sound wood [1 and 2]. Some large dead branches may have very large bases of sound wood that may protrude over a foot in length (0.3 meters). The temptation is to remove the swollen bases. If they are removed, large columns of rot will spread into the trunk. You must weigh appearance with health. Most tree owners will understand when you explain it to them. Explain also that dead branch removal is a health treatment because the dead wood is an energy source—cellulose, lignin, glucose—for fungi. Give the tree "a shower" by removing the dead and dirty parts. One note of caution. When dead wood is essential for wildlife, and where there is no hazard risk for humans, leave the large sections of deadwood for birds and other wildlife. Common sense and safety must be the rule.

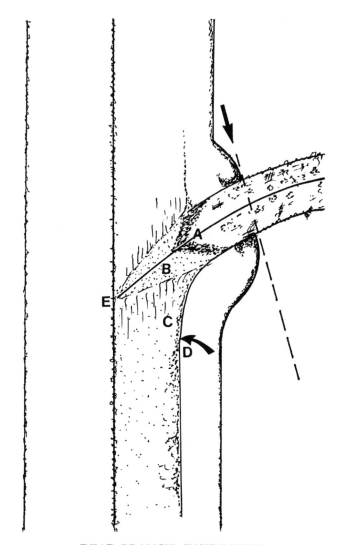

81. DEAD BRANCH, INSIDE VIEW

When dead branches are removed promptly, decay-causing fungi will be resisted by the branch protection zone at position A. When the dead branch persists or when the invading microorganisms are aggressive, the corewood [B] of the branch may be infected. When dead branches remain for a long time, and the infecting microorganisms are very aggressive, the wood in the trunk present at the time of branch death may be infected [C]. Then a barrier zone [D] will separate the infected wood from the sound wood that formed after the death of the branch. It is not well understood how C occurs and how D forms. The basic compartmented structure of the tree may be the primary answer to the limitations of the infection. If the pathogens are going to spread, it would be many-fold easier for them to spread vertically than outward in a radial direction. E is where the trunk pith and branch pith come close together but do not meet.

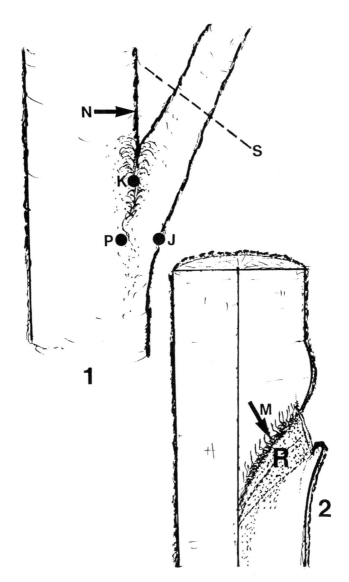

82. INCLUDED BARK

Included bark forms when bark of the branch and trunk squeeze together [1].
To remove a branch that has included bark, first stub the branch [S]. Cut upward
from point J to K. Point P is the bottom of the included bark. J is a point directly
outward from P. Care must be taken not to injure the trunk at N. After such a
cut is made [2], some rot [R] will develop in the base of the branch embedded
in the trunk. The included bark [M] resists upward spread of the rot.

104

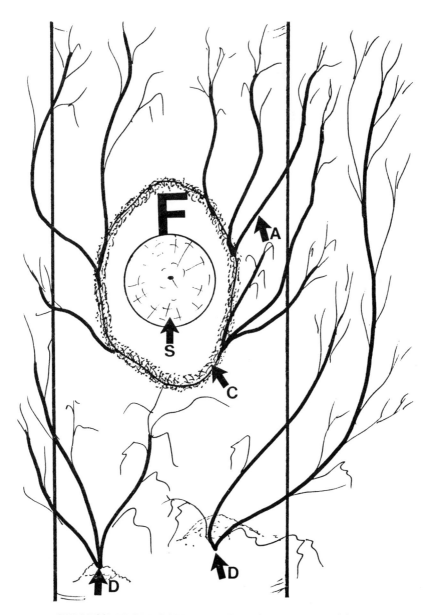

83. SPROUTS FROM CALLUS AND FROM DORMANT BUDS

Large ribs of callus [C] often develop after branches (S) are flush cut [F]. Because the callus is a meristematic tissue it may divide and form adventitious sprouts [A]. Dormant buds [D] may sprout below the wound (see diagram 76). Epicormic means sprouts upon the trunk. There are two types of epicormic sprouts: 1, adventitious from callus and 2, dormant sprouts from latent or dormant buds. Dormant buds may be meristematic points carried along in the cambial zone, and they do not have the appearance of buds, until released.

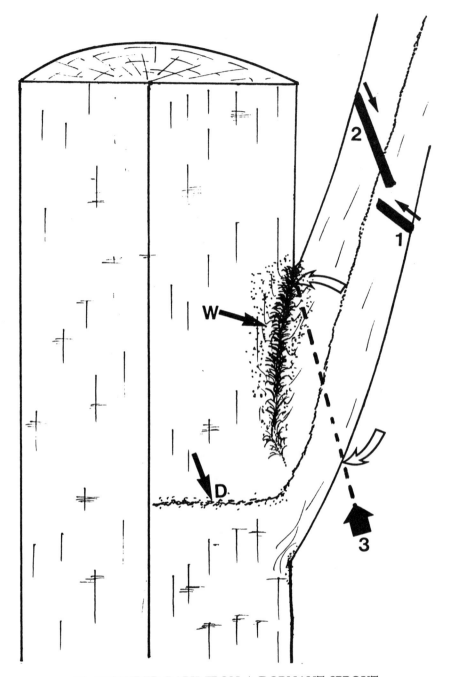

84. INCLUDED BARK FROM A DORMANT SPROUT

Dormant sprouts may grow upward rapidly and the bark of the trunk and sprout may be squeezed between the trunk and branch [W]. D shows the bud trace. Dormant shoots have no branch bark ridge. They are very poorly attached the first few years after they develop.

106

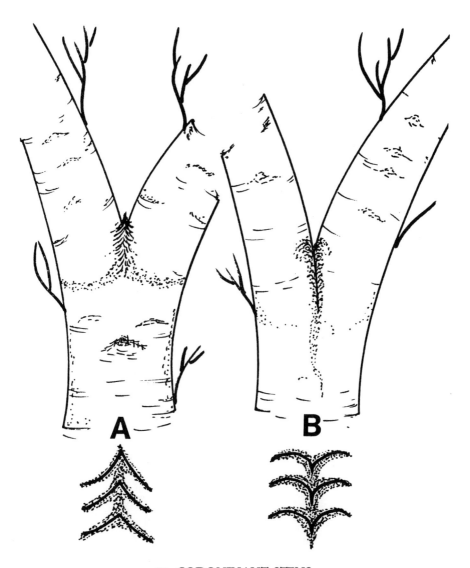

85. CODOMINANT STEMS

Codominant stems are stems of about the same size originating from the same position on a stem. When the stem bark ridge turns upward, the stems will have a strong union [A]. When the stem bark ridge turns inward, they will have a weak union [B]. The type of union and not the angle is the major factor affecting the strength of the stems. However, as the angle becomes tighter, the chances for type B unions increase. Climbers should not tie their support ropes through type B unions.

107

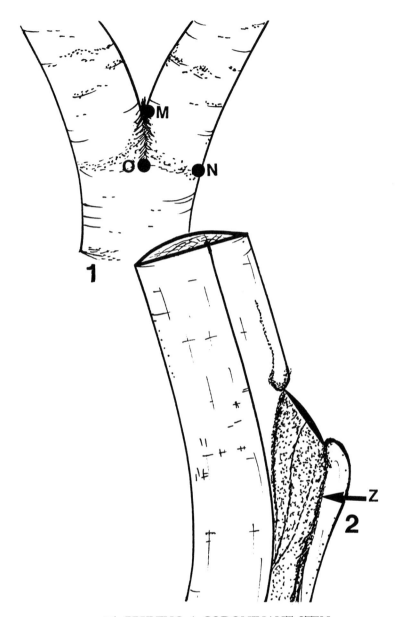

86. PRUNING A CODOMINANT STEM

When it is necessary to remove a codominant stem, first find the target points N and M [1]. O is the point at the bottom of the stem bark ridge and N is directly across from O. M is on the N side of the stem bark ridge within the crotch of the stems. After stubbing the stem, cut upward from N to M with great care. Some defect will develop in the stem [2] but it will be limited by the barrier zone Z. Codominant stems do not have protection boundaries; but the defect will be small if the correct cut is made.

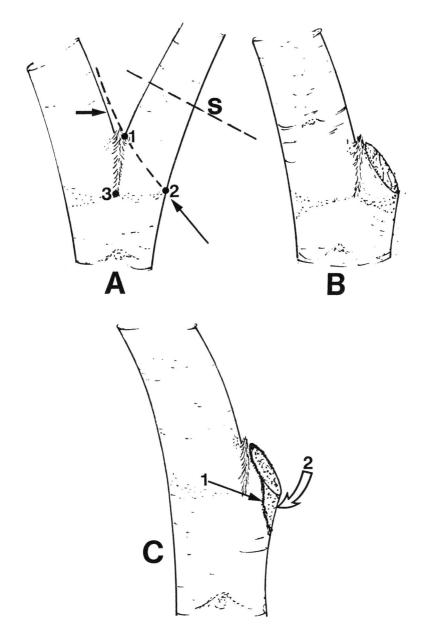

87. CODOMINANT STEM REMOVAL AND CAMBIAL DIEBACK

Correct removal of a codominant stem is shown in A. Stub the stem first [S] and then cut from 2 to 1. Use care not to injure the stem at the position of the arrow. B shows the result of a correct cut. On some trees [C] some cambial dieback [2] may develop below the cut, especially in cuts made in winter. The callus [1] will form under the bark. Cut away the dead bark after the callus has developed. Do not cut into the wood. Remove the bark by making very shallow cuts. Do not point the lower tip of the cut.

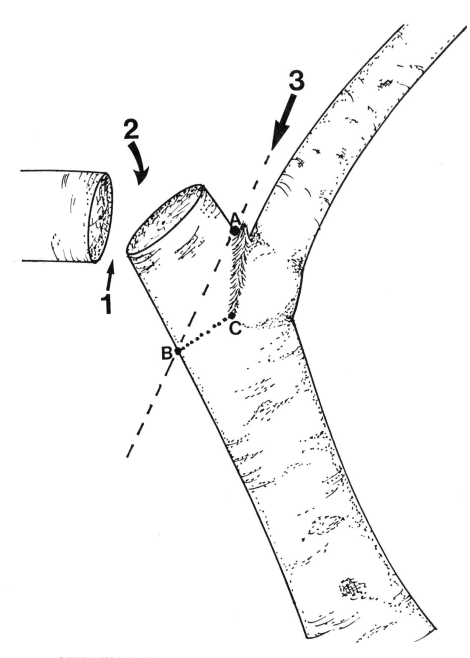

88. CORRECT REMOVAL OF A SMALL LEADER ON A YOUNG TREE
When it is necessary to remove the leader on a young tree, cut from A to B [3] after the top has been removed, 1 and 2. Point B is directly across from point C, the bottom of the branch bark ridge. The branch remaining should be at least one third the diameter of the stem that was cut.

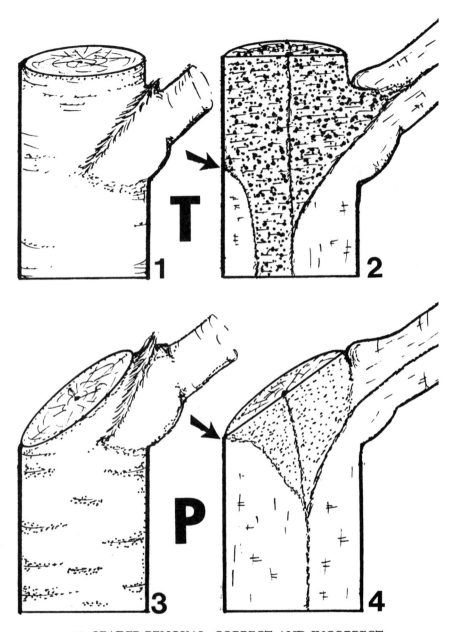

89. LEADER REMOVAL; CORRECT AND INCORRECT

T, flat top cut. 1, incorrect. 2, inside view. Arrow shows where cut should have been made. Decay develops rapidly in trunk stub. P, correct cut. 3 shows correct angle. 4 shows internal defect. Arrow shows where the tree began to wall off the infection. There is little cambial dieback and defect associated with the correct cut. There is no natural "built-in" protection boundary in leader stems. CODIT boundaries form and resist spread of infections.

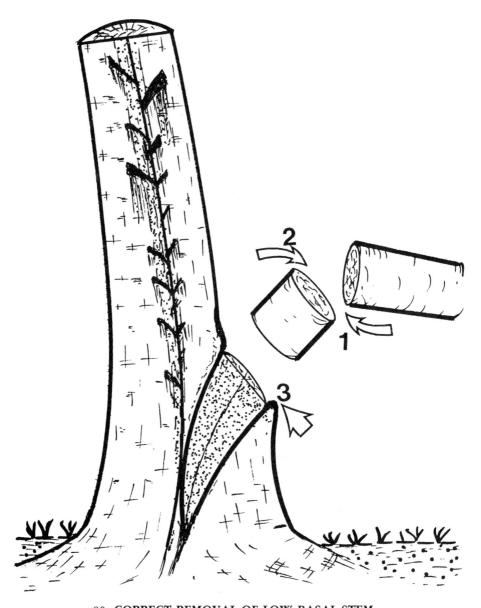

90. CORRECT REMOVAL OF LOW BASAL STEM

If the basal stem to be removed is living or dead, or if it has included bark, always stub cut first [1 and 2]. If it is a living stem, cut at the angle shown by the arrow [3]. If it is dead, cut as close as possible to the living wood that surrounds the dead stem. If it has included bark cut upward to meet the larger stem as shown by the arrow. Use care not to injure the larger stem. Defect may form in the corewood of the stem embedded in the base of the larger stem but the defect will seldom spread into the larger stem (S: 17). If a hollow forms, do not drill holes to drain water.

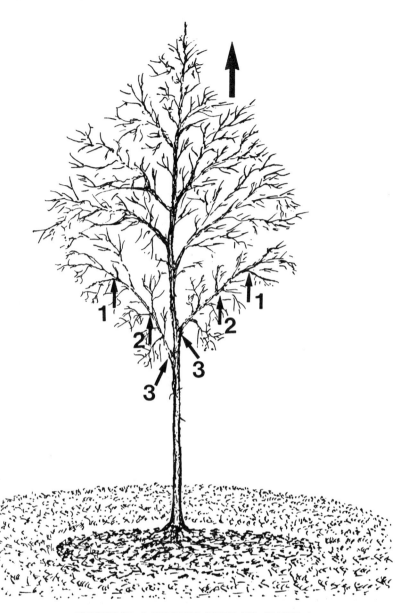

91. PRUNING A YOUNG TREE TO HAVE A
STRONG CENTRAL LEADER

To stimulate a strong central leader on a young tree, remove the lower branches in stages over the years: first year, 1; second year, 2; third year remove branch 3. Repeat upward on the tree. This will allow the young tree to grow without great amounts of foliage removed. This is the time in the life of a tree that much can be done to determine shape and to regulate growth. Street trees should have their lower branches at least 3 meters above ground. Correct training as shown here can bring this about without disrupting the early beauty of the tree. The best time for this type of pruning is just before growth starts in the spring.

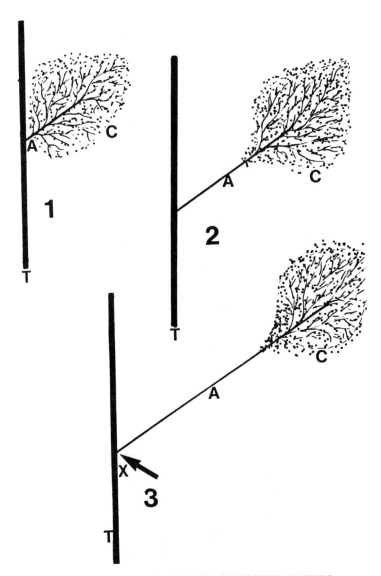

92. PRUNING LONG AND SHORT BRANCHES

The leaves or needles on the small branches must produce the glucose to supply the living cells in the roots, trunk [T], and branch. If the foliage volume remains the same [C] and the branch length [A] varies from 1 to 2, to 3, then care must be taken in how much is removed from C. Remember, A has hundreds of millions of living cells that depend on C for their energy. As A increases, the amount of pruning from C should decrease. Much can be taken from C in 1, at least one third. Less than one third can be taken from 2. If 3 requires pruning it should be at point X [arrow]. When foliage is removed from 3C, the entire branch will begin to wane. The best time to prune to regulate growth is just after leaves and needles have extended fully. Pruning at this time will cause slight injury.

114

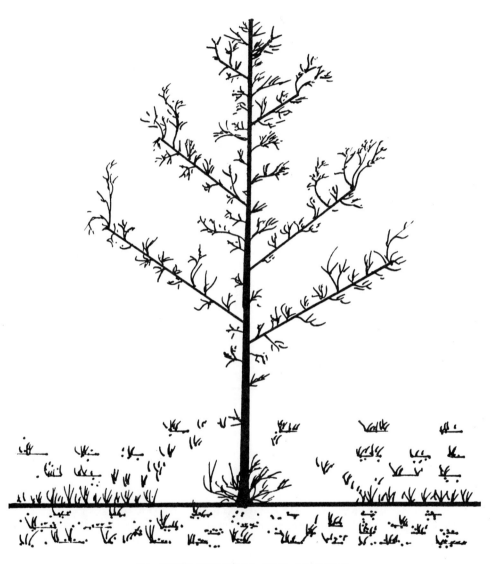

93. OVER PRUNING AND SPROUTS

Excessive sprouting indicates that the tree is using reserve energy to survive. When old trees, young trees, or branches produce many sprouts, it is a sign of over pruning or starvation. Some tree species are especially prone to sprouting. Pruning after leaves form may reduce sprouting. Remember, the sprout is there to return energy to the tree. Wait at least two to three years if sprouts are to be removed. When branches are tip pruned or over pruned, the sprouts and the entire branch may decline or die after three years.

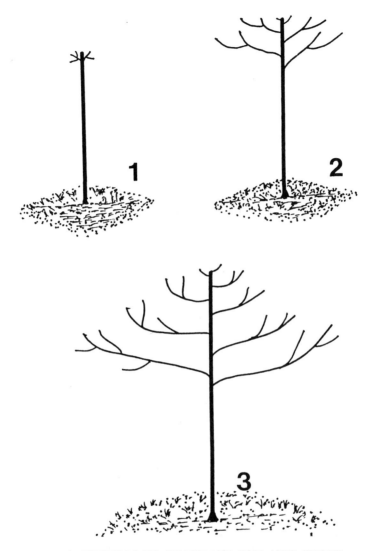

94. PRUNING TO REGULATE SIZE AND SHAPE

Pollarding, or high coppicing, are the terms given to the practice of regulating size and shape. To be done correctly, the desired shape is determined when the tree is young. A young tree is 100% dynamic mass. It has a cortex along the entire trunk. The framework can be a single stem [1] or a great variety of shapes [2 and 3]. Once the framework is established, all sprouts are cut back to the framework every year. In some cases where flowers are wanted, a few sprouts with flower buds are left on the framework. The all important feature of this practice is to establish the framework when the tree is young, and to cut back to the framework every year, or every other year on selected branches bearing flowers. Many types of tree mutilation have been called pollarding. *Topping large trees is not pollarding, it is a crime against nature.*

116

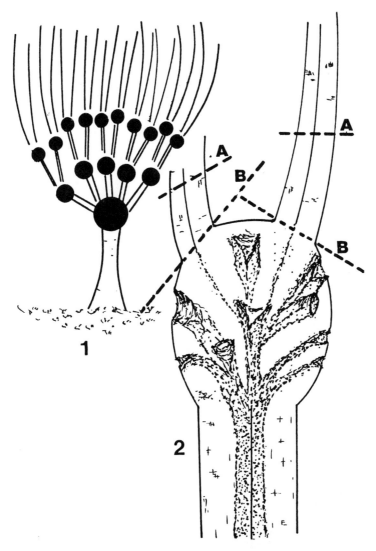

95. PLANE TREE AND TILIA PROBLEMS

A common worldwide problem with plane trees (*Platanus* species), and often with species of *Tilia* (lime, linden) is that the tops have been removed several times (black dots, 1) and now people want to know what to do to keep them safe. Of course removal is the best answer; but usually that is not realistic or allowed. In some cases the most defective ones are removed. Cables and braces are used in many of the trees. Risk of failure can be reduced by making all future cuts as shown in diagram 2. Plane trees usually compartmentalize very well. Do not cut into the swollen heads. Do remove the new sprouts when they begin to grow from a vertical to a horizontal position. Be on alert for dead and dying sprouts and remove them correctly [2] as soon as possible [A first, B second]. I hope we see the day when this horrible practice will not be done, or even allowed in our cities.

117

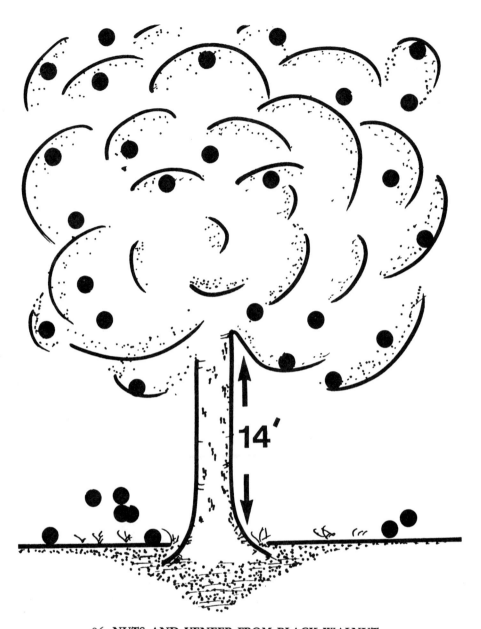

14'

96. NUTS AND VENEER FROM BLACK WALNUT

It is possible to grow black walnut for nuts and finally for veneer. To do this you must start early with the right tree. The tree must lend itself to pruning to 14 feet above ground before the first codominant stems begin to form. A clear trunk of 14 feet can yield a 12 foot veneer cant. Once the clear trunk is established, crown pruning should encourage codominant stems. Trees that do not lend themselves to this type of pruning should be culled early if nuts and veneer are wanted.

97. PRUNING TREES NEAR ELECTRIC UTILITY LINES

90% of the time, the removal of 3 branches can give 90% of the clearance. Time [T] is money [M]!

Guidelines [G] are given in 3 orders of pruning. Order 1 is the ideal. All branches will be removed correctly the first time the tree is pruned. Order 2 means that some pruning cuts less than ideal must be made to assure safe and reliable power. Order 3 means that many cuts must be made that are less than ideal to maintain safety for people and the power lines. As more trees are removed in Order 3 pruning, more trees will fall into Order 2. And eventually as Order 2 trees are removed, most new trees planted near lines will receive Order 1 pruning. Of course, the best solution is not to plant large-maturing trees near power lines (156,157).

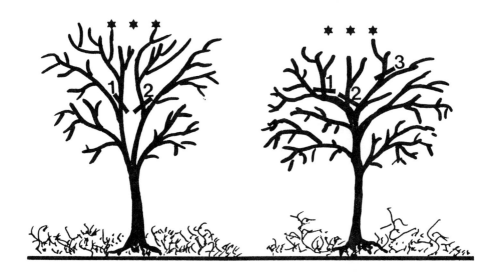

98. FIRST ORDER PRUNING

Remove only those branches growing toward the lines, or branches that when cut would produce sprouts that would grow toward the lines. Do not trim side branches. Note: * indicates position of power lines. All diagrams with the star signs are specifically for power lines. (Numbers show positions of cuts.)

120

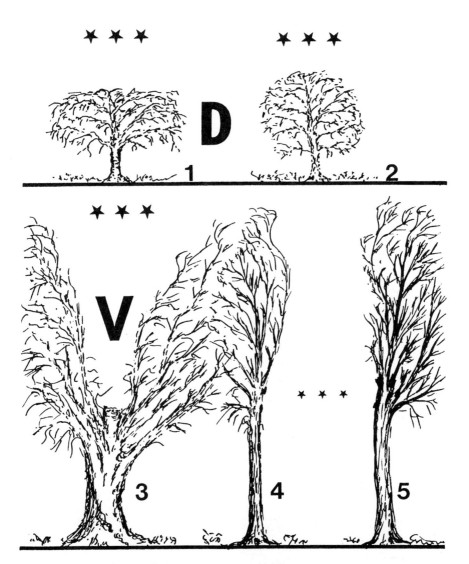

99. SECOND ORDER PRUNING — TREES AND POWER LINES CAN EXIST TOGETHER

If trees are to be planted near lines, choose dwarf varieties, or trees that have a small compact form [1 and 2]. Minimal amounts of pruning during regular pruning cycles will keep the trees attractive and clear of the lines. It may be necessary to remove the center [3] or sides [4 and 5] of large-maturing trees. When correct pruning starts early in the life of the tree, clearance can be sustained while keeping the trees healthy and safe. Trees and power lines can exist together if arborists, homeowners, and power companies all work together.

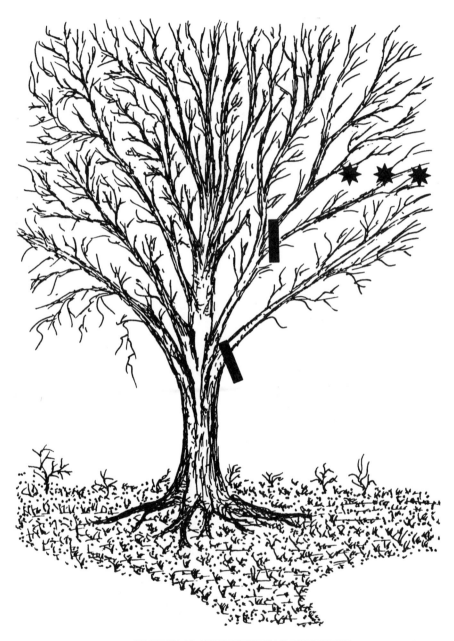

100. **NATURAL DIRECTIONAL PRUNING**
When side branches start growing toward the lines, remove only those branches
that are growing toward the lines.

101. TOPPING: A CRIME AGAINST NATURE

Topping is a worldwide tree mutilation practice that must stop! Topping not only destroys a tree's dignity, but it weakens the tree and makes it a high hazard risk. If a tree must be topped, then it is time for a new tree. Customer education is a major way to stop this practice. It will not be easy.

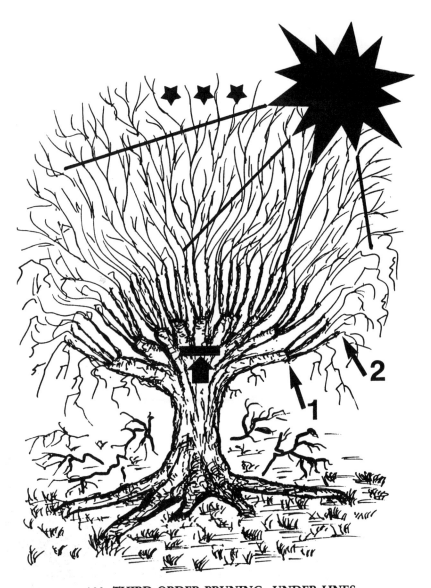

102. THIRD ORDER PRUNING, UNDER LINES

After several treatments of topping and tipping [Roundovers 1 and 2], there is little left to do except to remove the center, as shown here, or to remove the tree. Safety becomes the major problem. Sprouts growing from topping cuts are often poorly attached. Many cities have ordinances against topping. Professionals must work to stop this horrible practice. (For a booklet on pruning trees near electric utility lines, contact Shigo and Trees, Associates.)

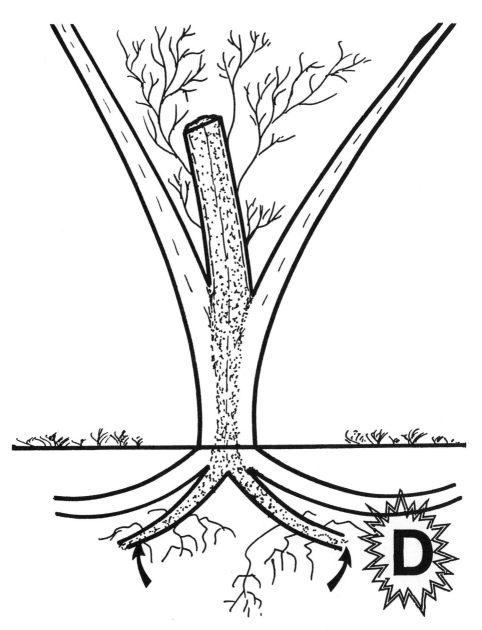

103. TOPPING AND ROOT DISEASES

When tops are removed the roots that normally get their food from the tops begin to starve [arrows]. Then the demons of D (see diagram 108) enter and cause a great variety of diseases such as wilts, plane tree canker *(Ceratocystis fimbriata)*, and root rots.

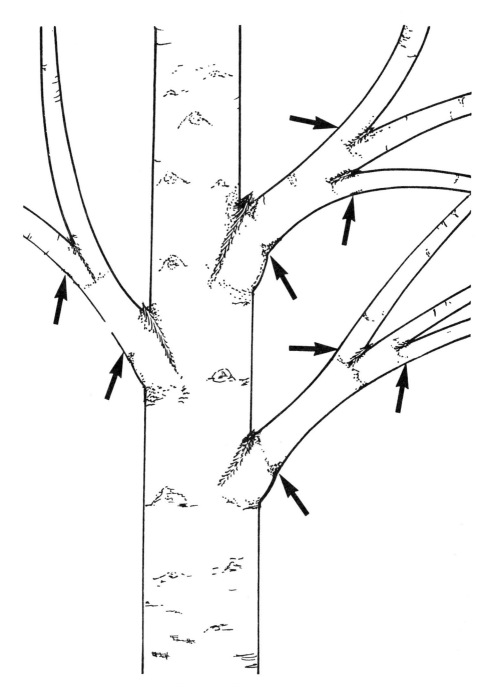

104. CUT AT BRANCH UNIONS

All pruning cuts should be at branch unions [arrows]. Do not make cuts between arrows.

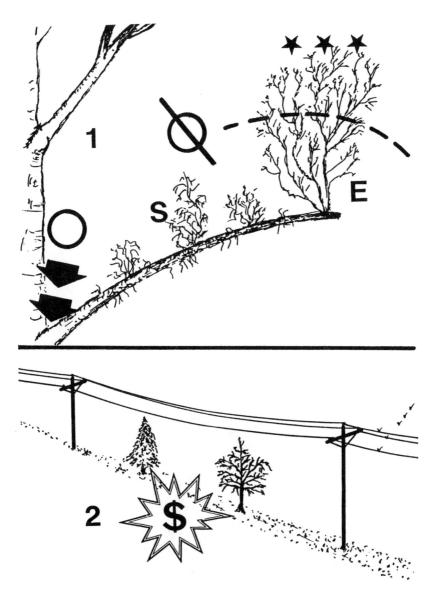

105. SPROUTS AND TRAINING YOUNG TREES

Two types of sprouts [1] grow after over pruning: elites [E] and suppressed [S]. The suppressed usually die in a few years, or they seldom grow very large. Elites grow from single buds and usually grow rapidly. Do not top elites. Do remove the entire branch [arrows].

Start training young trees during regular pruning cycles [2]. This practice will be good for the trees, lines, and economics of the power company.

Conifers and other trees that have a strong central leader should not be planted near power lines.

127

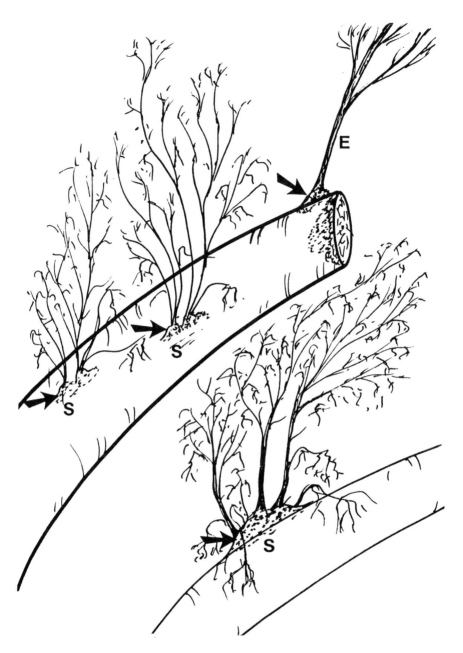

106. **ELITE AND SUPPRESSED SPROUTS**

Suppressed sprouts usually grow from bud clusters [S]. They are bushy and seldom grow rapidly. Elites grow rapidly [E]. It is best to leave the suppressed sprouts or remove the entire branch as shown in diagram 105. If sprouts must be removed, use care not to injure or remove the mound of wood at the sprout base [arrows] or many more sprouts will form. Most sprouts grow fastest the first three years.

128

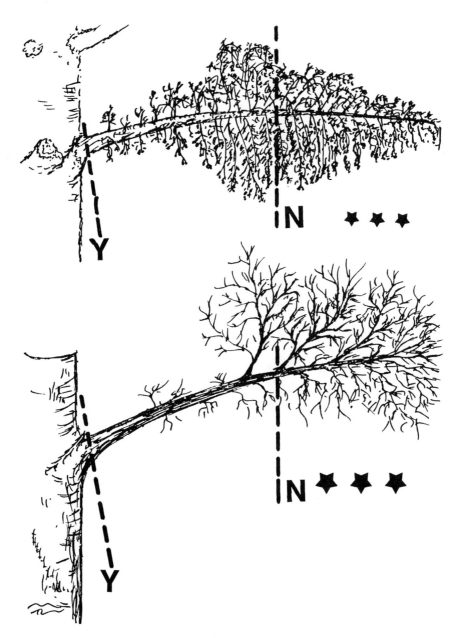

107. **TIPPING**

Do not tip long lateral branches [N]. It is best to remove the branch [Y]. Some tipped branches may live for many years, but most usually live for only a few years. Then they become a hazard to people.

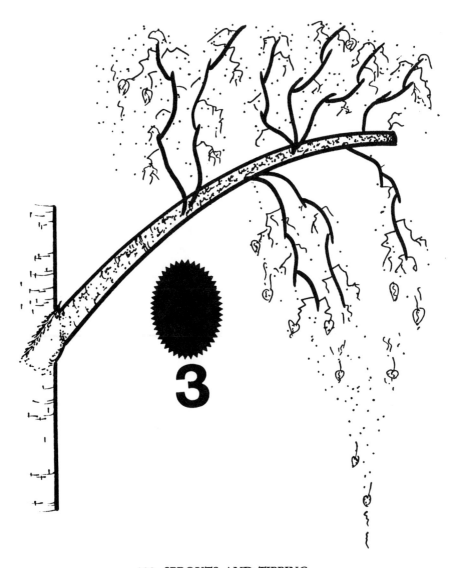

108. SPROUTS AND TIPPING

Sprouts usually grow for 3 years after a large branch is tipped, then most of them decline or die. On very vital trees, and on trees in warm climates, the sprouts may grow for many years. (Symbol indicates problems after 3 years.)

130

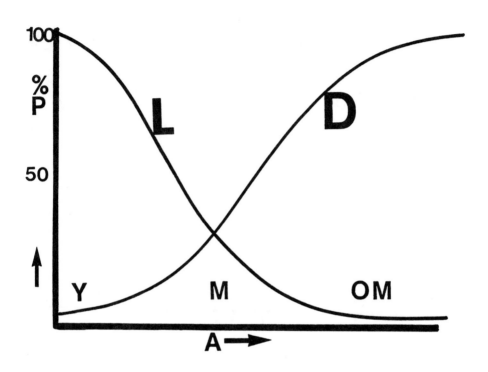

109. PRUNING DOSE: HOW MUCH TO REMOVE

The bottom horizon X axis shows age increasing [A]. The vertical Y axis shows percentage of wood removed increasing. When trees are young [Y] great amounts of living wood [L] can be removed. As the tree matures [M] less living wood should be removed and dead wood removal should increase [D]. As the tree approaches over maturity [OM] very little living [L] wood should be removed, and great amounts of deadwood [D] should be removed.

Many species of tropical trees grow very fast; but they still follow these patterns for pruning dose.

110. **STUMP SPROUTS**

After some species of trees are cut, many sprouts form the first growing season after the cut [1]. After 2 and 3 years, the number of sprouts still alive decreases greatly.

111. NEW TREES FROM SPROUTS

Healthy new trees can grow from stump sprouts. Wait at least 3 years to select the new tree, or trees if a clump is wanted. The best trees will grow from single buds low on the stump [1]. Avoid clusters of sprouts, especially when they are higher on the stump [2]. Never select a tree from a sprout growing from the callus around the top of the stump.

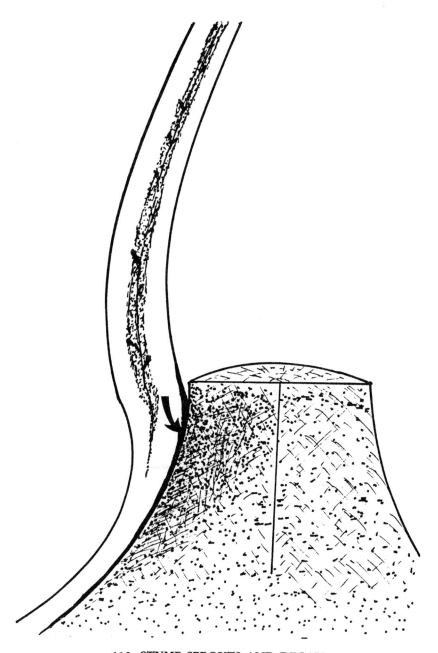

112. STUMP SPROUTS AND DECAY

Decay from the stump seldom spreads to the new sprout [arrow] (S: 17,168). Decay will spread from stump to sprout when the sprout grows so fast that it squeezes against the wood in the sound stump. Then a dead spot develops at the base of the sprout. When selecting a sprout for a new tree, make certain that the sprout does not have a dead spot resulting from squeezed bark. This is similar to included bark on branches. Sprouts low on the stump seldom have this problem.

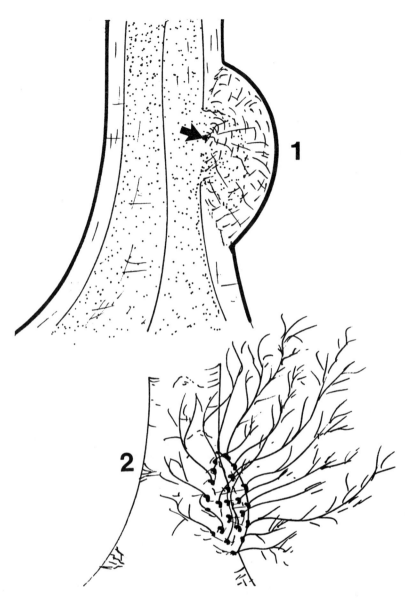

113. BURLS

Swollen spots or bumps on trees are called burls, tumors, cancers, galls, or bud fasciations. We know causes of some, but not all. Insects and microorganisms cause a great variety of galls on leaves, stems, and roots. Some burls start from a disruption at one point in the cambial zone, and the disruption continues for the life of the tree [1]. Viruses are thought to cause some of these cambial disruptions, as in stem pitting of some fruit trees. Bud burls or bud fasciations [2] occur where buds or sprouts have been removed from the same place over many years. Some trees have bud burls at the base; *Eucalyptus, Betula.* When the trees are cut, many sprouts will form from the basal burls.

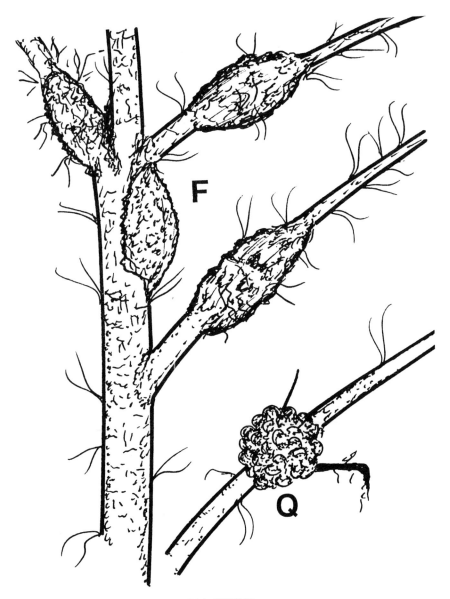

114. RUSTS

Rusts are fungi that are obligate parasites on green plants. Many rust fungi cause spindle-shaped swellings on stems [F, fusiform rust], round, gall-like structures [Q, gall rust], witchesbrooms, and many kinds of leaf and needle malformations. Many of the tree rusts also infect other plants as part of their life cycle. One way to control some rusts is to remove the plant that supports one stage of the rust fungi. Early attempts to reduce white pine blister rust were aimed at eradication of gooseberries *(Ribes)*. (For much more see 404.)

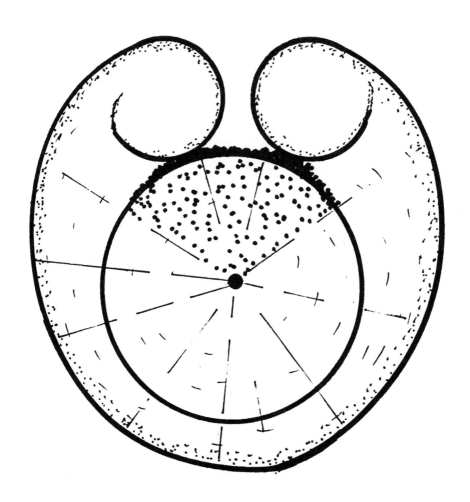

115. RAM'S HORNS

When woundwood grows rapidly, it often turns inward to form a ram's horn (shape). The wounds will not close because the bark of the ram's horns meet and seldom grow together. Treatments that stimulate rapid growth of woundwood often lead to ram's horns.

116. SHRUB PRUNING

Shrubs, like trees, are compartmented, woody, perennial, shedding plants. But, unlike trees, shrubs usually do not have a single large stem. A shrub has many stems or branches growing from a very short basal trunk. (A tree can fall on you and kill you; a shrub cannot!) Some shrubs should be pruned to the base every few years. All shrubs should have dead and dying stems removed. **Always prune a shrub from the inside first.** Do not tip prune shrubs. Make cuts at branch unions and do not injure collars.

138

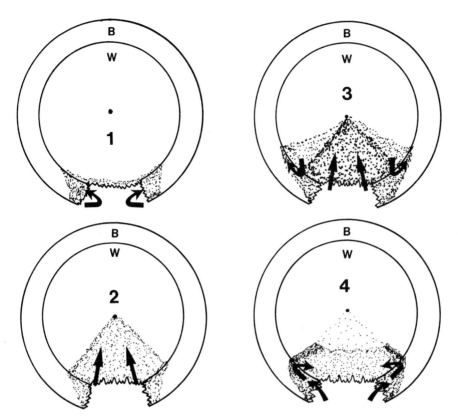

117 & 118. FOUR BASIC WAYS MICROORGANISMS INFECT
STEMS AND ROOTS

1. Annual Cankers

    Bark [B] is infected and only a very small amount of wood [W] is invaded. Boundaries in bark and wood wall off the pathogens after one tree growing season.

2. Wood Infections

    Wood [W] is infected and only a small amount of bark [B] is invaded. Compartmentalization resists spread of pathogens in wood; CODIT.

3. Canker Rots

    Wood [W] is infected first, and then the pathogens invade the bark [B]. Wood beneath the killed bark is then infected again by the pathogen. The pathogen alternates from wood to bark, and from bark to wood. In this pattern, the pathogen can continue to invade new wood by killing the cambial zone from the bark side inward. In this way, the pathogen is able to avoid compartmentalization for short periods (83,218; S: 31). Some canker rot pathogens produce wedges into the wood (A).

4. Perennial Cankers

    Bark [B] is infected first, and then wood [W] beneath the killed bark is invaded. Again, the pathogen grows from bark to wood, and back to bark, "avoiding" boundaries in the wood. The see-saw action of canker rot and perennial canker pathogens allows the pathogen to spread in a circumferential way, resisting compartmentalization for short periods.

139

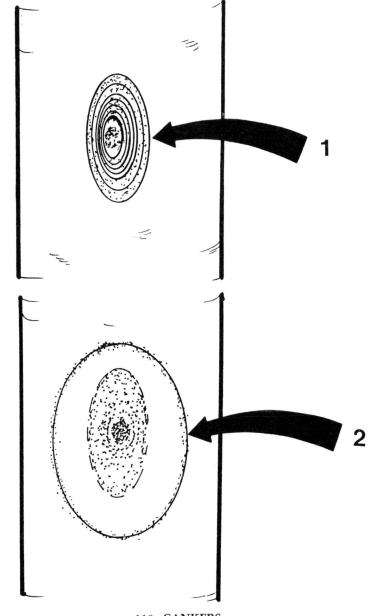

119. CANKERS

Cankers are localized dead spots caused by infections by pathogens. A lesion is any dead spot. When a lesion has a well defined margin it is called a canker [1].

When cankers are small, they can be cut out [2]. Bark must be removed far beyond the canker [2]. The best time to remove a canker is immediately after the leaves have formed fully. But, remember, most cankers are signs of other tree problems. On weak trees, new cankers often form, even when the old cankers are cut out effectively.

Cankers: 25,26,27to31,83,151,161,200,238, S: 15,172.

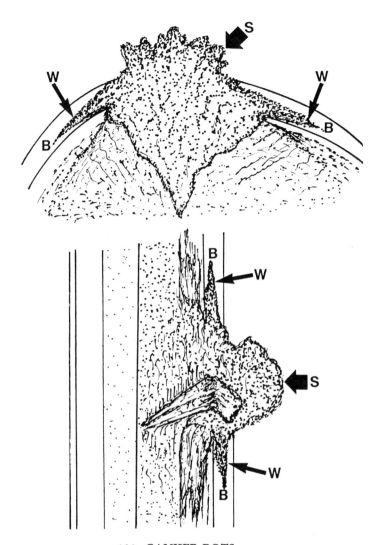

120. CANKER ROTS

Here are two views of a canker rot: transverse above, and radial longitudinal below.

After the pathogen becomes well established in the wood, it produces a hard mass of tissue [S] often called a sterile conk, which is a very poor term because it means a sterile fertile fruit body. Wedges of hard fungus tissue [W] form out in the bark [B]. Some pathogens form them into the wood. As the wedge expands, the cambial cells are killed. Then the fungus spreads laterally into the wood trapped beneath the dead cambium. Just as we are learning now in human physiology, there are many ways that pathogens can stall or stop an immune system or block defense. So it is with trees also. Tree pathogens have developed ways to circumvent compartmentalization temporarily. Because early decay studies on trees involved many canker rots, it is understandable why compartmentalization was not recognized.

141

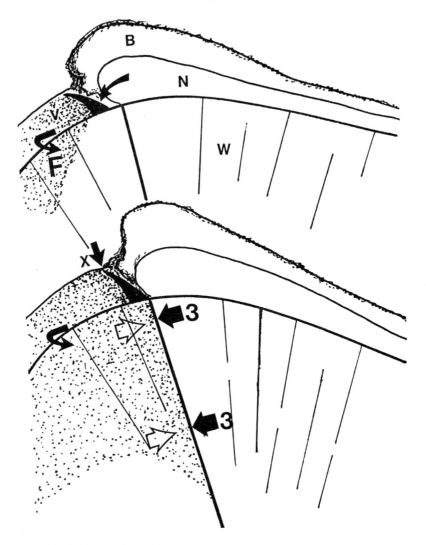

121. PERENNIAL CANKER IN A TREE THAT HAS STRONG COMPARTMENTALIZATION

Upper Diagram

In a perennial canker, the fungus [F] infects the bark first [V]. The tree responds by forming a wedge of woody tissues [arrow in new wood N] into the infected bark. The wedge usually does not close the gap between the infected bark and the bark [B]. The fungus then grows from the infected bark [V] into the dying wood [W] beneath the infected bark [arrow from V to F].

Lower Diagram

The spread of the fungus laterally in wood [open arrows] is met by a strong resisting force [closed arrow in wood, 3]. Strong walls 3 limit the lateral spread into the wood beneath the infected bark. The next growing season, the pathogen grows from the old infected bark [X arrow] into the new bark, and the sequence is repeated.

142

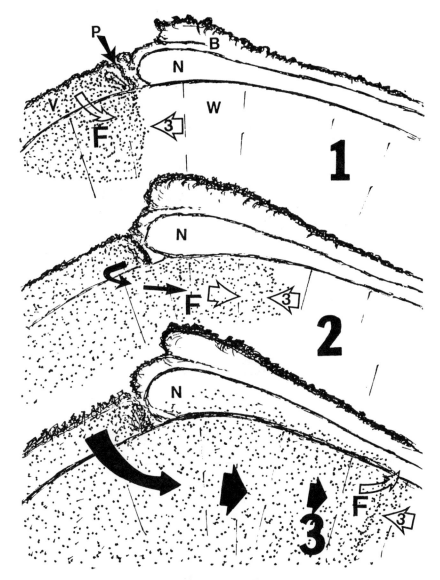

122. PERENNIAL CANKER IN A TREE THAT HAS WEAK
COMPARTMENTALIZATION

1. The fungus [F] infects the bark [V] and begins to grow in the wood [W] beneath the killed bark. The tree forms a weak wedge of woody tissues [P, arrow] into the bark. The new wood [N] begins to grow beneath the bark [B]. A weak wall 3 [open arrow, 3] forms in the wood.

2. The strong force of the fungus overcomes the weak resistance of wall 3, and the fungus spreads laterally in the wood.

3. The thin layer of new wood [N] is trapped and killed. Weak trees can be killed in one or two years. Many young aspens *(Populus tremuloides)* are killed this way by *Hypoxylon mammatum*.

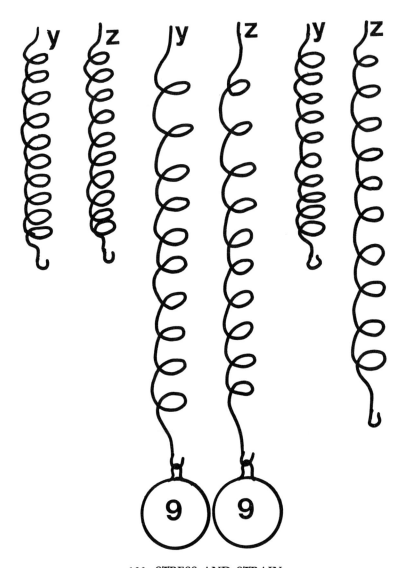

123. STRESS AND STRAIN

STRESS is a reversible condition where energy or other survival factors become limiting, and a system, or one of its parts or processes, begins to operate near the limits for which it was designed.

STRAIN is a nonreversible condition where a system, or one of its parts or processes, exceeds the limits for which it was designed. Think of two springs, Y and Z. They look identical. They are not made of the same material. When a 9 unit force is applied to both, Z stretches more than Y. When the agent causing the stretch—9 unit weight—is removed, Y returns to its original position. Z is twice as long. It has been strained (S: 184).

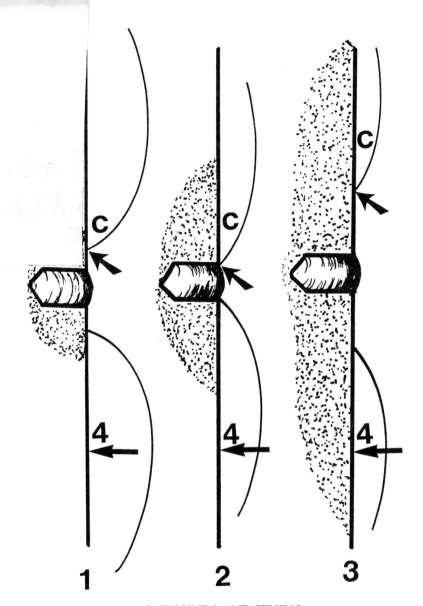

124. WOUNDS AND TIMING

1. Wounds made in spring at the time of leaf expansion will have moderate cambial dieback [arrow near wound], small columns of infection, and large ribs of callus and woundwood [C]. Arrow 4 shows the barrier zone and the size of the tree at the time of wounding.

2. Wounds inflicted during the summer, or midgrowth period, usually have very little cambial dieback [arrow near wound] and moderate growth of callus and woundwood.

3. Wounds inflicted in the fall, or after the growing period, will have a large area of cambial dieback [arrow near wound] and very small ribs of callus and woundwood (77;S: 73).

145

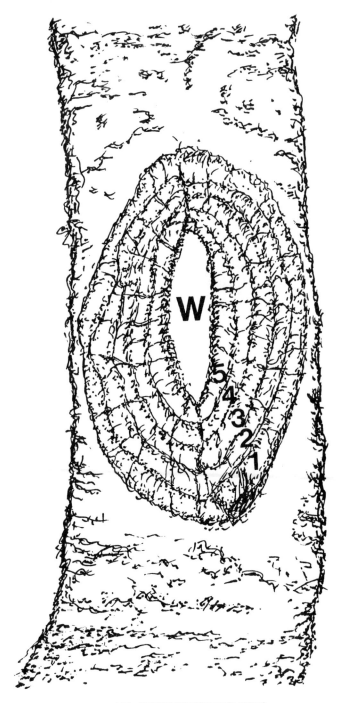

125. WOUNDWOOD RIBS

Ribs of woundwood develop about wounds [W]. The woundwood may close smaller wounds. On many wounds, the age of the wound can be determined by the number of woundwood ribs [1 to 5].

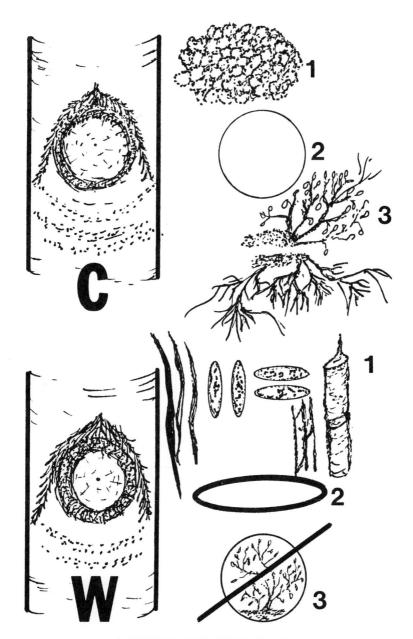

126. CALLUS AND WOUNDWOOD

Callus [C] has three characteristics: 1, homogeneous cells; 2, little or no lignin in the cell walls; 3, meristematic cells that can form adventitious sprouts or roots.

Woundwood also has three characteristics: 1, cells no longer differentiate; 2, cell walls with lignin; 3, cells not meristematic (180). [Be careful with the words callus, callous, and callose. Callus is defined above. Callous is an adjective that means toughened or hardened. Callose is a complex branched carbohydrate or polysaccharide that forms in phloem, usually in response to injury (S: 52)].

147

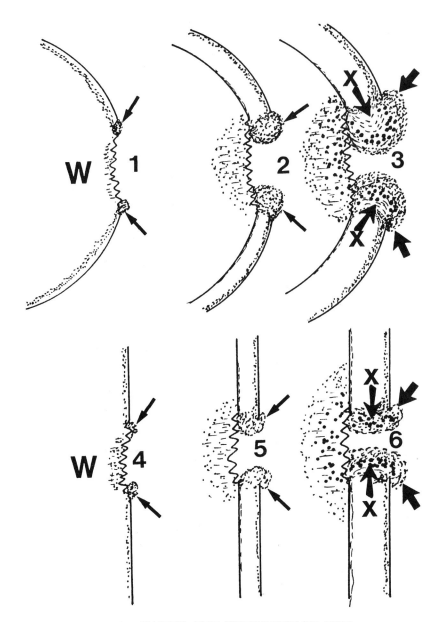

127. CALLUS AND WOUNDWOOD RIBS

Wounds [W] release pressure [1,4] and callus cells begin to form where meristematic cells are still alive [arrows]. The callus [2,5] begins to roll in on itself [arrows]. The cambial cells continue to form new cells from the inside [X arrows, 3,6]. The original callus cells slough off [arrows].

Callus forms first and will persist for a few weeks to a few months after wounding. When wounds are inflicted during the dormant period, callus will start to form when the tree growth starts in the spring.

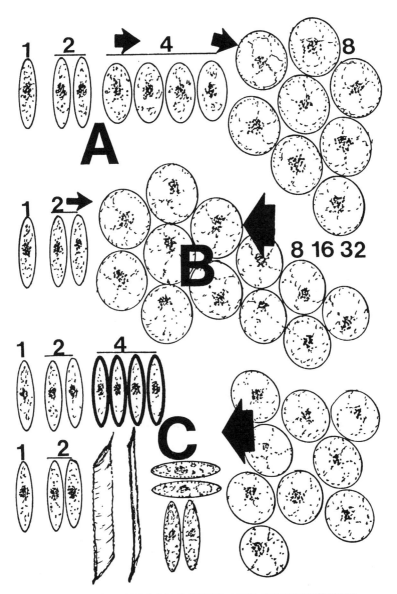

128. DEVELOPMENT OF CALLUS AND WOUNDWOOD

A. Meristematic cambial cell [1] divides [2], and division continues [4,8]. Because the wound releases pressure, all the new cells are round.

B. As the callus cells accumulate, they begin to exert a back pressure [large arrow]. The shape of the cells begins to change.

C. The new cells being formed begin to differentiate — vessels, fibers, axial and radial parenchyma — as the back pressure [arrow] increases. In time, the original callus cells are pushed off and only woundwood continues to form about the wound.

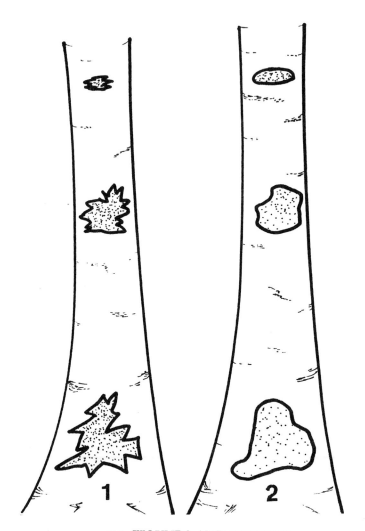

129. WOUNDS AND SCRIBING

Scribing wounds is a health treatment. Wounds [1] should be scribed as shallow as possible and enlarged as little as possible [2]. No need to scribe in the form of a vertical ellipse. Do not point tips. Make rounded margins. If callus has started to form, remove injured bark without disrupting the callus. Always remove injured bark and wood. **Do not dig into the face of the wound.** Clean soil and debris from the wound surface. Do not paint! Check the wound in a few months and cut away bark that may have died beyond the scribed area.

When wounds are inflicted during the growing season, wait until callus begins to form. Then cut away the injured bark carefully so as not to injure the callus. On shallow wounds inflicted during the growing season, it is possible to generate new tissues on the wound face if moist moss is applied within hours after the injury. The moss should be held in place by a plastic wrap. This treatment is more effective in warm climates (52).

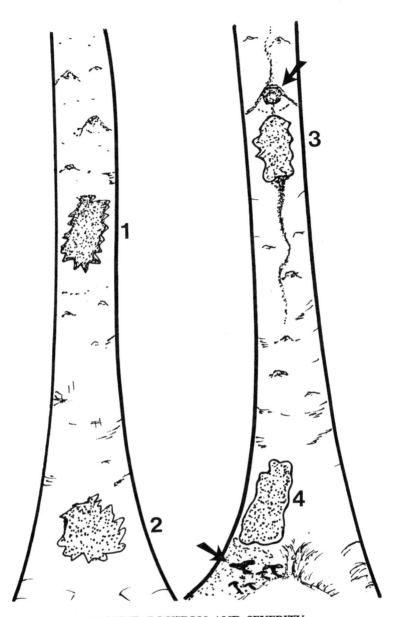

130. WOUND POSITION AND SEVERITY

Wounds on the trunk [1] are usually more severe than wounds at the base [2]. Wounds below or above open, large branch stubs often lead to cracks and extensive decay. Wounds at the base near a diseased root will cause extensive decay (S: 175). Wounds with bright, clean surfaces usually are associated with little or no decay (S: 20). Wounds with dark surfaces usually are associated with decay. Digging away the decay will not stop the process. Removing fungus fruiting bodies will not stop or stall the decay process. Check wounds periodically to be sure they are not weakening a trunk or branch and thus leading to a high hazard risk.

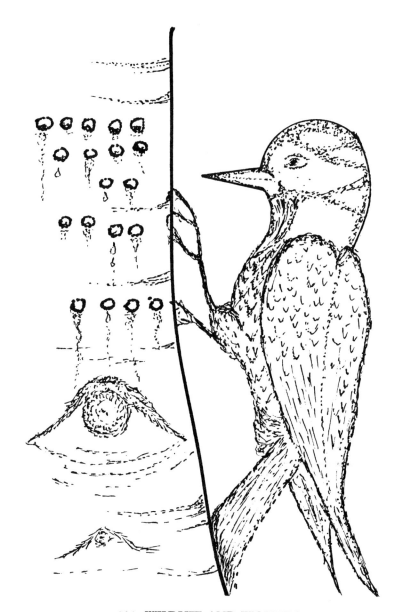

131. WILDLIFE AND WOUNDS

Wounds are inflicted by birds, squirrels, deer, bear, porcupines, beavers, and many other small animals (283; S: 9,15,26).

Animals wound trees for reasons that support their survival.

Unless the wounded branch or tree poses a high hazard risk for people or property, the tree or branch should not be removed (S: 181). Protective guards can be used to keep rodents away from young trees. Remember, sapsuckers are migratory birds, and any destructive action against an endangered species or migratory bird is a serious crime.

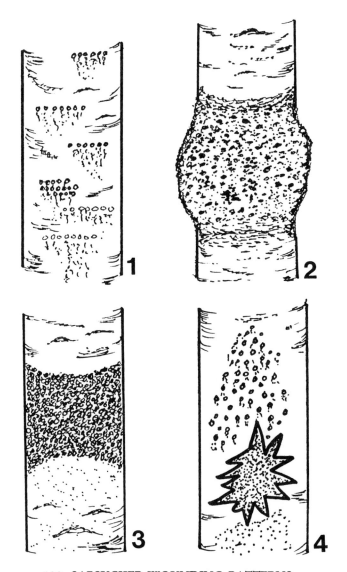

132. SAPSUCKER WOUNDING PATTERNS

Sapsuckers are woodpeckers that have a special spoon-like tongue for lapping sap. The major food for the birds is insects, especially ants. However, the birds will eat small amounts of inner bark and sap. They do mix the sap and inner bark with insects and feed this mixture to their young. Sapsuckers are territorial birds. Their nest usually will be within 100 meters (300 feet) of the wounded trees. Sap flowing from wounded maples will be infected by dark fungi; and the bark of the tree will be black. Black bark on many tree species indicates sap flow or sap dropping from sucking insects, especially aphids. The birds drill rows of holes [1], or they will concentrate on one area [2,3]. The area may be fusiform or spindle-shaped as in birches [2], or the concentrated wounds could kill a branch or trunk [3]. Sapsuckers often drill holes above other wounds [4]. (S: 9,26).

153

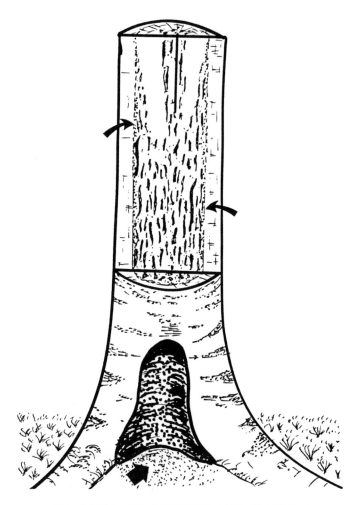

133. ANTS AND TERMITES AND WOUNDS

Ants live in trees and eat away from the tree. Termites eat infected wood in the tree and usually live away from the tree (17,145,182). (Some termites in the tropics build homesites in the branches of trees. They are still living outside of the wood.) Ants and termites follow the CODIT patterns with their galleries. They stay within the compartments [arrows] that are first infected by microorganisms. Ants clean the compartments and thus regulate the spread of decay (A). (Remember, the chambers in the tree are the ants' home. They are "careful" not to stimulate rot in *their* home.) Termites "methodically" mine and digest the wood in the compartments. Ants and termites are "careful" miners. They leave pillars, boundaries, and supports behind. If it were not for these supports and compartmentalization, the ants and termites would cause the tree to fall soon after it was infested and everybody would lose! Wood dust indicates ants (large arrow).

Insects: 7,44,58,98,138,168,169,183,184,187,230,248,249,296,316,385; S: 7,10,23.

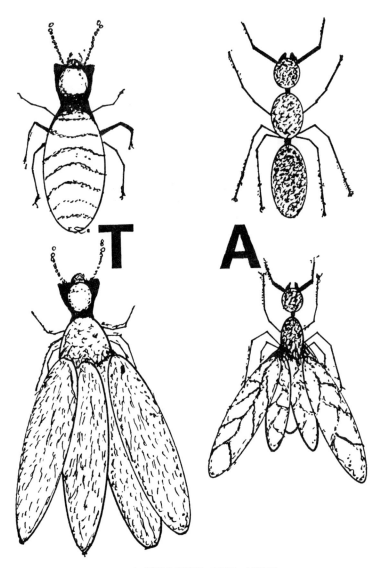

134. TERMITES AND ANTS

Termites [T] are social insects (145). They live in colonies. Termites are small, flat, soft-bodied insects sometimes without eyes. The antennae are like small round balls on a string. The abdomen is broadly joined to the thorax. In the winged adults, the wings are equal in size and usually much larger than the body.

Ants [A] are also social insects that live in colonies. Ants have elbowed antennae, and their abdomen is divided into two distinct regions. Ants have a strong constriction or "waist" between the thorax and abdomen. The wings are unequal in size on adults.

Termites and ants are often confused (7). Termites are sometimes called white ants. Before you consider any treatment, be sure you know whether you have an ant or termite problem. Always read labels before you use any product.

155

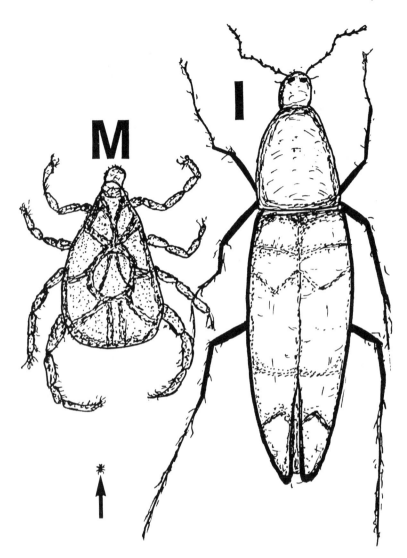

135. **MITES AND INSECTS**

Insects [I] are air-breathing arthropods with a distinct head, thorax, and abdomen. They have one pair of antennae, three pairs of legs, and usually one or two pairs of wings in the adult state.

Mites [M], spiders, ticks, and scorpions belong to the Class Arachnids. They are air-breathing arthropods that have a body comprised of two regions; the cephalothorax and abdomen. They have six pairs of appendages of which four pair are legs. They have no antennae.

Mites cause a variety of leaf galls. Most of the time the galls cause little injury. However, when the galls are very numerous, the leaves may die.

If you know you have a mite problem, use a product designed for mites. If you have an insect problem, use a product designed for insects. Always read labels carefully first.

156

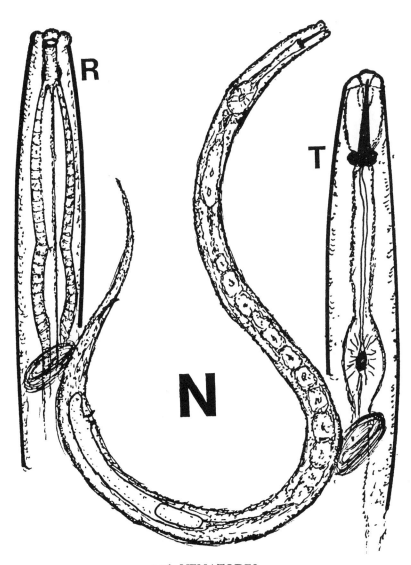

136. NEMATODES

Nematodes are small roundworms. They live in water, soil, plants, and animals. Nematodes are often called eelworms because of their shape. Most soil inhabiting nematodes are about one millimeter in length. They cannot be seen by the naked eye. They are transparent. Many feed on microscopic organisms in the soil. They have a tube-like mouth that takes in organisms as a vacuum cleaner [R]. Others have a spear-like structure in their mouth parts [T]. These forms infest roots. Some are vectors for viruses also. Be suspect of nematode problems when general decline or low vigor is a symptom. If nematocides are to be used read the label very carefully first.

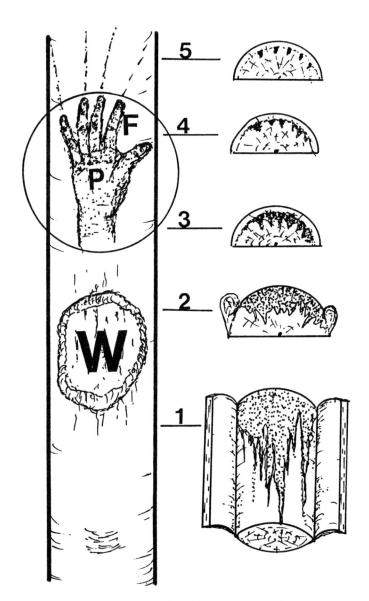

137. WOUNDS AND PALM AND FINGER PATTERN
OF INVASION

After wounding [W], pathogens spread above and below the wound within the
tissues present at the time of wounding. If the wood that formed after wounding
was pulled back [1], a pattern similar to a hand with a palm and fingers would
be seen. When transverse sections are cut above or below the wound [2,3,4,5] the
patterns appear as if you are cutting transverse section through the palm [P] and
fingers [F]. If you cut a section at 5, and then 4, you see that the wound is beyond
or proximal to 4 and not beyond 5 (S: 58,101).

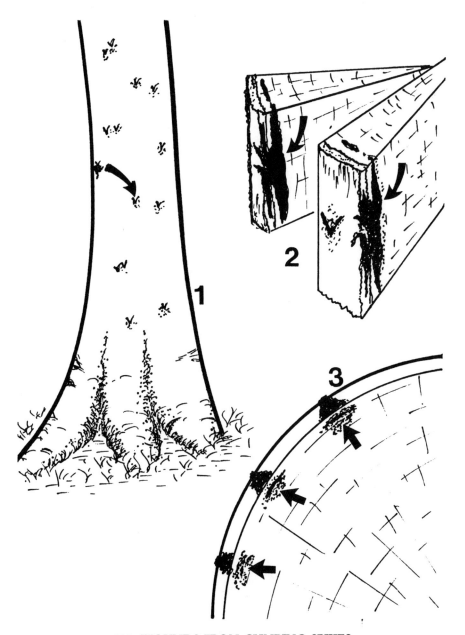

138. WOUNDS FROM CLIMBING SPIKES

Puncture wounds made by climbing spikes cause injuries that could lead to cankers or to infection courts for fungi that cause serious diseases such as oak wilt (105,168,169). The wounds mar the beauty of the bark [1]. The puncture wounds [2,3] are perfect sites for infections by the fungus that causes oak wilt. It is interesting to note that the same people who advocate flush cuts and wound dressings, often use spikes.

159

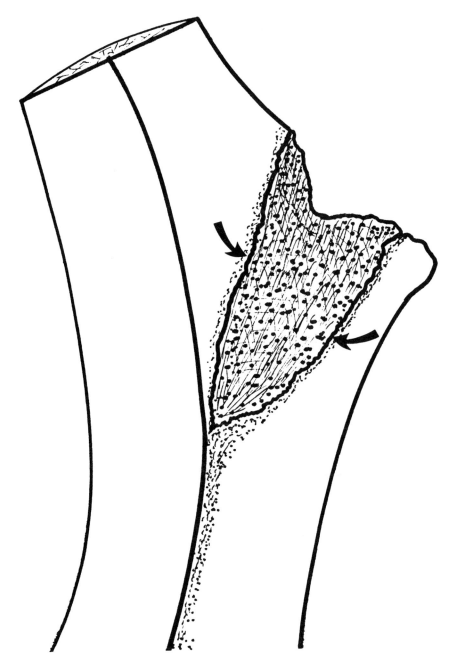

139. CAVITIES FROM DEAD STEMS

When codominant stems or leader stems die, decay may lead to a cavity. Usually the cavity has strong boundaries [arrows]. If the boundaries are broken, decay will spread rapidly into the surrounding sound wood [47]. Remember, water does not cause rot! Microorganisms do. If the cavity must be filled for aesthetic reasons, then use some type of nonabrasive material such as an expandable foam.

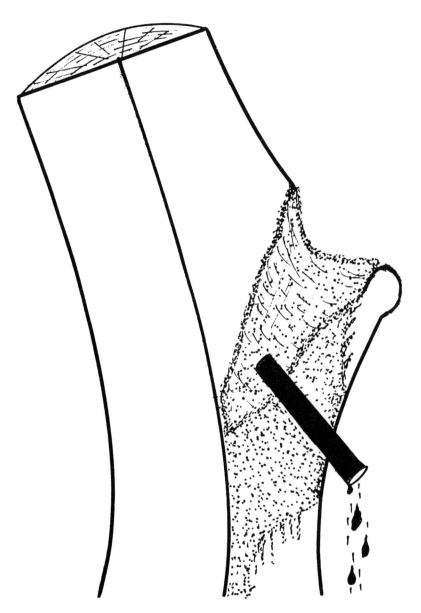

140. CAVITIES AND PIPES

Pipes inserted below cavities break the boundaries and decay will spread rapidly out to the wood present at the time of drilling. Many times the drilling leads to cambial dieback, and a new surface wound is created. Draining water will not stop or stall decay. When a cavity is filled with water, decay will not spread. Decay-causing fungi have very exacting requirements for growth; too wet or too dry, too much oxygen, not enough oxygen, too high pH, or too low pH will stall their growth (see references for decay).

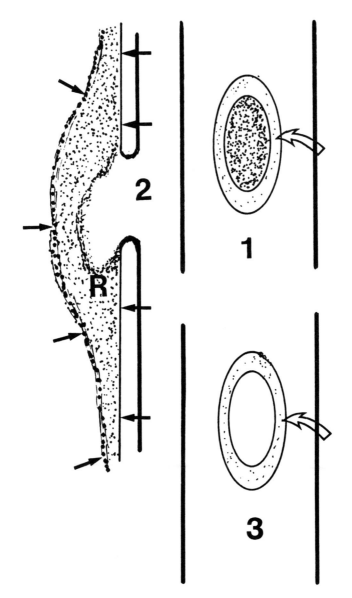

141. CAVITIES AND WOUNDS

Cavities often develop from old wounds and flush cuts [1]. The cavity is there because the protection boundaries separate sound wood from decayed wood — CODIT. Rot [R,2] may be advanced or only incipient; but it will still be compartmentalized [arrows]. If the cavity must be treated because the owner insists, then remove some of the decay, but **do not dig into the soundwood. Do not break boundaries!** Do not paint. The cavity could be left open [3], or filled with a foam. Cavity filling will not stop rot, and it will not strengthen the trunk even if rods are inserted (340).

When boundaries are broken, rot will spread faster and the tree will be weakened.

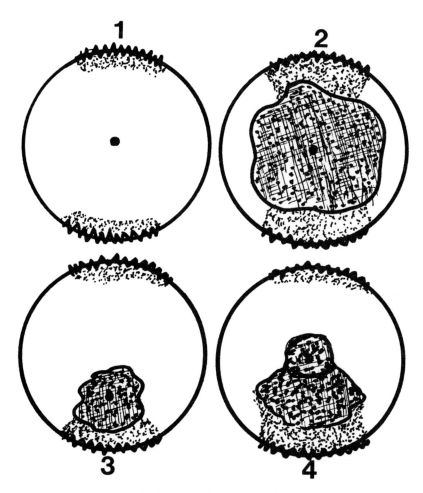

142. WOUND DRESSINGS

There are no data to show that wound dressings stop rot. To have a wound dressing experiment, control and dressed wounds must be dissected after at least 5 years. If there are no controls, there is no experiment. Here are some examples that show how any material can be made to *appear* beneficial or not beneficial: 1, Wounds on a sound tree, if treated or not, will have very little decay. 2, Wounds on a weak or defective tree, if treated or not, will have extensive decay. 3, Wounds on an eccentric tree with internal defects, if treated or if control is on the upper side, there will be little or no decay. If treated or if control is on the lower side, decay will develop rapidly. 4, Wounds on trunks that have decay on one side, if control or treated wound is on the upper side, little or no decay will develop. If the control or treated wound is on the lower side, decay will develop rapidly. As new wounds approach old internal injuries, the likelihood for decay increases (see diagram 149). Some individual trees of a species are such strong compartmentalizers that very little defect develops after wounding regardless of the treatment.

Wound dressings: 35,68,102,212,360; S: 43,50,69,90,95,140,150,163.

163

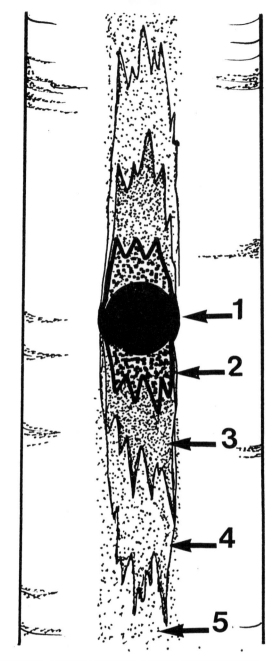

143. WOOD ALTERATIONS AFTER WOUNDING

1, Wound; 2, Tissues that died as a result of the wound; 3, Discolored wood associated with microorganisms; 4, Discolored wood resulting from tree's response to wounding; 5, Healthy-appearing wood in early stages of alterations toward a more protective state. Tree alone is responding in 4 and 5. Tree and microorganisms are associated in 3. Microorganisms are interacting with other microorganisms in 2.

Wound response: 319,320,321; S: 61,63,78,107,108,137,143,158,171,178,188.

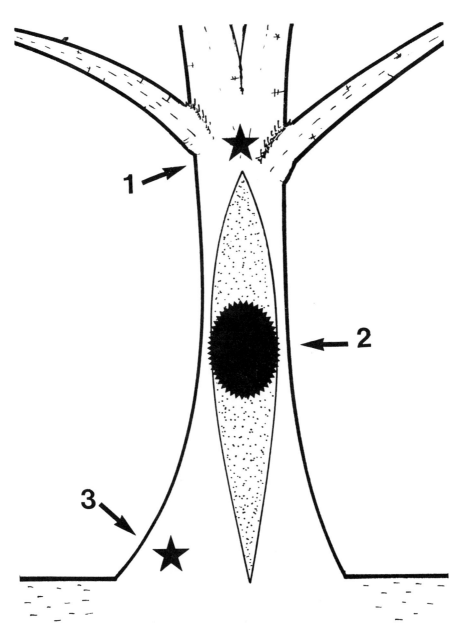

144. STRONG AND WEAK PORTIONS OF THE TRUNK
AGAINST WOUND ROTS

The stars show the strong portions of the tree (S: 16,17,18,20). Wounds inflicted below healthy living branches [1], and on the tree base [3] resist decay much more effectively than wounds inflicted 1 to 3 meters above ground [2]. If wounds must be made for any reason, they should be made as close as possible to area 1 or 3. Weak areas start again on roots below 3. Area 2 is weak because that is the position on the trunk where most old large branches died.

145. DRILL BITS; SHARP OR DULL MAKES A DIFFERENCE

When holes must be drilled for rods, tapping maples, or for other reasons, use a very sharp drill bit [1]. Dull drill bits make ragged cuts that lead to more decay [2]. When tapping maples for sap, sharp drill bits should be used (378,379; S: 111,117). The same can be said for increment borers (53,195). When drilling into a tree, use care not to twist and pull away the bark. Injured bark leads to cambial dieback and larger wounds. If possible avoid drilling when bark is loose in the spring and in the autumn at leaf fall. If holes are used for pins to move trees, drill above major roots and make holes as low as possible on the trunk. Do not plug drill holes with dowels or wound dressing (195).

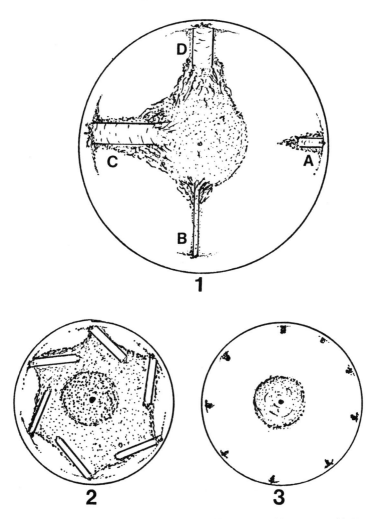

146. HOLE SIZE, ANGLE, AND DEPTH AFFECT AMOUNT OF DISCOLORED OR DECAYED WOOD

1. Small shallow holes cause the least injury [A]. Very narrow holes deep into the trunk cause little injury [B]. Large deep holes that touch other columns of infected wood cause the greatest amount of injury [C and D].

2. Slanted holes cause large columns of discolored wood. Discolored wood is dead wood. Large columns of discolored wood decrease greatly the energy storage capacity of the tree.

3. Small, shallow holes, no deeper than 2 growth rings, cause the least amount of injury, especially when there are no other large columns of infected wood in the tree; and when the tree is a strong compartmentalizer. Remember, it is not so much the hole that causes the injury as it is what substances that are put into the hole (S: 91,103,105,120,132,160,181).

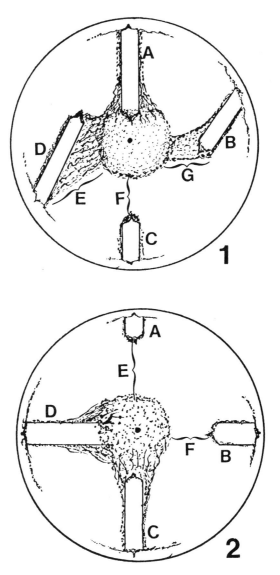

147. HOLES AND INTERNAL INJURY

1. A, Straight large hole penetrating internal column of infected wood B, Slanted moderate-sized hole, close to internal column G, Trapped wood that dies and discolors C, Smaller hole where distance F is far away from the central column D, Large slanted hole, and E where wood died and discolored.

2. A,B,C, and D are holes of the same diameter but different depths. As the distance between the top of the hole and the internal column decreases — E,F — the wood between the hole tip and the column dies and discolors. As holes get closer to other holes or to older columns of infected wood, new columns of infected wood form rapidly (S: 111,117).

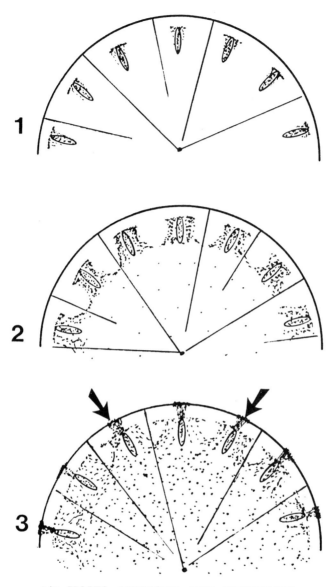

148. HOLES, GENETICS, AND CHEMICALS

Size, angle, and depth of holes are only some of the factors that affect internal injuries. Some trees are strong compartmentalizers [1] and others are moderate [2] or weak [3] (196,300,302,303,323). The same hole will result in dramatic differences in different trees (S: 92,93,97,122,123,124,155,165). The substances or chemicals put into or forced into the hole with pressure are the most important factors affecting internal injury. Most chemical injections result in pattern 3 with some holes that do not close [arrows]. When holes do not close, that is a sign of serious internal injury. The tree should not be injected and injured again. Old injection holes cannot be used for a second injection.

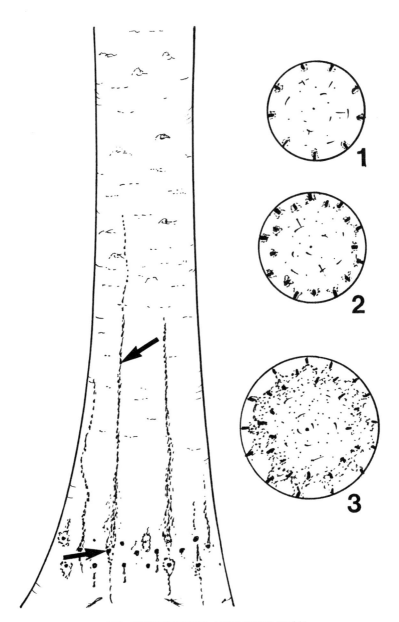

149. INJECTIONS AND IMPLANTS

I have seen trees that have died from injections and implants! I have dissected hundreds of elms that had many injection holes (S: 103,132,181). The long columns of discolored and decayed wood associated with the holes greatly reduced the amount of healthy wood available for storage of energy. I have seen large cracks and cankers associated with injection holes [arrows]. Even small holes with small columns of defect will cause internal injuries [1]. As the treatments continue, the columns of discolored wood coalesce [2 and 3]. Research must find better ways to treat trees with chemicals. I know it can be done!

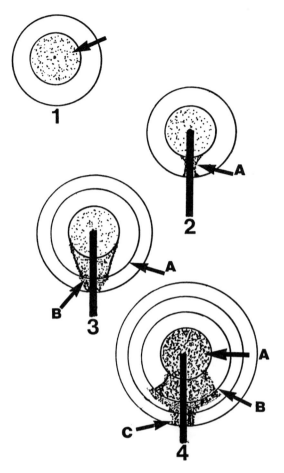

150. DRAIN TUBES FOR WETWOOD AND FOR WATER
IN CAVITIES

Columns of wetwood and cavities with water are compartmentalized in trees [arrow 1]. When large drain tubes are inserted, bark is killed, sapwood is injured, and the protection boundary about the column of wetwood or the cavity is broken [2]. The wetwood organisms or decay-causing fungi spread into the injured sapwood [A,3] and into the bark injured by the drilling [B,3]. A new reaction zone forms in the sapwood and the zone resists spread of the pathogens. If the tube does drain wetwood, decay will develop [A,4]. A new protection boundary will form [B,4]. If the hole was drilled during the growing period, a canker or an area of dead bark will develop [C,4]. A boundary will form about this infection also. It is primarily the injury caused by drilling that causes the bark dieback and cankers and not the wetwood fluids. If wetwood fluids were the primary cause of bark killing, then there should be large dead areas below all the large branch stubs on elms and poplars where wetwood fluids flow. **Too often we seek to blame others for the injuries we cause.**

171

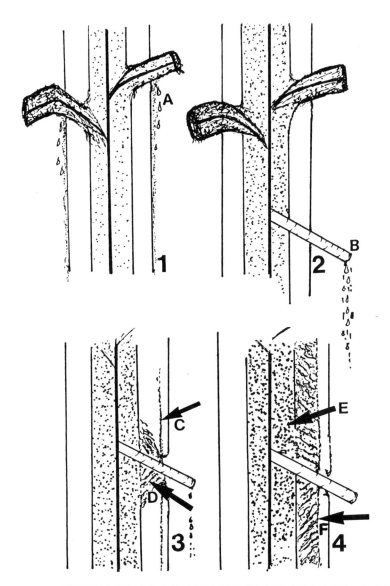

151. WETWOOD ASSOCIATED WITH OLD BRANCH STUBS

Wood in the trunk present at the time branches die is often infected by wetwood-causing pathogens in many tree species. Wetwood fluids often flow from the stubs [1,A]. The fluids kill the algae, lichens, and mosses on the trunk. Often the fluids are used as a food source by fungi. White spots or bleached spots on the bark are signs of wetwood ooze. Tubes have been used to drain the wetwood fluids [2,B]. The drilling starts new columns of infected wood [3,D], and a new barrier zone forms [3,C]. The wetwood dries and decay develops [4,E] and new columns of wet-wood will be walled off by a barrier zone [F,4]. Wetwood is a disease of wood, but it is also a type of biological protection wood (A,B). So long as the wetwood is present, decay will not develop. (Wetwood is a term used for both a disease of wood, and for the wood altered as a result of the disease.)

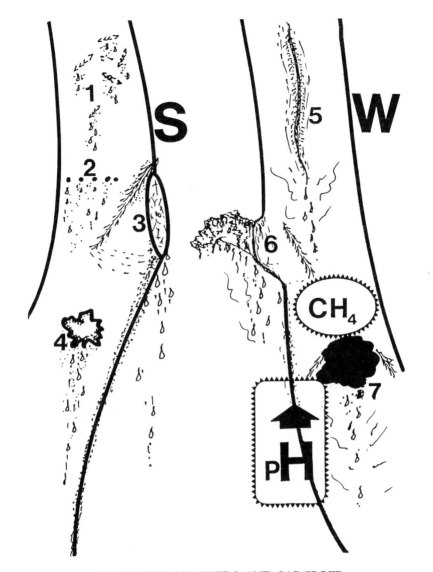

152. WETWOOD FLUIDS AND SAP FLOW

Wetwood is a disease of wood—sapwood, heartwood—caused by bacteria that can live with little or no free or gaseous oxygen. The bacteria are called anaerobic organisms. Their growth in the wood alters the cell membranes; and moisture, pH, and microelements increase in the infected wood. The gas methane—colorless, odorless— is produced by the bacteria. The wetwood fluids are often colonized by fungi and other bacteria and slime or ooze flows from the infection court. The slime or ooze often has a very foul odor. The wetwood fluids should not be confused with normal flow after wounding [S:1, squirrels; 2, sapsuckers; 3, pruning wounds; 4, mechanical wounds]. Wetwood fluids have a foul odor and the bark flora are killed [W: 5, cracks; 6, old stubs; 7, canker rots with masses of fungus tissue]. When holes are bored into large columns of wetwood, the escaping methane will burn if lighted with a match. The pH of wetwood may be 8, or as high as 9.

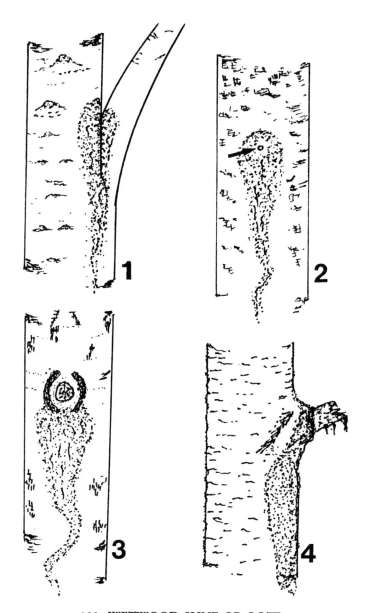

153. WETWOOD SLIME OR OOZE

Wetwood is a common disease of many species of trees—elms, oaks, ashes, poplars, horse chestnuts, willows, birches. Some common infection courts for the bacteria are dead spots caused by included bark [1], insect galleries [2], flush cuts [3], and old dead stubs [4]. Included bark between roots and root stubs are common underground infection courts. The branch crotch with included bark is the major infection court on many trees. Wetwood may start in the roots and spread toward the trunk.

Wetwood: 56,232,239,306,307,362,380,387; A,B.
Bacteria: 137,206,239,258,306,307,310,380; S: 36,37,39.

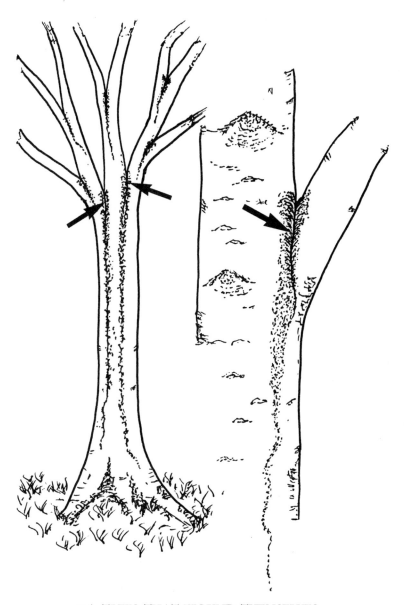

154. TREES THAT WOUND THEMSELVES

Included bark often leads to a dead area where the branch squeezes the trunk. Included bark can be found on many species of trees. However, some tree species, and especially some new varieties or cultivars of species, are very prone to included bark and dead spots [arrows]. Some examples are Modesto ash, varieties of Tilia, Bradford pear, and thornless locust. Wetwood often starts in the dead spots within the crotches. Also, the dead spots start cracks when there are temperature extremes or high winds. Then the cracks are called frost cracks, wind shakes, sun scald, or even lightning injury. Trees with included bark should not leave the nurseries. But, they do!

175

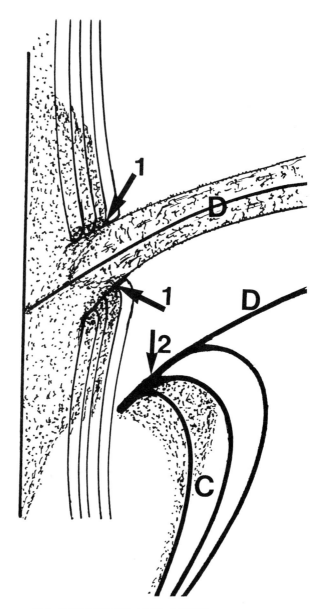

155. WETWOOD AND ASPEN

When branches die on aspen, *Populus tremuloides*, the base of the branch [D] dies and hardens. Most aspens have very weak branch protection zones (A). The hard, dry branch base may stall the spread of pathogens from branch to trunk. However, as the trunk tissues grow about the hard branch base, they squeeze inward and kill the cambium in the same way as included bark does (arrows 1 and 2, enlarged]. Then dead spots develop that are perfect places for development of wetwood [C]. Later when the hard branch stub does rot, the wetwood is replaced with other microorganisms, and some may cause decay or canker rots such as *Phellinus tremulae*.

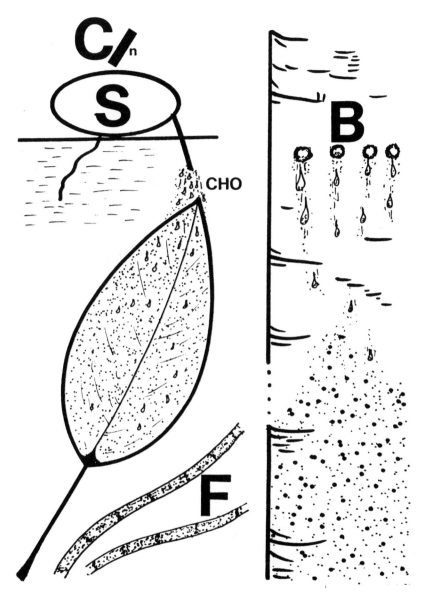

156. BLACK SOOTY MOLD AND BLACK BARK

The carbon nitrogen ratio in tree sap is far in excess of carbon to nitrogen [C/N]. When sucking insects [S] take in sap, they often excrete the excess carbohydrate [CHO]. The sugary liquid falls on other leaves or plant parts. Fungi [F] with dark hyphae grow on the parts covered by the sugary liquid, and the parts appear sooty. When sapsuckers or boring insects drill into trunks, sap may flow on the bark [B] and, again, the bark appears sooty or black because of the dark fungi [F] growing on the sugary sap.

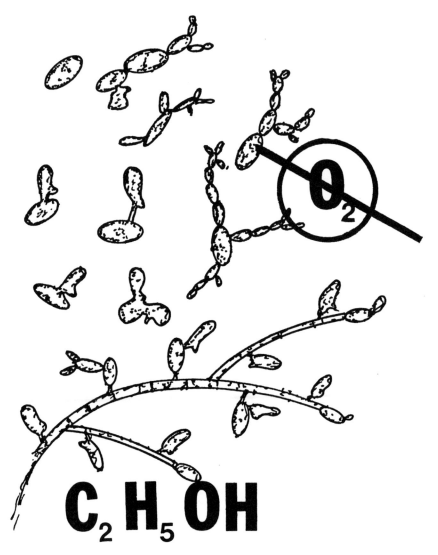

157. YEASTS

Yeasts are fungi. They are usually single-celled; but they often bud to form long chains of cells. Some yeasts do have filamentous hyphae. Yeasts have the ability to ferment carbohydrates. They break down glucose to form carbon dioxide and ethanol, C_2H_5OH. This fermentation process takes place when oxygen is very low or absent. Yeasts often grow in sap that flows from wounds. Squirrels wound maples and birches in early spring and the sap is eaten later after the yeasts have grown in it. Bubbles formed by the fermentation process can be seen on stumps that were cut in the spring.

158. LEAF AND NEEDLE DISEASES

An almost endless number of fungi and bacteria infect leaves and needles. Some pathogens not only infect the leaves, but go into the developing shoots— anthracnoses. Even though many of the diseases may not kill the tree, the diseases leave the tree in an unsighlty state. Needle diseases of all types are serious problems on trees grown for Christmas trees. Diseases that infect young developing leaves and needles do threaten the vigor of trees. Before you consider a treatment for a leaf or needle problem, make certain you know the cause. Leaves and needles may have obvious infections, but the real cause of the problem may be some other agent that is weakening the tree and predisposing the leaves and needles to infection (147).

179

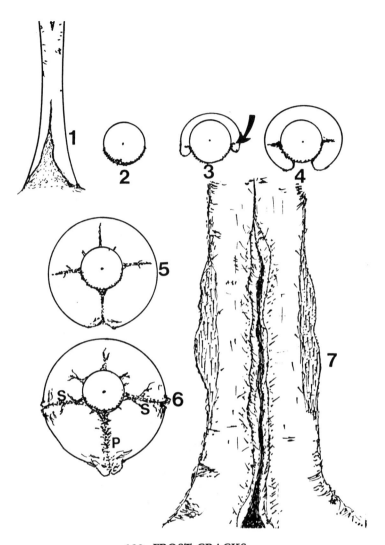

159. **FROST CRACKS**

There are two basic types of cracks: Those that start in the outer bark and spread inward to the cambial zone or to the phloem — bark cracks. Those that start from the inside and split outward to the bark — wood cracks (S: 14,148,176,183,200). Wounds, flush cuts, cankers, branch and root stubs, and dead spots from included bark in branches and roots start the internal cracks. Then some other factors such as temperature extremes, drought, or wind cause the cracks to split outward. The diagrams show the usual sequence of events from wounding [1 and 2], wound-wood inroll with cracks [3 and 4], formation of additional internal cracks [5 and 6], and the appearance of the cracks on the trunk [7]. The primary cracks [P] may close, but once the secondary cracks [S] split the bark, they will rarely close. The shallow bark cracks seldom kill cambium. Rapid growth is a common cause of bark cracks.

180

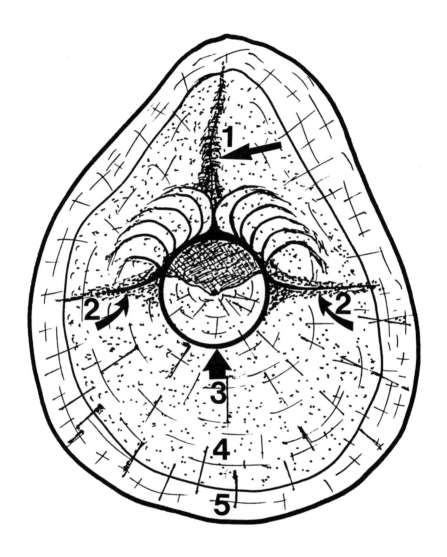

160. CRACKS: PRIMARY AND SECONDARY

After wound closure, the cracks remain in the trunk. The primary crack [1] may stay closed for long periods. The secondary radial cracks [2] often split out to the bark. The barrier zone [3] indicates the size of the tree at the time of wounding. The heartwood is 4, and the sapwood is 5. The cracks are perfect sites for wetwood-causing bacteria. Reaction zones resist the spread of the pathogens associated with the cracks.

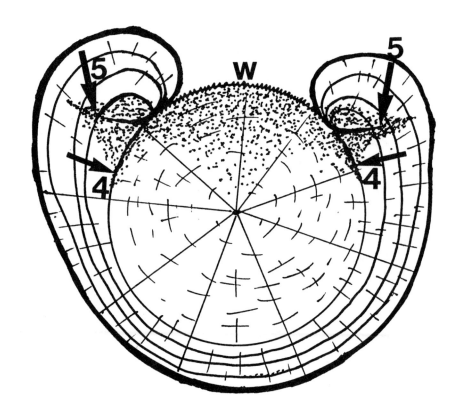

161. CRACKS AND WOUNDS

After wounding—mechanical wounds, flush cuts, etc.—the callus, and later, the woundwood may roll inward. The pressure of the inrolling woundwood may squeeze the barrier zone [4] from the outside, and a crack may develop beyond the barrier zone into sound wood [5]. As the wound closes [W] the internal cracks may continue to spread outward. Reaction zones form and resist the spread of the infected wood associated with the radial cracks. When temperature extremes occur or when winds are high, the radial cracks may split out to the bark.

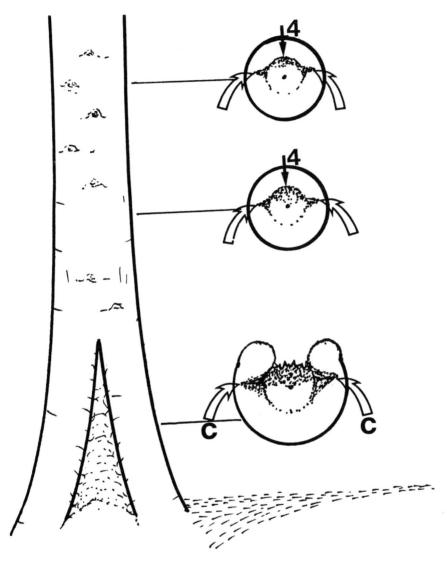

162. CRACKS AND CONFUSION

When transverse cuts are made through a wound, the internal radial cracks associated with the inrolling woundwood can be seen easily [C]. However, as cuts are made above the wound, the pattern of discolored wood appears as if the barrier zone [4] has been breached by the pathogens [arrows] (222,279). Not understanding the cracks and the columns of discolored wood associated with them has led people to disbelieve the concept of compartmentalization.

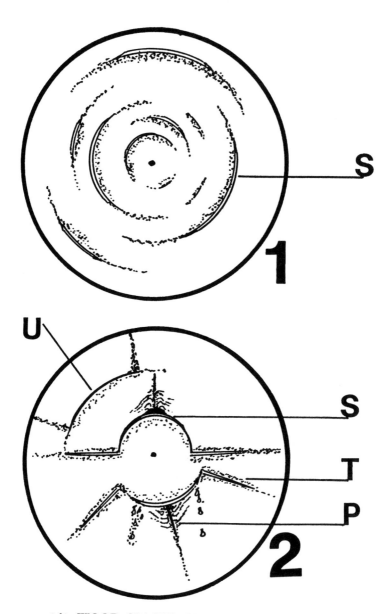

163. WOOD CRACKS: RING AND RAY SHAKES

Ring shake is a term used to describe circumferential separations in wood [1S,2S]. Ray shakes are associated with barrier zones. The barrier zone is a strong protection zone but a weak structural zone. As the shakes propagate beyond the wound, the wood may tear and ragged edges result (222,279). Ring and ray shakes are often associated [2] (S: 9,41,46). The primary crack [P] and the secondary cracks [T] are sites that often contain the wetwood pathogens. In a sense, the wetwood "lubricates" the cracks and benefits the tree because the possibility of trunk splitting is reduced (S: 200). It is amazing to see how nature "corrects" or adjusts problems that could cause death.

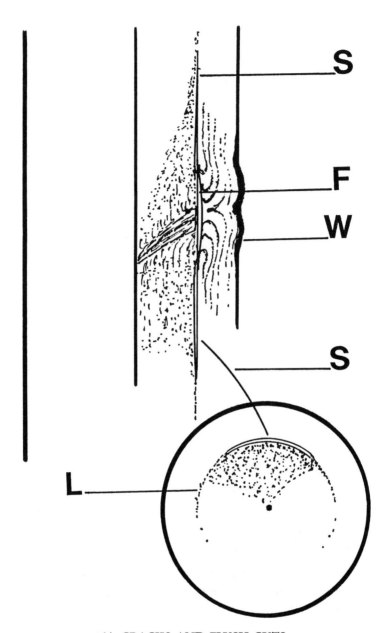

164. CRACKS AND FLUSH CUTS

Flush cuts [F] remove the branch protection zone and wound the trunk [H]. The barrier zone that forms after wounding often separates to form a ring shake or crack [S]. There may be a circumferential weakening far beyond the wound [L]. When woundwood closes the wound, wood [W] is the correct term for the tissues. The woundwood may roll inward to form a "ram's horn" and the wound will never close completely. Then primary and secondary cracks may develop.

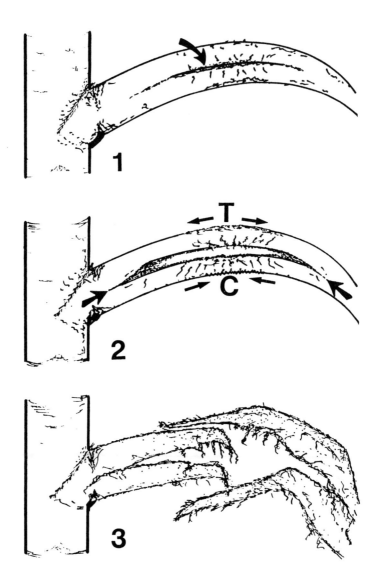

165. CRACKS AND BRANCH FAILURE

Cracks in lateral branches are common starting points for branch failure [1 arrow]. So long as the crack is moist and so long as the crack can propagate or continue to split, the branch will bend. When the crack meets resistance to further propagation [2, large arrows in branch] tension [T] develops above and compression [C] develops below (S: 176,183). If the moisture begins to decrease, the branch will fail (S: 200). Failure can occur when there is no wind. The splinters will point downward when this type of failure occurs. When high winds lead to the fracture of the branch, the splinters will usually point upward. Branches that fail during high winds usually crack as the branch bends upward. Branches are not well constructed for upward pressures. Also, do not confuse branch cracking with branch pull out from the trunk.

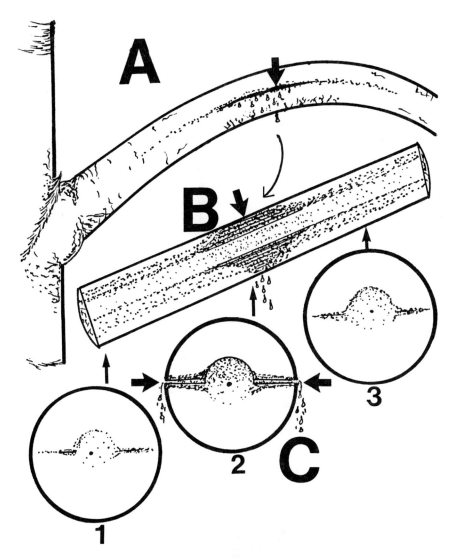

166. CRACKS AND WETWOOD

Internal cracks are perfect sites for the development of wetwood. Cracks with wetwood often develop where flush cuts removed smaller branches from large lateral branches [A]. Dissection of A radially through the cracks is shown in B. Diagram C show tansverse sections of B at points shown by the arrows. The dissection in B is through points shown by the arrows in C,2. So long as the wood along the crack is moist, the branch will bend. Most of the time there will be no decay associated with the crack. Decay-causing fungi rarely grow where moisture and pH are high (397).

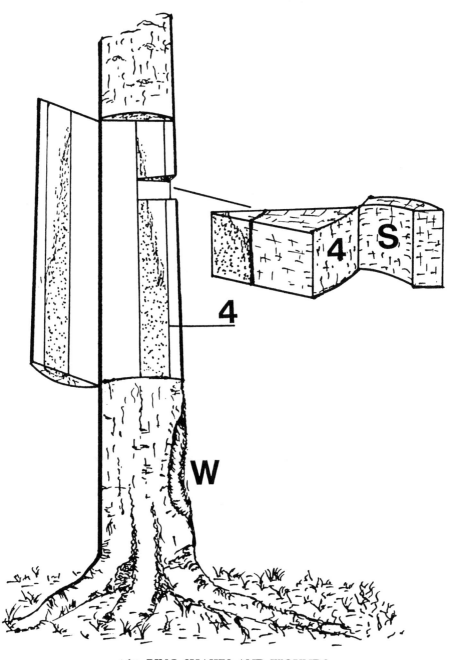

167. RING SHAKES AND WOUNDS

Wounds [W] are common starting points for ring shakes [S] (222,279). Barrier zones resulting from wounds [4] may separate to form the shakes. The column of discolored and decayed wood associated with the wound will develop as a cylinder or tapered cone while the barrier zone will occur along the wood present at the time of wounding.

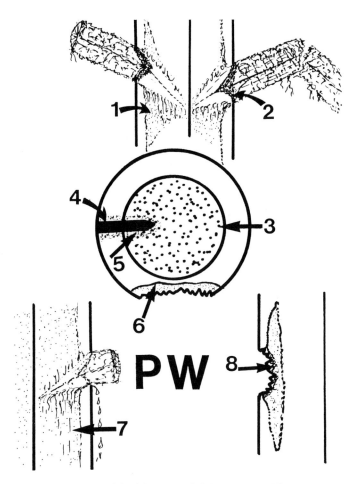

168. PROTECTION WOOD SUMMARY

Protection wood is wood that is more resistant to infection than healthy sapwood: 1, False heartwood; 2, Branch protection zone; 3, Heartwood; 4, Discolored sapwood; 5, Discolored heartwood; 6, Reaction zone; 7, Wetwood; 8, Surface, hard, dry wood. The barrier zone is also a type of protection wood. Other types of protection boundaries are in bark (27,28,31,238), petioles, pith, nonwoody roots, and leaves and needles.

Many types of pathogens have easy access into twigs and tips of roots through dead and dying tissues. The pathway to the trunk or to the trunk and other roots is made difficult for the pathogens because of the protection zones at the bases of twigs, branches, and root branches (214,374). When reserve energy is low and protection zones are weak, the pathogens spread rapidly. Mature trees have thousands of infections that are compartmentalized. When tree parts die or when wounds are inflicted, infections will take place. Trees survive by constantly compartmentalizing the infected tissues (S: 174,185). Strong compartmentalization depends on a full supply of reserve energy. **Where does the energy come from? Let us now turn to this very important subject of *energy*.**

(Professor; please review basics of physics (123), before you go on.)

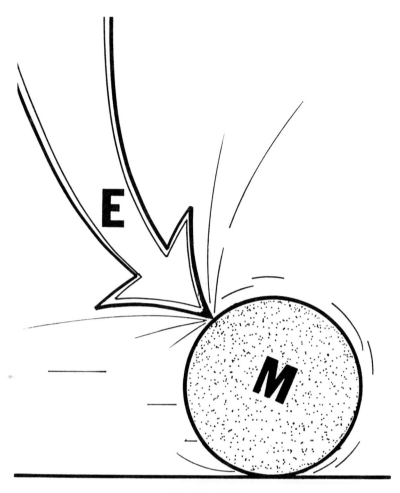

169. ENERGY

Energy is the force that moves matter (123). Energy is needed to maintain the order of a system. When energy becomes limiting, parts and processes of the system begin to lose order, and disorder begins to increase (107). To survive, the system must then reduce its mass to maintain order within the limits of the amount of energy available. There must be sufficient potential energy to supply enough kinetic energy to maintain the order of the system. Orderly growth of a system — kinetic energy — can occur only when there is an excess of potential energy. When growth is stimulated beyond the limits of potential energy available to maintain order; then the energy reserves are lowered to accommodate the increase growth, or mass of the system. The system is larger at the expense of a depleted energy reserve or potential energy. And, when reserves are low, defense is low. And, when defense is low, pathogens attack. It is so simple! Yet, when energy reserves are high, the system can sustain moderate periods of stress due to drought, flooding, insect injury, wounds, transplantation, etc.

Remember, in business it takes money to make money. The same can be said for trees. It takes energy to get more energy. There is no "free lunch". Every action has an "up front" cost.

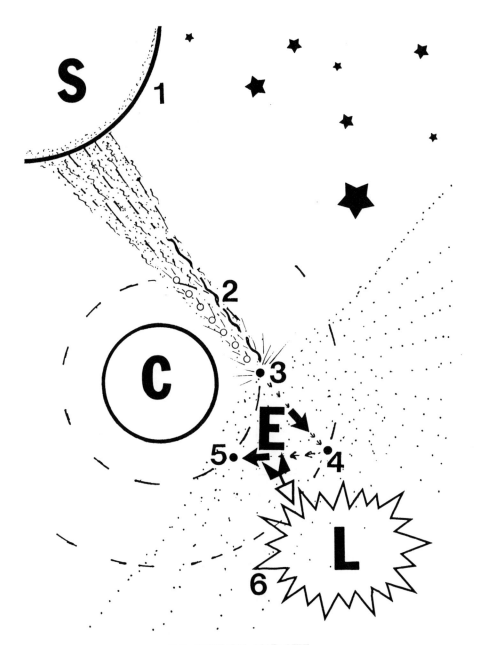

170. ENERGY AND LIFE

Energy comes from the sun [1] in the form of waves or particles—photons—[2] striking an electron [3] on the chlorophyll molecule [C], and moving the electron to a higher orbit [4] (60,124,292,123). As the electron moves back to its original orbit (5) some of its energy of movement is captured in a substance called glucose. Most of the life [L] on this planet is dependent on this process. Some organisms get enetgy from chemical reactions and from heat and chemicals coming from vents in the floor of the ocean and deep fresh water lakes (51).

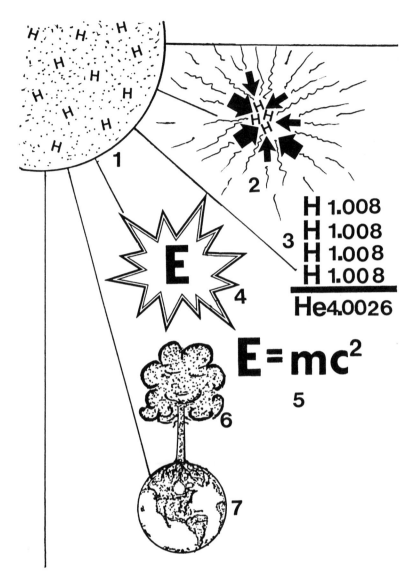

171. ENERGY AND MASS

Hydrogen [H] in the sun [1], under extremely high temperatures and pressures [2] is fused to form helium [3] (292). This process is called fusion (123). For every four atoms of hydrogen, one atom of helium is formed [3]. The atomic weight of hydrogen is 1.008 and helium weighs 4.0026. What happens to the "lost" mass?

In the fusion process, mass is converted to extremely high amounts of energy [4 and 5]. $E = mc^2$ means energy equals mass times the speed of light squared. The energy [4] from the fusion process streams from the sun in the form of waves or particles—photons. Only 0.1% of the energy from the sun that hits the earth is trapped by plants (396). Trees trap 50% of that energy [6]. This is the major benefit of trees to our living world [7].

192

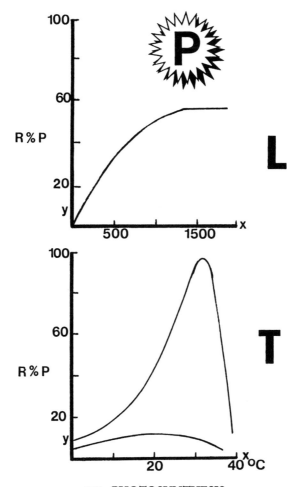

172. PHOTOSYNTHESIS

Photosynthesis is an energy trapping process (51,60,123,106,270,273,289,292, 352,401). The energy from the sun is stored in glucose, which comes from carbon dioxide and water. The energy of the sun splits the water molecule which then bonds with carbon dioxide to form glucose. Oxygen is given off in the process. Light [L] and temperature [T] regulate the efficiency of the process in chlorophyll. On the two graphs, relative percentages of photosynthesis [R%P] are shown on the Y axes. On the upper graph, [L] intensity of light in foot candles is on the X axis. On the lower graph [T], temperature is shown in centigrade on the X axis. The lower curve on the T graph shows that photosynthesis will remain low regardless of temperature when light is low. Light drives the process; but the process is most efficient when light intensity is near 1500 foot candles and temperatures are between 28 and 35 degrees Celsius. When temperature rises above 40 degrees Celsius, the efficiency of the process decreases rapidly, regardless of the amount of light.

193

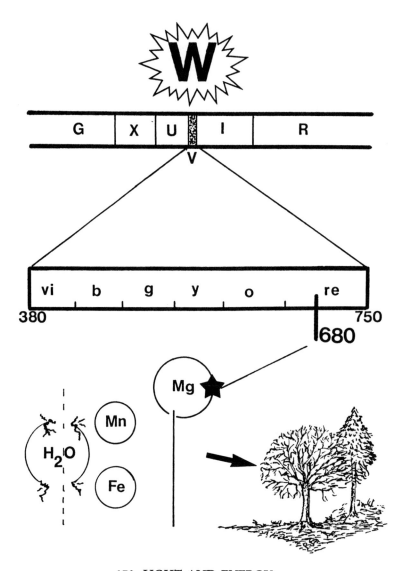

173. LIGHT AND ENERGY

Visible light [V] makes up a small part of the waves [W] present in our atmosphere: gamma, shortest, G; X-rays, X; ultraviolet, U; infrared, I; and radio waves, longest, R. The visible range is from violet [v] to blue [b], green [g], yellow [y], orange [o], and red [re]. The waves of visible light go from 380 to 750 angstroms. An angstrom is 1 ten-billionth of a meter. Different chlorophyll pigments—a,b,c— trap light best at different wave lengths. Chlorophyll a [Mg] which is most common in green plants, traps at 680 and 700 best. Manganese [Mn] and iron [Fe] are essential in the process of splitting water—H_2O. When manganese and iron are lacking or low, the process stops or decreases and energy is not trapped.

$P_2 O_5 \quad H_2 P O_4 \quad HP O_4$

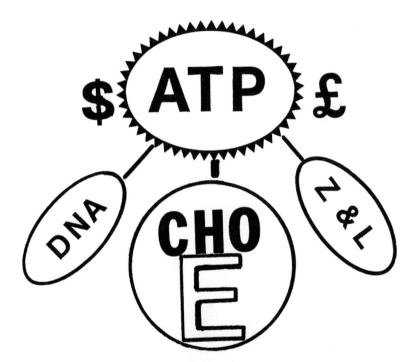

174. ATP: UNIVERSAL BIOLOGICAL CURRENCY

Phosphorus is absorbed in different forms. The first part of photosynthesis involves phosphorus to form a substance called ATP—Adenosine Triphosphate. ATP holds energy in its bonds. It is the international currency. It is like liquid assets. ATP supplies the energy to make processes proceed. Phosphorus is a part of DNA and enzymes [Z]. ATP is involved in making lipids [L] and carbohydrates [CHO]. ATP pays the bills to make these essential substances, and many more! This is why trees require phosphorus. And, this is why mycorrhizae are important. They are very active in absorbing phosphorus (120,207,343,367,398).

195

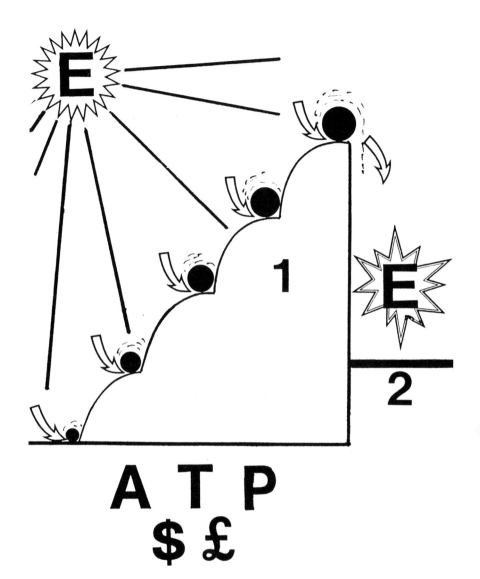

175. ATP AND ENERGY

The first part of photosynthesis involves the trapping of energy in ATP. The energy [E] is trapped in the bonds that hold the atoms together. It is similar to cocking a spring and locking the spring in the cocked position. When the lock is released, the spring moves. As ATP is formed and as the energy accumulates, it is similar to rolling a ball up a hill. However, here, the ball gets larger as it goes up the hill. At the top, one final push sends the ball down, and *most* of the energy used to push the ball up is released to do the work; to make something move: metabolism, growth, reproduction, defense. Energy is the force that moves matter.

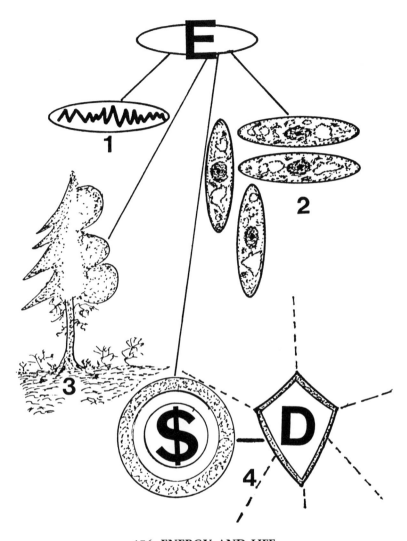

176. ENERGY AND LIFE

Energy is required to maintain the living processes in the cell—metabolism [1]—to make more cells—growth [2]—to make more trees—reproduction [3]—and to keep the defense system ready at all times [4](60). All of the energy must be stored in living cells. Proper allocation of energy for 1,2,3, and 4 is essential for survival. The tree must metabolize and grow, or it dies. When energy reserves are low, and little is left for defense, the pathogens attack. Please remember, energy must come *out* of the system first before growth, metabolism, and reproduction take place. And fertilizers DO NOT add energy, they do not feed trees, they add elements essential for growth, metabolism, reproduction, and defense. Too often this causes the defense budget to suffer and the pathogens attack as the tree uses stored energy to grow bigger, faster.

197

177. LIGHT AND PHOTOSYNTHESIS

That light [L] drives photosynthesis [P] has been proved by many experiments (60). When plants are put into the dark [D] photosynthesis decreases over time [T]. When light returns, so does the trapping of energy. Do not confuse this simple statement with the light and dark reactions of photosynthesis. The light reaction traps energy from waves or photons as the electrons on the chlorophyll molecule are forced to a higher orbit; and then return to their original orbit. The energy is trapped in ATP. This is the first part. As many ATP molecules accumulate, they are used to make glucose. This second part is not dependent on light, so it is often called the dark reaction of photosynthesis. The trapping of energy is a highly ordered process. The details of the process are far beyond the scope of this book; but I strongly suggest that you explore this marvelous process by reading about it in a book on biochemistry (352) or molecular biology (60).

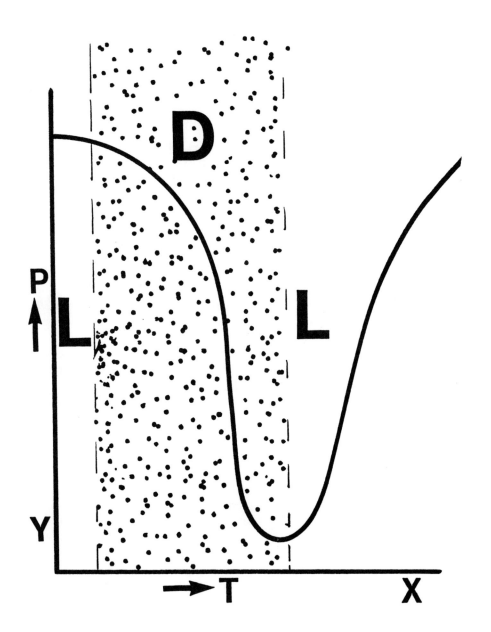

178. RESPIRATION: ENERGY RELEASE

Key words: sun, hydrogen, fusion, helium, mass to energy, waves or photons, chlorophyll, electron out of orbit, electron return, energy trapped, ATP, dark reaction, glucose, fuel.

Glucose ($C_6H_{12}O_6$) is like a mobile battery. It is soluble in water. Glucose is the fuel for life. Energy is trapped in the chemical bonds that hold glucose together (352). The chemical bonds are like cocked and locked springs. Each ATP supplies the energy as a ratchet wrench that gives the spring an advance until all the springs are cocked and locked in place. So it is with glucose. When the locks are systematically released, the spring moves and makes something nearby move. That is work; to move matter. The process of using potential or stored energy to "run" the biological "machine" is called respiration [R]. The "unlocking" of the glucose to release the energy is called glycolysis [glyc = sugar; lyse = split or break down, G]. The process is highly ordered. The second part of respiration is called the Kreb Cycle [K] where CO_2 is given off. The third part is called the electron transfer chain [ET]. In the end, each glucose molecule "makes" 36 ATP molecules, and ATP is like liquid money. It pays the bills for metabolism, growth, reproduction, and defense.

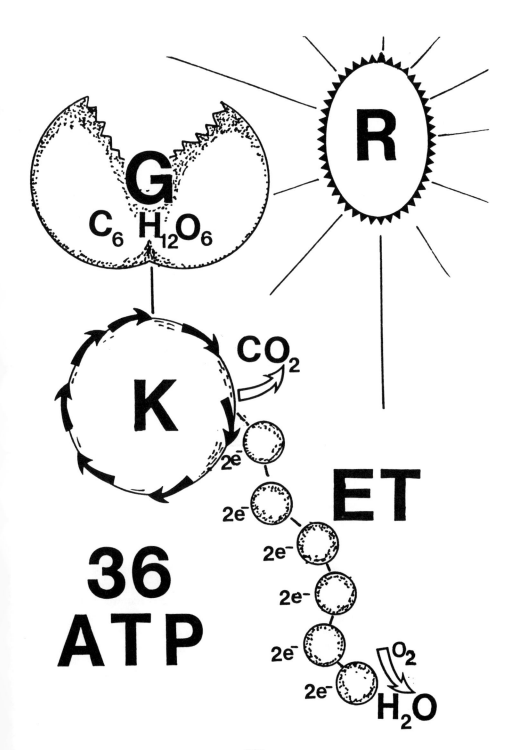

179. TREE PUMPS

In a sense, a tree is like an oscillating pump or seesaw. One part moves the other part so long as energy is supplied. There is no perpetual motion machine. Any machine or pump that does not receive fuel will eventually stop. In a tree, one part of the pump traps energy [$C_6H_{12}O_6$] and the other part supplies the water and the 13 essential elements [H_2O & 13E]. The top cannot function without the bottom and the bottom cannot function without the top. The living network — symplast — and the transport systems — xylem, phloem — maintain connections between the top and the bottom. The top and bottom move as a seesaw or as an oil pump — up and down, up and down. The pump maintains a dynamic equilibrium. This means that it appears to be balanced when any observation is made at any one time. Yet, the pump is constantly in motion meaning that one part — top, bottom — is *always* up or down and away from the other part. When movement stops or becomes balanced, life stops.

Again, balance is the equalization of opposing forces. Balance means that motion stops. When movement ceases, the system stops — death. The balance of nature is a myth. Natural systems survive because they keep moving as dynamic equilibrium and dynamic oscillation.

When one part — top or bottom — is threatened or made smaller, the other part will adjust *if* the injury is *not* beyond the limits of the system and if there is enough time. Now comes the part that most people do not, and cannot understand. As the pump adjusts to a smaller mass, the energy in the parts that are shed are first transferred to the parts that will remain. When the "balancing act" — removing top to compensate for killed roots — is tried by tree workers, the living parts are removed BEFORE they have had a chance to return their energy to the system. **Then the imbalance is made worse, not better.** After parts die, then remove them, never before. More on this later, and the seesaw later also. (Can you remember playing on a seesaw when you were a child, and the other person suddenly got off when he or she was at the bottom? Down you crashed. It hurt! A tree hurts too when you suddenly alter the seesaw with improper treatments!)

202

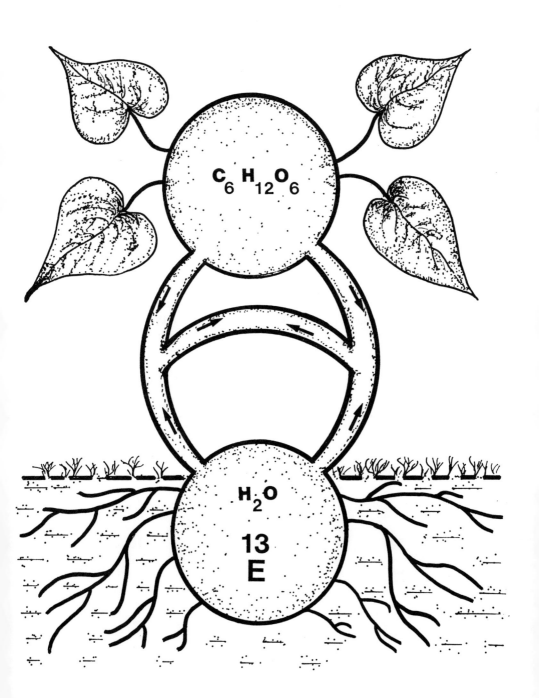

180. AGING

Aging is the process of fulfillment of the genetically programmed information in an organism, or its parts, over time, as affected by environmental factors, and by other living systems that would use the energy of the host system. In a sense, aging is like the playing of a cassette tape. At the moment of conception or fertilization, the tape begins to receive and combine information from both parents [I]. At the time of birth, the tape is ejected and must now play out the information while providing its own energy source [2,E]. How long and how well the tape plays is dependent on environmental or abiotic factors [3] and on other biotic systems that would drain energy from the host system [5]. Then the parasitic system uses the energy to run its tapes or to reproduce [4]. As the abiotic and biotic factors affect the host system over time, the playing of the tape can be long or short, or it may have interruptions. This is aging (B).

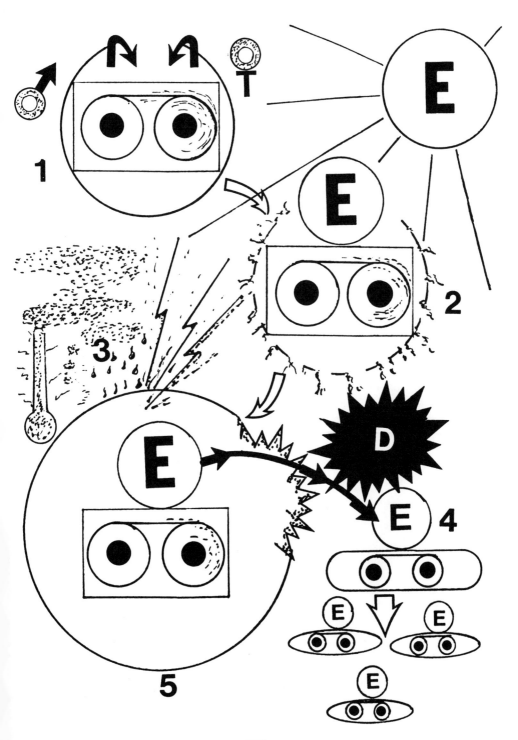

181. LIVING AND NONLIVING SYSTEMS

Living and nonliving systems—weather—constantly interact and adjust to each other. Again, in a sense, they are like a pump or seesaw and the rules of dynamic equilibrium and dynamic oscillation are effective. They appear in balance only because we find it difficult to perceive the constant changes that take place between the two systems. We know that the environment [En] can affect living systems. And, we have seen in our time how living systems can affect the environment—cut all the trees, and clouds that bring rain begin to decrease, and drought begins. I see host [H] and parasite [P] as interacting systems for the benefits of each so they can survive against the pressures of an ever-changing environment. When a host system or its parts cannot maintain order because of decreasing energy, then another system—parasites, pathogens—begins to use the energy at the lower amounts to maintain order in their system. The energy that comes into living systems will be used. When we think of pumps or seesaws, dynamic equilibrium and dynamic oscillation, and energy to maintain order, the subject becomes very simple and very clear (149).

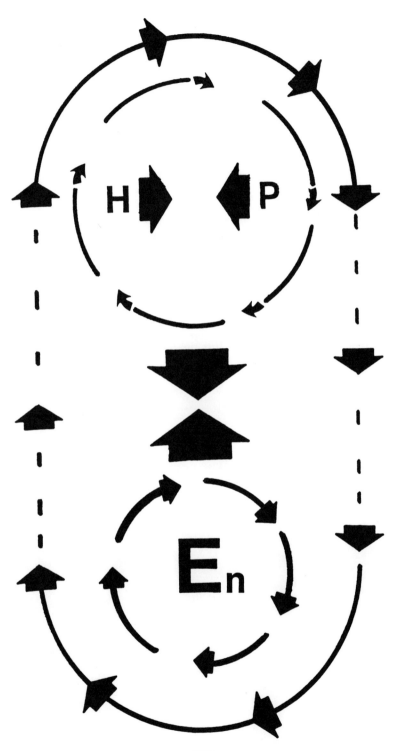

182. SURVIVAL FACTORS

Survival is the ability to stay alive under conditions that have the potential to kill. (In nonliving systems, survival is the capacity to remain in a functional state under conditions that have the potential to disrupt that state.) Survival of a living system is dependent on eight major factors: 1, Energy; 2, Genetic programming; 3, Space; 4, Water; 5, Essential elements; 6, Temperature; 7, Time; 8, Concentrations of the factors. Too much or too little water or elements will kill. Temperatures too high or too low will kill. A professional understands the concentrations of survival factors that are best for the trees and their associates. How much, means DOSE. A professional knows the dose, not just the recipes!

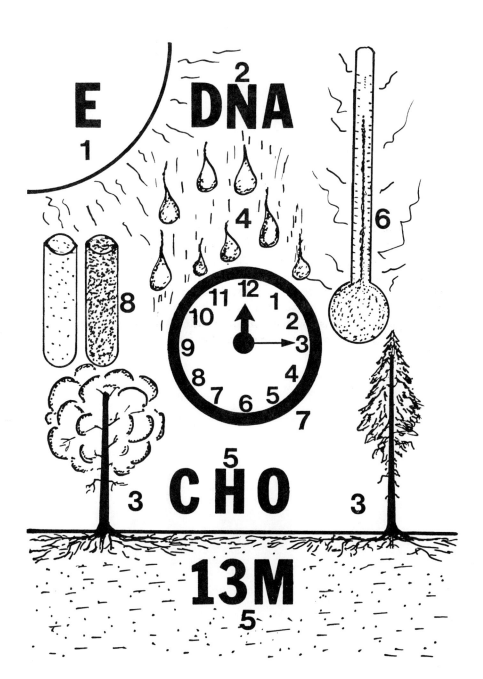

209

183. DEMONS OF D

Living systems die 3 ways: 1D, depletion of energy (infection, starvation); 2D, dysfunction of parts and processes (genetics, toxins, poisons); and 3D, mechanical disruption of parts and processes to a point beyond restoration or compartmentalization and generation of new parts. I call these agents the Demons of D because they all start with D: die, death, decomposition, discoloration, decay, dieback, decline, depletion, dysfunction, disruption, degeneration, and the list goes on. The Demons of D are involved in energy drainage that leads to stress and strain, and sometimes death. Once we begin to see the tree and its associates as a highly ordered system that must maintain that high order by keeping its energy reserves high, then treatments will be simple and effective.

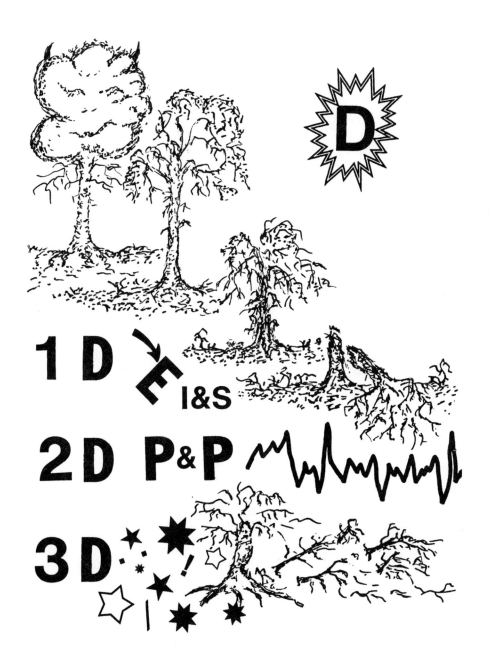

1 D **E** **I&S**

2 D **P&P**

3 D

184. INFECTION AND THE DEMONS OF D

Infection is the establishment of an energy transfer between two different species' systems. When the energy transfer increases the disorder of a part, or the entire system of the donor, or host, and increases the order of the receiver, or pathogen, the process is called disease. When both systems benefit from the energy transfer, then the process is called symbiosis.

The diagrams show the process of disease. When energy reserves are high [$], defense is high [1]. When energy reserves begin to decrease, potential pathogens infect [2]. The pathogen [stippled circles] transfers energy to its system [3]. While the donor system loses energy, the pathogen gains energy, and begins to reproduce [4]. The new pathogens mature and wait for new hosts to attack [5], or they may infect the original host until it dies. The pathogen uses the energy to maintain order of its survival factors.

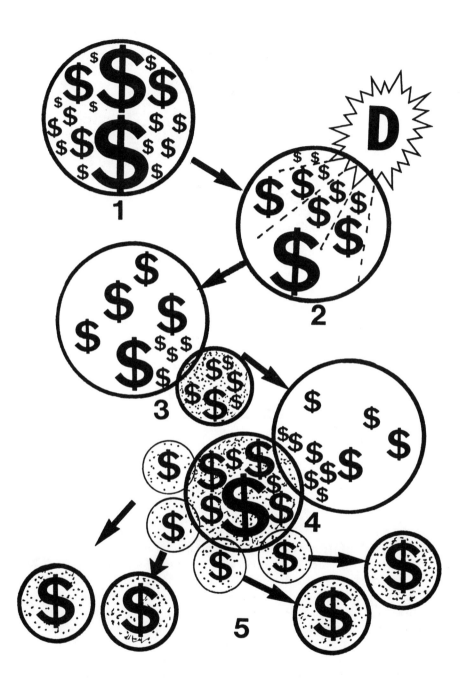

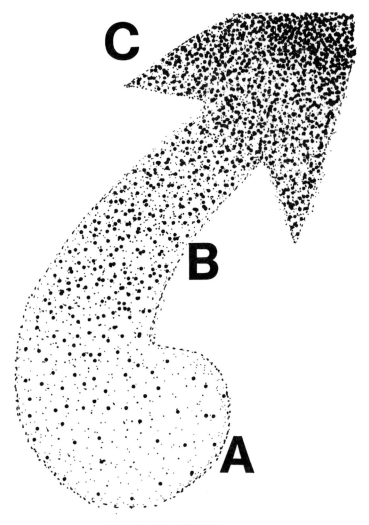

185. GRADATIONS

The Grand Living System is made up of many factors that require energy to maintain the order of the parts and processes. In our discussions, focus is usually on one part or process at a time to simplify learning. However, please do not lose sight of the many interacting ingredients of this story. There are no absolutes: there are no sharp lines or distinctions between the parts and processes. Yet A is significantly different from B, and C is even more different from A. But, all the dots are gradations from A to C. When I discuss energy, there is always more because life depends on at least 7 other survival factors. My focus on energy is because I believe it is the force that moves matter; but also energy keeps the movements orderly, and energy keeps the matter orderly. More on this now as we go to enzymes and other parts and processes that keep the tree system alive and well; and orderly.

214

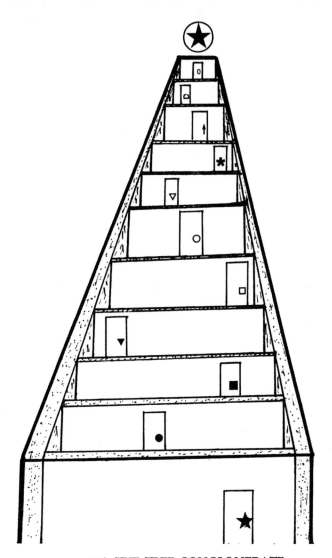

186. THE TREE CONGLOMERATE

The tree system is like a giant business conglomerate because it has many units or parts that operate in different ways. Yet, all units belong to the home office; the tree system. And, there are processes in the different parts that are similar—biochemical pathways. A living chemical pathway is like a series of rooms, all with doors at different places, and all doors with different locks that require individual keys. The aim of the pathway is to move through the rooms while using as little energy as possible. To do this, the keys must be ready as each new door is approached. The keys are enzymes. Enzymes are chemicals that catalyze reactions without being consumed by the reaction. The key opens the door. The key remains the same and can open the door again. When doors do not open, rooms fill with substances that could stop the flow through the rooms. This is how many herbicides and pesticides function (2,4,66). They disrupt the keys, and disrupt the pathways of life.

215

187. ENZYMES

Enzymes are protein-based molecules [Z] that often incorporate macro and microelements (60). Enzymes make it possible for chemical reactions to take place faster under lower temperatures than they would occur in the abiotic world. They catalyze the reactions. They are like chemical keys [1]. When parts of the keys are altered by removing an end piece or substituting another part in the end piece, the key may go into the lock, but it will not turn the lock. Then the lock is not in the position to receive the correct key even if it became available [2]. Enzymes may be altered or destroyed by extremes in pH and when temperatures begin to increase above 40° Celsius (100°F) [3]. Poisons and chemicals designed to kill often alter or destroy a specific enzyme or one of its parts. In this way the chemical can be highly selective to a species. However, some biological pathways have shunts, or detours about a room. This is how they may "escape" when a pathway is disrupted. We need to know more about these shunts so we will have the ability to treat trees poisoned by vandals.

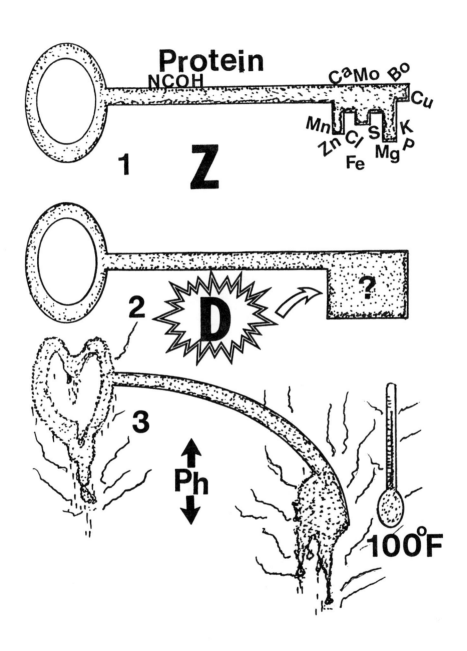

217

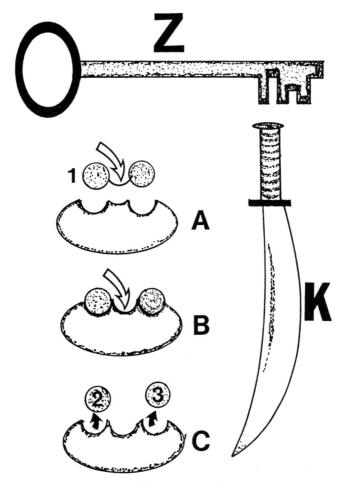

188. ENZYME FUNCTION

The word enzyme comes from the discovery of the substance in — en — yeast or fungi; — zyme. It was first found in yeast, which is a fungus [Z]. As a molecule comes in contact with the enzyme [1,A] it "fits" within the enzyme structure [B]. Then the molecule is altered [2,3] and leaves the enzyme [C]. Enzymes may also be thought of as chemical knives [K]. The knives cleave long chain molecules and split large molecules into smaller ones [A,B,C]. Of course, both explanations are highly simplified accounts of enzyme function. The enzymes make it possible for processes to go on at high rates at lower temperatures. If enzymes were not present, the cell processes would go very slowly. To speed the process, temperature would exceed the limits that would keep the cells alive. The enzymes regulate many natural processes. Microelements are essential parts of many enzymes. When microelements are low or lacking, many enzymes will not function. Reminder; every time something moves, energy is used. There is a constant cost for doing the business of life.

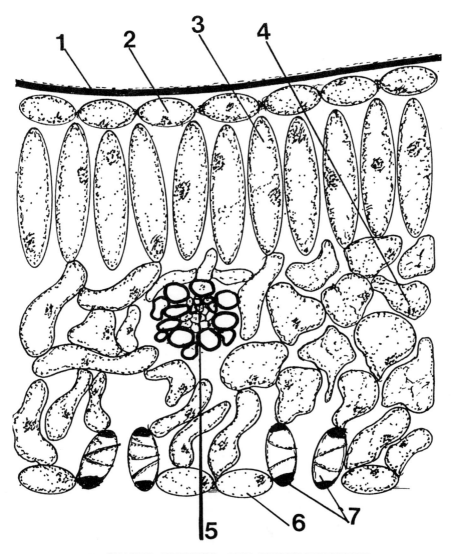

189. LEAVES, NEEDLES, AND PHOTOSYNTHESIS

Here is a transverse section through a leaf: cuticle of waxy materials [1], epidermis [2], palisade layer [3], spongy mesophyll [4], phloem and xylem bundle [5], lower epidermis [6], and guard cells for a stoma. The waxy covering protects the leaf from water loss. The internal cells have many chloroplasts that contain chlorophyll. Most transport bundles—xylem, phloem—are near the lower surface. The guard cells regulate the opening into the stoma. Leaves contain a great amount of air space.

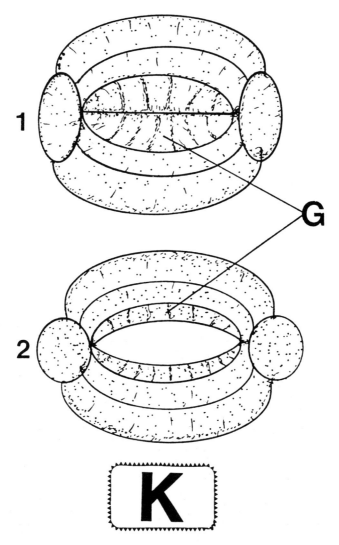

190. GUARD CELLS

Guard cells [G] regulate the opening and closing of the stomata. When the stomata are open, moisture will leave the leaf. However, the stomata must remain open to receive carbon dioxide from the air. Another tradeoff; stay open for CO_2 and moisture leaves; close to maintain moisture, and no CO_2 is absorbed. The guard cells are like long balloons reinforced with bands [G]. When starch is changed to glucose and potassium enters the guard cells [1] the osmotic pressure makes the cells turgid and they expand to open the stoma [2]. When potassium moves out, and sugar is changed back to starch, the cells become flaccid and the stomata close [1]. And, again, the movement of potassium into and out of the cells, and the conversion of starch to sugar, and sugar back to starch, requires energy. There is a cost for every action.

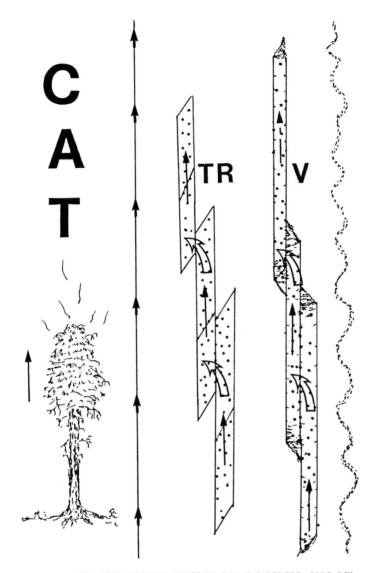

191. WATER MOVEMENT FROM ROOT TO SHOOT

Before water movement is discussed we need to understand CAT first. C means *cohesion* of the water molecules. Water is a polar molecule. It has strong positive and negative ends. It is like small magnets. The molecules clump together. Pour water on glass and it will form beads or mounds because of cohesion. The vessels [V] and tracheids [TR] in trees are small, long capillaries with inner walls that have a great variety of textures. The column of water in a cohesion state "clings" or adheres to the capillary walls—**adhesion** [A]. So water molecules cling or adhere to the capillary walls and the molecules also "stick" together to form long "ropes" of water in the capillaries. T is transpiration. As the water leaves the stomata it is as pulling the "rope" of water upward. The "rope" of water is so strong that it could stay intact within the capillaries for a distance of over 1500 feet (461.5m). The smaller the diameter of the capillary the longer the "rope" can be.

221

192. ROOT ABSORPTION OF WATER AND ELEMENTS

Water and the 13 soil elements essential for life are absorbed through nonwoody roots—root hairs [RH], mycorrhizae [M]. (The diagram below the dotted lines with the stars shows a magnified section through the areas of the dotted lines.) Water (H_2O) moves through the epidermis [EP] and through the walls of the cells—apoplastic movement. When water reaches the endodermis [EN] it must move through the cells—symplastic movement—because the endodermis has cells lined with suberin [CS]. This boundary of suberin is called the Casparian strip [CS]. It is impermeable to water. The elements [1E] in solution move through the living cells—symplastic movement—through the pericycle [P] and into the transport system [X]. Symplastic movement requires energy. Water and elements do not "just move" into plants. There is a cost.

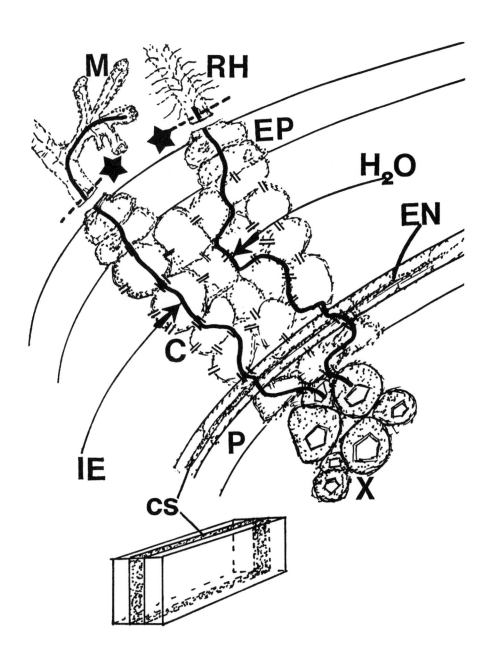

193. TRANSPORT FROM ROOT TO SHOOT
AND FROM SHOOT TO ROOT

First the parts: phloem sieve tubes 1, radial parenchyma 2, phloem companion cells 3, phloem fibers 4, cambial zone 5, wood fibers 6, vessels 7, axial parenchyma 8. Nonwoody roots [R] transport water and elements [WE] to the leaves through vessels or tracheids. The leaves transport photosynthate or glucose [G] to the roots through the phloem. Radial transport of water, elements, and photosynthate takes place through the symplast and the apoplast. Indeed, the tree is a pulsating master pump with countless smaller pumps throughout the system. Let us now look at one of the most fascinating series of pumps that move photosynthate from shoot to root—phloem transport.

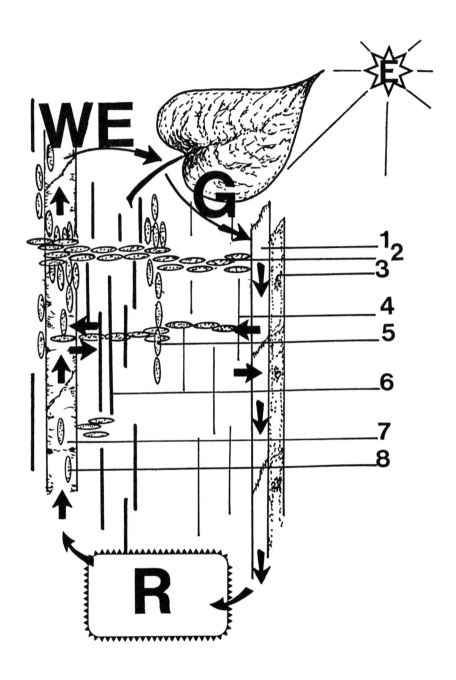

194. PHLOEM TRANSPORT

First the mechanism — osmotic pressure. The leaves pump photosynthate or sugars [G] into the phloem sieve tubes. There is a high energy cost [$] for this action. The loaded sieve tube is surrounded by water [W]. The water moves into the sieve tube and a very high turgor results. When the turgor increases and the cell wall can no longer expand, the photosynthate is moved to the next connecting sieve tube. The process repeats as the photosynthate is "squeezed" from one sieve tube to another. When materials reach the roots, energy is required to unload into the root symplast. Along the way from the leaves to the roots, photosynthate is moved into the symplast of the branches and trunk. (Photosynthate does not go from trunk into branches. See branch diagrams.) And, again, there is an energy cost for this movement.

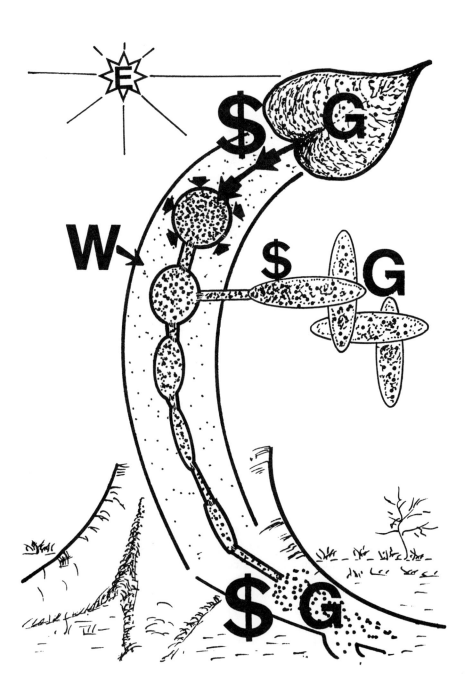

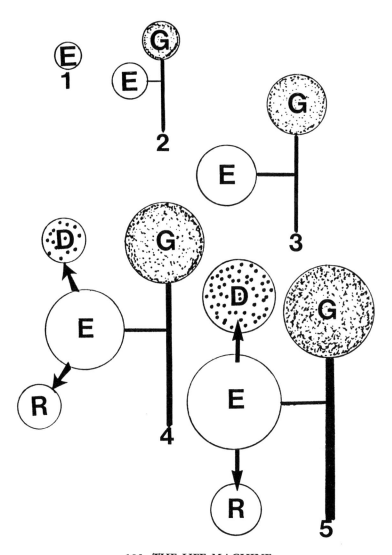

195. **THE LIFE MACHINE**

All life starts with reserve energy [E], or on somebody else's reserves — seeds, cuttings, egg, fetus in a placenta [1]. In trees, growth starts from the reserve energy [G]. Energy is replenished in reserves — starch, oils — needed to start growth again the next growing period [2]. As growth continues, so does the requirement for more and more energy reserves [3] needed to start a system that is increasing in size. As the tree system grows, the demons of D begin to drain energy as wounds are inflicted and as twigs and branches die. At the same time, the tree begins to develop reproductive parts [R], and more energy is used [4]. As the tree grows, the demands for defense, reproduction, and metabolism increase [5]. We will see now that the system must make some adjustments for allocation of energy. Growing at the same fast rate may not be the best answer for survival.

228

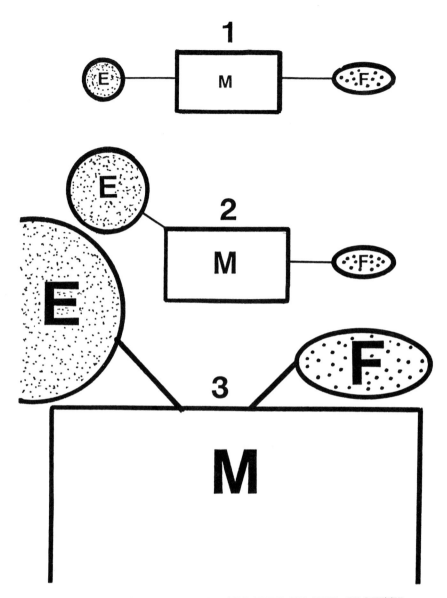

196. POTENTIAL AND KINETIC ENERGY AND GROWTH

A small motor [M] can be started by a small battery [E] and the motor will run for a long time on a small fuel supply [F]. The battery is the reserve energy or potential energy for starting the motor. The fuel keeps the motor going. As the motor runs, kinetic energy is used. As the motor size is increased, a larger battery is needed to start it. If the fuel tank is not increased, the motor will operate for a short time [2]. As the motor increases in size, the battery and fuel tank must also increase [3]. As a tree increases in mass, the potential and kinetic energy must also increase. Let us discuss next what can be done to help the tree along the way.

229

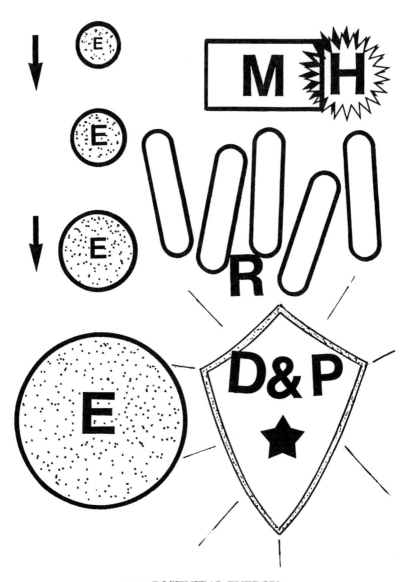

197. **POTENTIAL ENERGY**
The battery or potential energy [E] can be increased in a tree by keeping the tree healthy—correct pruning, watering, fertilizing, and protecting the tree from wounds and abuse [MH]. Reproduction [R] drains energy. Deblossoming sprays [NAA, naphthalene acedic acid] can be used to reduce reproduction and to conserve energy (49). Tulip flowers in Holland are cut off as soon as color and variety are noted. The practice is designed to benefit vital growth of the bulbs. Defense and protection come from reserve energy. Defense is a dynamic action to assure survival. Protection is a static feature that resists spread of pathogens.

230

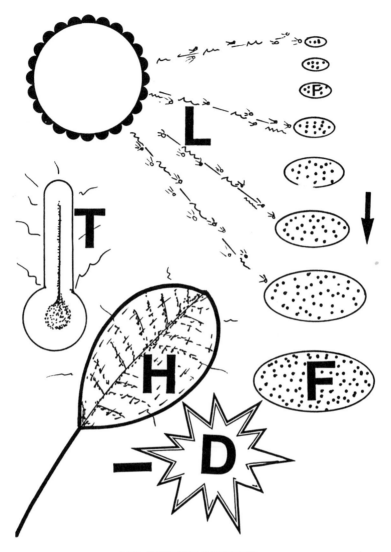

198. **KINETIC ENERGY**

Light in the form of waves or photons is the ultimate energy source [L]. Healthy leaves will trap the energy of the sun [H]. High temperatures [T] above 40° Celsius decrease photosynthesis even when light intensity [L] is high. Keep the demons of D away. Remove deadwood and protect the tree against root injury and compaction. Kinetic energy is energy an object has because it is in motion. The tank holds the fuel [F] used for keeping the object in motion.

Even if your car battery is fully charged, and the fuel tank is full, the motor will not start itself. Some energy source must turn a key or activate the battery in some way. In a sense, a seed is the same as a slowly running motor. When the time and environmental conditions have played their parts, the seed motor speeds up, — growth — kinetic energy from potential energy stored in the seed.

231

199. NITROGEN AND ENERGY

When chemicals and materials that release nitrogen [N] to a tree are added to the soil, a long chain of events start. Potential energy is used to absorb the nitrogen. Energy is used to produce amino acids and a long list of nitrogen-containing compounds. In the end, more tissue is produced and must be maintained — growth [G] — and then the new tissues must return energy to the system. The all important point to remember is that energy [E] flows *out* of the system first, and then, if all goes well, the debt is repaid. However, that is still not the entire story, because the system is larger now and the reserve energy must be greater than the amount that was present when the stimulation of growth started.

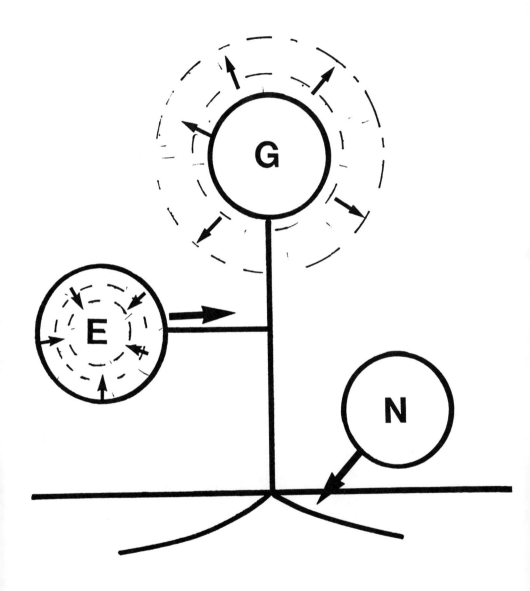

200. NITROGEN AND GROWTH

Nitrogen [N] is a gas that makes up almost 80% of our atmosphere. Except for urea [U], plants seldom absorb organic molecules through nonwoody roots. Urea is an exception because it is a highly polar molecule — strong + and − ends. Most of the nitrogen absorbed by plants is in the form of the nitrate anion — NO_3^-. Nitrogen may also be absorbed in the form of the ammonium cation — NH_4^+. Nitrate or other forms are absorbed by the symplast. Once inside, most of the nitrogen is used to make amino acids [1]. Some NO_3^- may be transported in amino acids before it is used. The amino acids then combine to form peptides [2], polypeptides [3], enzymes [4] and other proteins [5]. These actions take place in living cells and result in more protoplasm [6], more DNA and RNA and more chlorophyll [CHL] in larger leaves. All of these processes take energy out of the system.

234

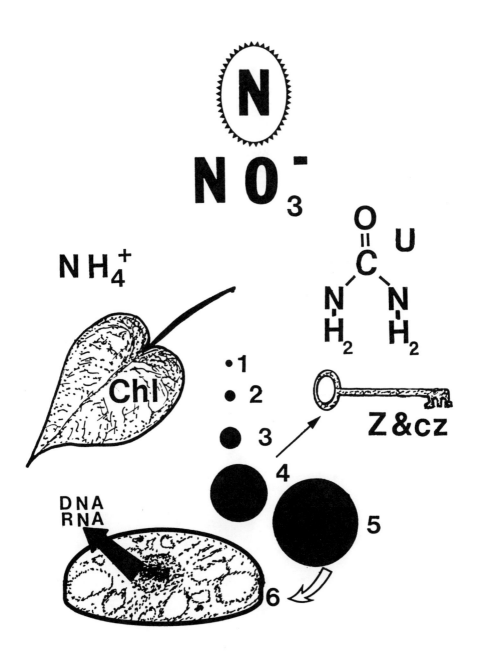

201. NITROGEN PATHWAY

Nitrogen in the form of nitrate anion, ammonium cation, or polar organic urea, is dissolved in the water about the nonwoody roots — the rhizosphere (99,100). The dissolved elements contact the rhizoplane or root walls [RW]. Energy is required for the movement of the elements into the roots [R]. The dotted lines show that the RW may be about a root hair or mycorrhiza. Some nitrogen may form ammonium ion and then go directly to amino acids. Some nitrogen may be transported as nitrate ion; but it will still form nitrogen-based compounds at some point. All along the pathway every chemical reaction requires energy in the form of ATP.

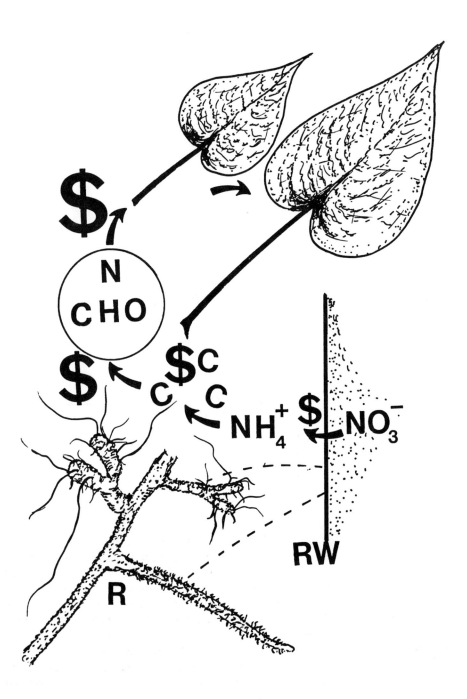

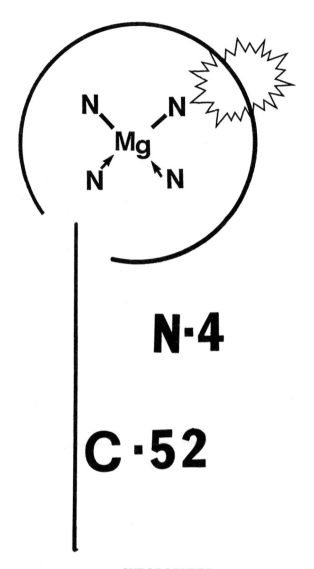

N·4

C·52

202. CHLOROPHYLL

Chlorophyll is a molecule that starts the energy trapping process. The molecule has magnesium [Mg] at its center with 4 nitrogen [N] atoms bonded to it. A long chain of carbon and hydrogen atoms attach the molecule to a membrane. The molecule has a series of double and single bonds with carbon that make it a very receptive light absorbing pigment. Such a compound is called a polyene. My diagram is a very simple representation of the general structure of chlorophyll. My major point is that it takes 4 nitrogen atoms and 52 carbon atoms [C] to make one chlorophyll molecule. And, again, the energy to make one molecule must come out of the system first; and the chlorophyll contains a great amount of carbon and only a small amount of nitrogen.

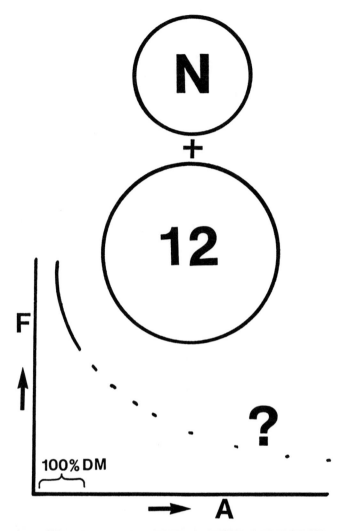

203. NITROGEN AND OTHER ESSENTIAL ELEMENTS

No doubt about it, nitrogen [N] is a key element essential for growth of all organisms. Nitrogen appears to be the limiting factor for growth of trees. Yet, trees have grown for hundreds of millions of years within the limits of nitrogen available to them. I believe it is time to separate nitrogen from the other 12 essential soil elements when we consider fertilization. In many cases, elements other than nitrogen are low or lacking in the soil. Adding more nitrogen and stimulating growth can make the deficiencies all the worse. We know so little about fertilization of mature trees. The graph shows relative amount of common fertilizers increasing on the Y axis [F] and age of the tree increasing on the X axis [A]. Young trees are 100% dynamic mass, so they respond the same as annual plants do to fertilizers. As trees age and the ratio of dynamic mass to static mass changes, we know less and less about the amounts of fertilizers required, if any, for healthy growth.

239

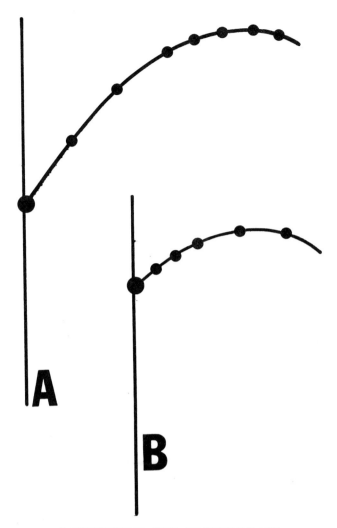

204. FERTILIZERS AND GROWTH RATE

Strange, it seems that some of the people who fertilize trees to grow faster are the first to top and mutilate trees to make them small again! Adding nitrogen will stimulate growth and make the leaves greener, most of the time. We should fertilize for health. The common answer to the response of fertilization is that the growth rate increases—from A to B. (From dot to dot is the amount of annual growth.) First, are you fertilizing a healthy tree to keep it healthy? Or; second, are you fertilizing a stressed or sick tree to help it regain health? Next, what elements are low or lacking in the soil? And, what are the soil, water, pH, light, and element requirements of the tree to be treated? Do you have the wrong tree in the wrong place? Before we discuss fertilization further, let us give a brief look at soils.

Fertilization: 97,98,150,186,204,205,260,294,389; S: 53,56,87.
Roots: 37,41,59,85,99,100,136,190,207,271,272,275,276,277,352,364, 381,382,387; S: 131,142,146,161,180.

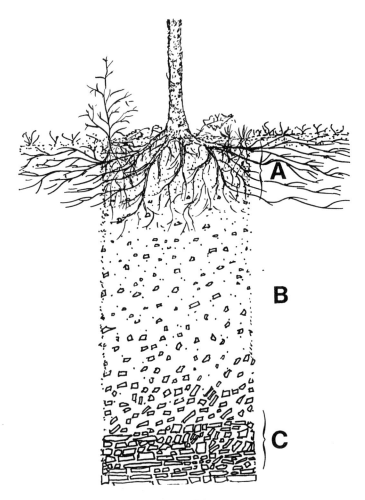

205. SOIL PROFILE

Soils are extremely variable; however, most soils have three horizons. The top A horizon has organic matter, the lower B horizon is a leached zone, and C is the parent material for the area. Tree roots and their associates, the fungi, bacteria, and actinomycetes, grow best in the A horizon. Mycorrhizae are often near the surface. In deep sandy soils, roots may grow many meters downward. Most soils in the tropical rainforests have a very shallow A, or none at all. All forest litter is decomposed rapidly by termites and fungi. The sunlight rarely reaches the forest floor. Many species of trees have adapted to many soil types. Learn the type of soil you have and the tree species that grow best in that soil. Then plant those trees. Problems start when the wrong tree is planted in the wrong soil. The tree may not die; but it will tolerate the poor soil and have insect borers, cankers, and many other man-caused problems.

Soil: 206,228,297,308.

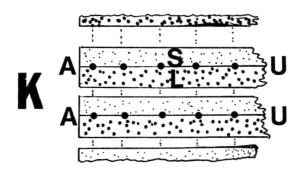

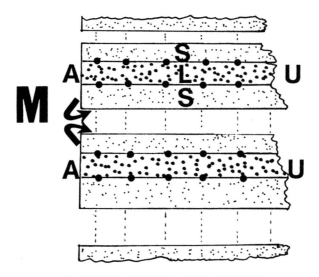

206. CLAYS, STABLE AND SHRINKING

Some clays shrink and expand greatly; others do not. Why?

Clays are particles or crystals of alumina [L] and silica [S] mostly. Most clays, such as kaolite clays [K] are "sandwiches" of silica and alumina held together with oxygen bonds [dots]. The "sandwiches" are so closely packed that water can enter only from the edges [A and U]. Montmorillinite clays have triple-decker "sandwiches" with alumina [L] between the two silicas [S]. The spaces between the crystals are large, and water can enter all along the long surfaces [bent arrows]. The clays absorb water rapidly and expand and then they lose water rapidly and shrink. Trees often get blamed for the shrinking or expanding soils that crack foundations of buildings, because roots absorb water from the soil. Most of the time the real problem with cracked buildings is due to poor engineering and poor building methods. Removal of the tree could make the situation worse not better.

Soil: 206,228,297,308.

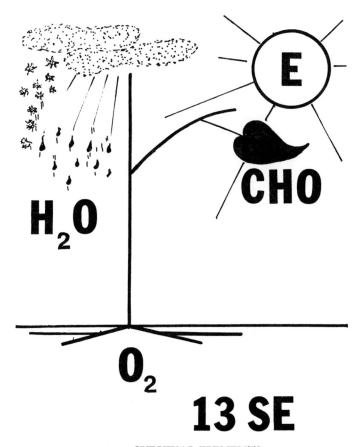

207. SURVIVAL ELEMENTS

All living things require at least 16 essential elements (60). Carbon, hydrogen, and oxygen combined make up carbohydrates. The bonds that hold the CHO together are high energy yielding bonds (352). Carbohydrate is tree food. The 13 essential elements in the soil are absorbed as positive ions—cations—or negative ions—anions. The ions do not have energy bonds that can be used by living things. The 13 soil elements should be called elements (106). A NUTRIENT IS THE COMBINATION OF AN ENERGY SOURCE WITH AN ESSENTIAL ELEMENT THAT DOES NOT YIELD ENERGY. Oxygen is required for respiration. Photosynthesis builds the CHO molecules, and respiration takes them apart. Photosynthesis "uses" carbon dioxide and water and "gives off" oxygen. Respiration "gives off" carbon dioxide and water and "uses" oxygen to "burn" the fuel to release energy. Note that we start with carbon dioxide and water and end with carbon dioxide and water. The energy is held in the bonds, not the elements. The energy bonds are like cocked, locked springs.

(Professor; review basic biochemistry)

(Review Energy: 50,72,85,122,124,204,205,236,256,266,287,288,341,382,383, 386,387,392)

243

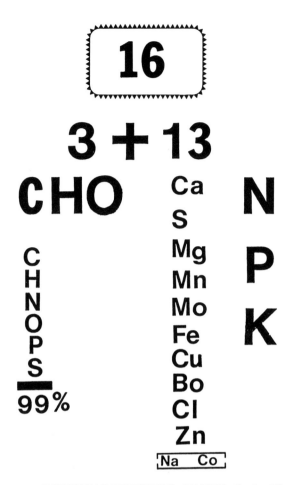

16

3 + 13

CHO

Ca
S
Mg
Mn
Mo
Fe
Cu
Bo
Cl
Zn

Na Co

C
H
N
O
P
S
——
99%

N

P

K

208. ESSENTIAL ELEMENTS OF LIFE: 3 + 13

Organic molecules contain carbon. Organic chemistry is the chemistry of carbon. Carbon, hydrogen, and oxygen make up compounds called carbohydrates. Plants build up organic molecules and animals and microorganisms break them down (292). On a weight basis, about 99% of most plants are made up of carbon, hydrogen, nitrogen, oxygen, phosphorus, and sulpher. The other elements are called microelements. They should not be called *minor* elements. Indeed, when they are lacking, life stops. This is not a minor role. Sometimes a few of the elements are called macroelements: nitrogen, phosphorus, potassium, calcium, and magnesium. Sodium [Na] and cobalt [Co] may also be required in very micro amounts. Cobalt may be essential for the mycorrhizal fungi. Selenium is found in some desert plants. Nickel is required by the bacteria that form galls on leguminous trees. The bacteria fix nitrogen. Silicon may be required by some plants and animals. Some soils are lacking in some essential elements. Boron [Bo] must be added to grow pines in some areas of the world. A healthy tree depends on the correct amounts of essential elements in the soil.

Elements and microelements: 40,84,125,150,185,186,369; S: 33,55,60,62.

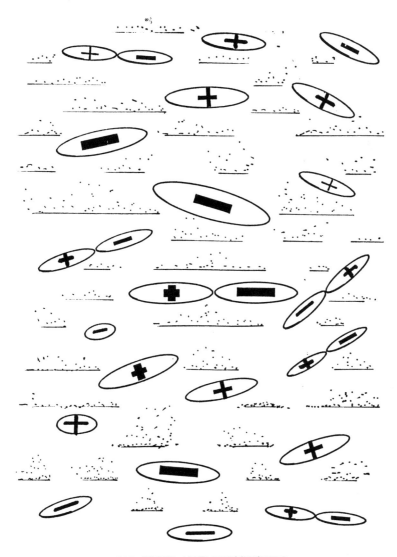

209. IONS AND FERTILIZERS

Ions are charged atoms or molecules. Some ions have a positive charge — cations — and others have a negative charge — anions. When fertilizers are put into or on the soil, the ions become available in the water. Quick release fertilizers are those that release the ions as soon as the materials dissolve in the soil water. Slow or controlled release fertilizers are of two basic types: 1, The chemical granules are coated with materials that must wear away or dissolve away before the fertilizer granules are able to dissolve in the soil water. 2, The essential elements may be bonded with carbon to form organic molecules. The microorganisms must break down these molecules before the ions are released into the soil water. Once the ions enter the soil water they are like small magnets or submarines with a positive or negative charge.

Fertilization: 97,98,150,186,204,205,260,294,389; S: 53,56,87.

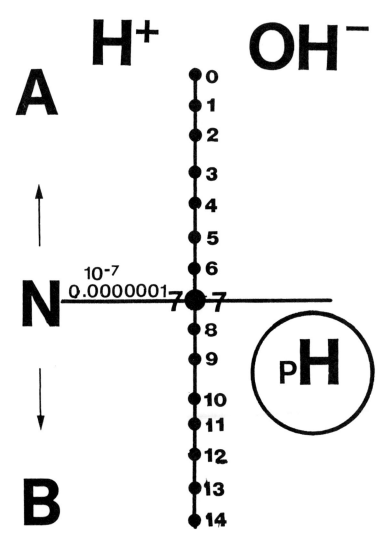

210. THE pH SCALE

The pH scale is used to define the degree of acidity or alkalinity of a solution. The "p" stand for "power" and the "H" stand for the concentration of hydrogen ions. The scale is from 0 to 14. The lower the number the stronger the acid [A], and the higher the number the stronger the base [B]. At the neutral point [N] there is an equal amount of H^+ and OH^- ions. In pure water there is 0.0000001 moles of H^+. (A mole is the amount in grams for the molecular weight of a substance. Because hydrogen has a molecular weight of one, a mole of hydrogen would be one gram of hydrogen in one liter of water.) This is expressed as 10^{-7}, or for convenience as pH7. The pH values cannot be averaged, because they represent logarithms.

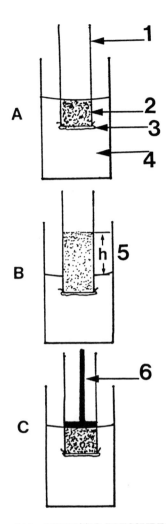

211. OSMOTIC PRESSURE

Osmosis is the diffusion of water through a differentially permeable membrane. This means water will go both ways through the membrane; but other substances, or ions will not move through the membrane. In A, a tube with an open bottom [1], has water and substances dissolved in it—solute—[2], and a membrane is tied at the bottom [3]. The entire tube is in a larger tube which contains water [4]. In B, the water from the larger tube moves into the smaller tube and the water and solute in the smaller tube rise [5] to the height of h. In C, if a piston is placed in the smaller tube [6], and a force is applied to lower the water and solute in the smaller tube to the level of the water in the larger tube; that force is equal to the osmotic pressure that first moved the water and solute upward in the smaller tube. Osmotic pressure is a major force that moves many substances in trees. Loading solutes into confined places is an energy demanding process. (See phloem transport, diagram 194, and see basic chemistry; 106,292.)

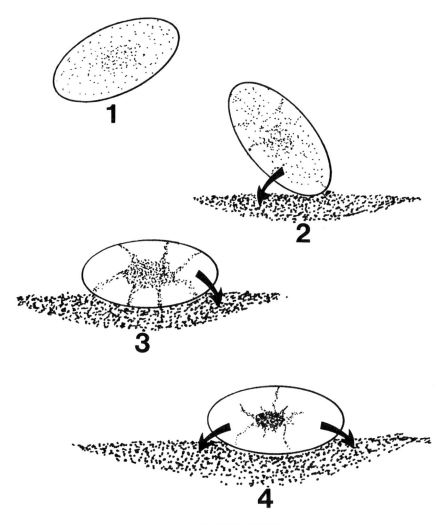

212. PLASMOLYSIS

When water moves out of a cell to the point where the protoplasm shrinks and breaks away from the cell wall, the cell will die. The process is called plasmolysis. For example, when a bacterium [1] "lands" on a salted ham [2], water moves from the bacterium to the salted surface [3] and the protoplasm shrinks and breaks away from the cell wall, resulting in death of the cell [4]. It is important to point out that water will flow both into and out of the bacterium. But, the flow will be much greater outward than inward. We often speak of the salt index or the salting effect of fertilizers. High salt index means that a high amount of the materials in the fertilizer will form ions rapidly when in contact with soil water. And, when high amounts of ions are available, the probability of plasmolysis of roots is high.

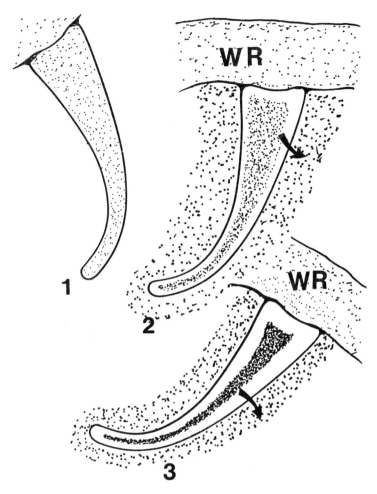

213. **ROOT PLASMOLYSIS**

When nonwoody roots [1] growing from woody roots [WR], are suddenly surrounded by ions from fertilizers [2], the water in the nonwoody roots flows outward [3], and the root will die if the cells are plasmolysed. This phenomenon is easy to see on grass and annuals; but not so easy to recognize on mature trees.

How to apply fertilizers is always a question. So much depends on the soil type, other plants such as grass, and the elements that are low or lacking in the soil. You cannot or should not separate addition of fertilizers with how they are applied, and that water should always be a part of the treatment. Tools that release fertilizers slowly as the tool penetrates the soil appear to be best where grass and other plants are near the tree. If nitrogen is the target element, then surface application is the best. Applying fertilizers deep into the soil — beyond 30 cm. or 12 inches in most cases — makes little sense to me. Applying fertilizers into drill wounds in trunks — injections — also makes little sense to me. (A tourniquet will always stop a nose bleed. All treatments must be weighed against the side effects.)

249

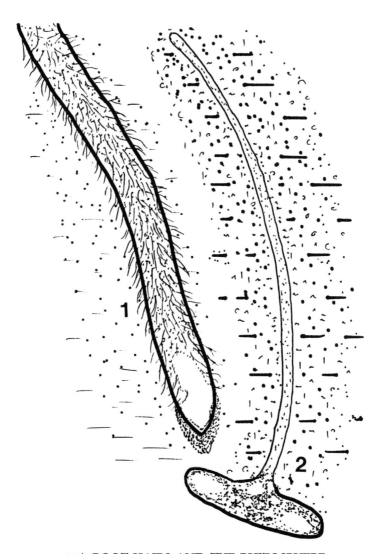

214. ROOT HAIRS AND THE RHIZOSPHERE

Root hairs [2] are extensions of single epidermal cells on nonwoody roots [1]. The root hairs extend greatly the absorptive surface of the root. They are like heat radiation grills on a radiator. The hairs and epidermal cells of small nonwoody roots, and the soil and water and microorganisms surrounding them, make up the rhizosphere (99,100). The rhizosphere is a unique area where root, water, elements, and microorganisms all seem to "melt" together in a gel or "soup". The rhizosphere is a niche that serves the survival requirements of tree and associates. The root hairs may live for a few weeks or longer; but they soon become a part of the "soup". The recycling elements in the rhizosphere is a world of its own. My point: The rhizosphere is the business end of the tree. It is absolutely essential for the lives of many organisms. It is very fragile! Construction is an enemy of the rhizosphere because soil is compacted and oxygen is reduced.

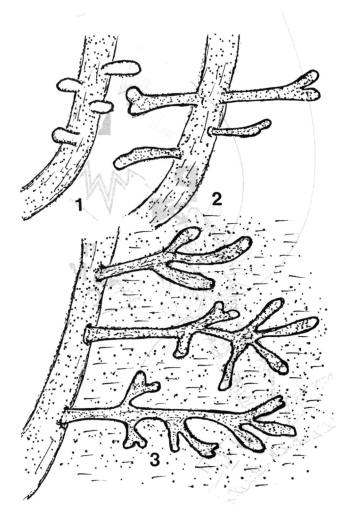

215. MYCORRHIZAE: THE OTHER ABSORPTIVE STRUCTURES

Mycorrhizae are nonwoody structures composed of root and fungus tissues. The structure is not root, nor is it fungus; but both.

Mycorrhiza means fungus root. There are basic types of mycorrhizae: those that have most of the fungus tissues on the outer surface — ectomycorrhizae; and those that have the fungus tissue inside the root and cells — endomycorrhizae. And, as always in nature, some forms are between these two types. Many mycorrhizal fungi form mushrooms as fruit bodies (285). As the nonwoody root begins to emerge from a small woody root (1), a fungus infects the root [2], and a great variety of branching and swollen structures result [3]. The mycorrhizae facilitate the absorption of elements, especially phosphorus, zinc, manganese, and copper. Most mycorrhizae form near the soil surface where leaf and twig litter is being decomposed. Mycorrhizae of many trees, such as beeches, can be found in abundance in the leaf litter. Compaction destroys the habitat for these mycorrhizae.

Mycorrhizae: 120,207,213,234,343,367,398.

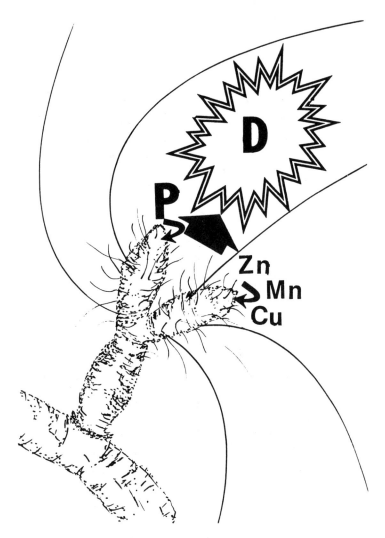

216. MYCORRHIZAE AND THE DEMONS OF D

The vegetative tubes, or hyphae, of the mycorrhizal fungi often extend far out beyond the rhizosphere and often attach to decomposing leaves and other plant litter. The hyphae greatly extend the absorptive area for the tree. The fungi also protect the tree from pathogens [P](207). The tree and fungus have a mutualistic association—symbiosis. The tree benefits because of more efficient absorption of elements. The fungi benefit because they obtain some carbohydrates from the tree. Also, when the mycorrhizae die, some of the fungi digest the structure. Other types of nonwoody structures involve bacteria and actinomycetes. Bacteria form nodules on the roots of many plants in the legume family. These nodules fix nitrogen which means that atmospheric nitrogen is combined with oxygen or hydrogen to form nitrate or ammonium ions which can be absorbed by the tree. On the carob trees, bacteria nodules are sometimes found on the trunk and large branches. Actinomycetes interact with the tree to form nodules called actinorhizae. They also fix nitrogen. They are found on a wide variety of trees (181,297,318).

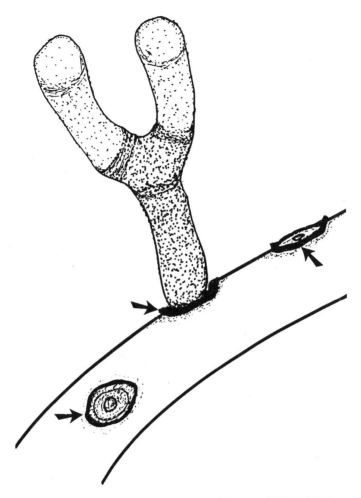

217. MYCORRHIZAE AND ANOTHER BOUNDARY

Tree defense depends greatly on strengthening existing boundaries and building new boundaries after wounding and after nonwoody parts die (A). Mycorrhizae are ephemeral; they live for a short time. How short, I do not know; but being a nonwoody structure it is highly unlikely that they live more than a year. It is common to see new mycorrhizae forming close to others in all stages of aging and dying. A close look at mycorrhizae will reveal a base or "cup" that holds the structure [arrows]. The "cup" is like a doughnut with a hole in the center. As the mycorrhiza begins to die, the hole is closed. If the hole does not close, it becomes an easy entrance point for root-infecting pathogens. Conditions that might prevent closure could be compaction or flooding. Remember, with leaves the abscission layer starts to form and then the leaf dies and usually falls away. Shed means a boundary separates the leaf from the tree. Shed does not mean cast away. Mycorrhizae are shed also. They begin to die and then the boundary forms. They cannot fall away. They will be digested in place. There is probably as much root tissue (or more) formed and shed under ground as leaves above ground.

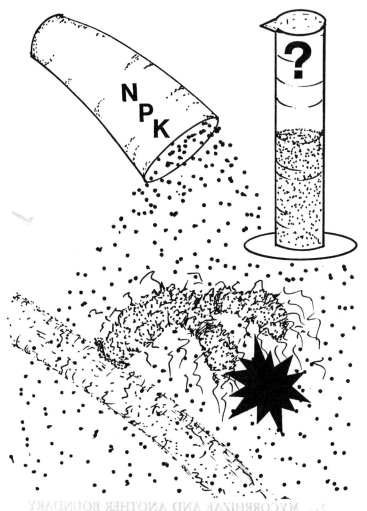

218. MYCORRHIZAE AND FERTILIZERS

Fertilization may decrease or increase the amount of mycorrhizae on roots (120,343). Overfertilization, especially with high amounts of nitrogen, may decrease mycorrhizae (292,343). I do not know at what concentrations the increase or decrease starts. The only way to determine the concentrations that decrease mycorrhizae is to have some measure of the abundance of mycorrhizae before fertilization and after treatment. It is easy to examine a few roots and to observe the number of living and dead mycorrhizae present. Even on well established lawns, a small section of grass can be removed and tree roots can be examined. Then the section of lawn can be replaced with no visible sign of disturbance. Until such observations are made the "dump-it-on" treatments will continue. When in doubt it is better to apply very low amounts and repeat the treatments than to apply a single large dose. A professional knows dose and timing. An understanding of dose and timing will come as the system is understood. (For excellent reviews of this subject, see pages 526 and 527 in reference 292, and reference 343.)

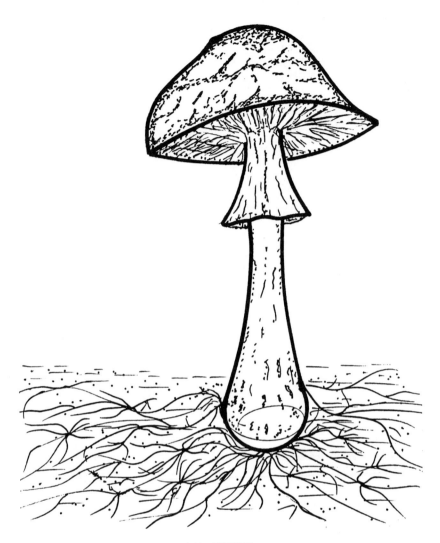

219. FUNGI

Fungi are organisms that get their energy by breaking down or decomposing organic matter; living and dead. The fungi are the original recyclers. As they decompose matter, they release carbon dioxide and return nitrogenous compounds and other materials to the soil. They belong to the Kingdom Fungi. The vegetative parts are multicellular tubes called hyphae. Only rarely are fungi single-celled. The single-celled forms are yeasts. The fruit bodies of the fungi are extremely variable from structures so small that they can hardly be seen by the naked eye, to large woody structures that could weigh up to 30 pounds (13.3kg) or 40 pounds (17.7kg). The mushroom is the fungus fruit body most commonly seen and recognized. The mushroom is the structure that produces the spores. Some mushrooms are very poisonous. Unless you really know your mushrooms, do not eat them. Leave collecting to the experts.

Now is the time to introduce the subject of mass; the mass/energy ratio.

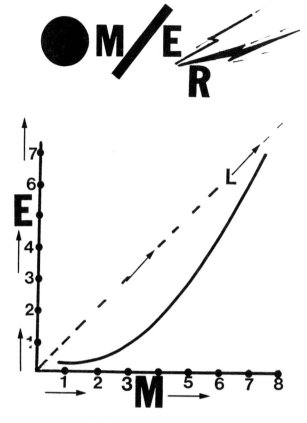

220. MASS/ENERGY RATIO

No system can increase in mass beyond the limits of energy available to maintain order with all of its parts and processes. Mass is the amount of matter regardless of space occupied. Here I use the word to indicate the amount of parts and processes in the tree system. As the mass of a tree system increases [M] the amount of energy [E] to maintain order in all parts and processes begins to follow an exponential—exponents—curve not a linear curve [L]. This explains why the growth rate of young trees is so rapid and the growth rate of older trees is so slow even though trees are generating systems. Again, as the tree system increases in mass, the amount of energy required to maintain order in the parts and processes increases as some exponent and is not a linear increase. On the other hand, trees are the largest organisms because they developed ways to work with this law for relatively long periods. Trees shed parts and wall off parts and alter parts to be protection wood. Walled off parts and protection wood then become static mass. Energy is required to bring about static mass; but once formed, no additional energy is required to maintain it. So the tree forms layers of dynamic mass over the expanding core of static mass. The core/skin hypothesis. (The paper by R.C. Hardwick (127) *must* be read because it serves as the basis for many of the concepts presented here.) (Do not confuse mass with weight. Your body mass is the same on earth as it is on the moon. Your weight on the moon is much less than your weight on earth. Weight is determined by the force of gravity acting on mass.)

256

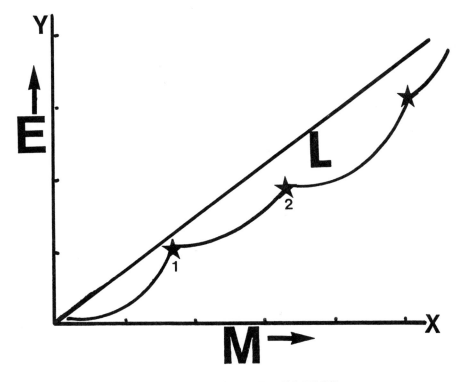

221. TREE SYSTEM ADJUSTMENTS

As the tree system gets larger [M] and older, the demands for energy [E] increase as some exponent because new and greater demands for energy begin to develop. The tree system begins to reproduce and this takes large amounts of energy. Twigs, branches, and roots begin to shed and energy must go for protection zones. Wounds begin to accumulate and the defense budget must be increased. Energy is required to alter wood to a more protective state. Larger growth means more energy to establish new cells and to maintain the energy for metabolism. At the same time, more energy must be stored to accelerate the system in spring. To survive, the tree system sheds, walls off, and alters wood to a more protective state. This is a way of bringing the energy [L] curve down again (stars 1,2,3). But, please note that even these actions do not stop the energy curve from moving upward. A major reason is that the adjustments themselves require energy. We are back to the reason why there is no perpetual motion machine, no 100% use of energy in a machine, and no absolutes. And when parts of the systems do not have enough energy to maintain order, the pathogens take over. When too many parts are lost, the entire system may stop.

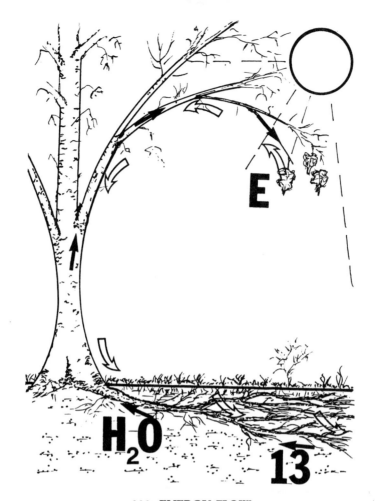

222. ENERGY FLOW

Energy trapped in the bonds of carbohydrate [E] is transported from source—tissues that contain chlorophyll—to sinks—tissues that require energy but do not trap it [open arrows]. (Source is a common term in plant physiology that indicates where a substance originates. Sink is a term that indicates where a substance goes, and is not transported to another location.) Water and the 13 soil elements essential for life are transported from the source—soil—to the sinks—cells that are not able to absorb them, but do require them [dark arrows]. To trap energy requires energy; to absorb water and elements requires energy; to transport all substances requires energy; and to incorporate the substances into the tree system requires energy. Every action and reaction has a cost. There is no perfect machine. There is nothing free. Add to all of this the energy loss caused by so many old treatments that removed defense systems: covering wounds, drilling holes, digging into sound wood, removing tops, cutting large roots, and the list goes on. It is a wonder trees have survived! Arboriculture should mean tree care, not tree injury for profit. Modern Aboriculture hopes to change this.

Energy: 50,72,85,122,124,204,205,236,256,266,287,288,341,382,383,386,387,392

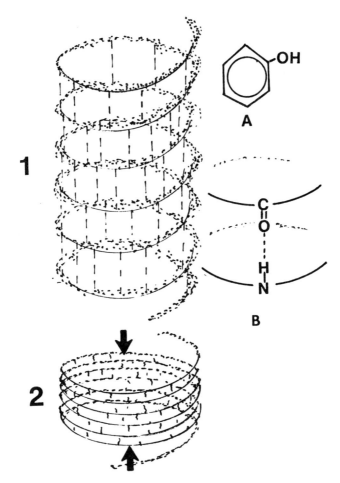

223. TANNING

Tanning is a process of adding phenol-based compounds [A] to proteins [1] and chemically removing the bonds [B] that hold the protein molecule in place. When the hydrogen bonds are oxidized, the protein molecule collapses [2] and enzymes of another organism cannot fit within the collapsed molecule to digest it (292). The protein molecule is like the slinky toy for children. Imagine the toy held apart by toothpicks [1]. Then remove the toothpicks — hydrogen bonds — and the toy collapses [2]. That is tanning. Trees may tan their leaves and the tanned leaves act as a protective measure against digestion by insects and fungi. Much research has been done to determine whether a tree attacked by insects, sends chemical "signals" to other trees not yet attacked. The "signals" stimulated the tanning process. It appears that such "messages" are sent. Please understand that trees do not reason or think out these actions. Giving purpose to actions that are beyond reason is called teleology. Teleology is a good teaching device so long as the principles of natural systems are understood.

Review pysiology: 5,6,101,103,104,122,190,223,238,253,254,267,287,341,342, 349,359,393,395,407,408.

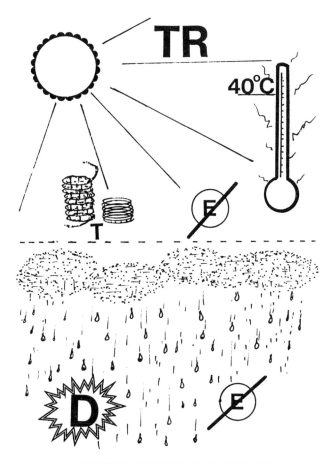

224. TROPICAL TREES AND ENERGY

You would think that tropical trees with all the heat, rain, and light available to them would be the most massive trees in the world. Not so. Trees along the northwestern coast of the United States of America and the southwestern coast of Canada attain biomasses many fold greater than most tropical trees. Trees in New Zealand and parts of Australia also grow to massive sizes. Trees in cold climates use energy to stay alive at cold temperatures (103,104,274). In very warm climates, trees use a great amount of energy to tan leaves and to form protection boundaries against the ever present termites, other insects, and a great number of pathogens. So, their defense budget must not only be high; but it must be high all year. Then add to this the slowing of enzyme systems as temperatures rise above 40° Celsius. And more, when the rains come, the light is low. And, the insects and pathogens are high in numbers. Competition is intense for survival in the tropics. Most tropical trees grow very fast when young, and then, if they survive, growth rate is slowed. Of course there are always exceptions such as some *Ficus* species that form prop roots, and one tree can occupy almost a hectare of land.

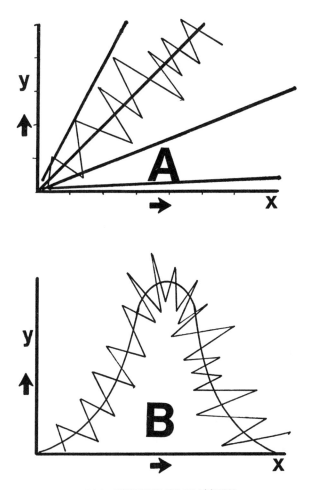

225. CURVES IN NATURE

Linear curves [A] are straight lines between a horizontal base and a vertical line at 90° to the base. Linearity means that for every unit outward on the base—X axis—there is a unit increase on the Y axis that fits a straight line. Linearity means that you can predict what will happen as one or the other factor changes. In nature, linearity may occur for short durations. And when it does, it will really be a series of vibrations or a jagged pattern along the linear curve.

The bell-shaped curve [B] is another natural curve. And, again, the real pathway is usually a jagged pattern along the bell-shaped curve.

In theory the curves appear applicable and correct. Yet, in real life, there is no equal reaction for every action. Again, we are back to the desire for a perfect machine; a perfect system. It does not work that way. Machines have friction. Natural "machines" have energy drains. When mathematicians look at nature, they say that it is chaotic because it does not fit their "nice" formulae (107). Natural systems vibrate or resonate about linearity, and the bell-shaped curves. Knowing this can help in understanding many natural phenomena, such as insect cycles and disease cycles.

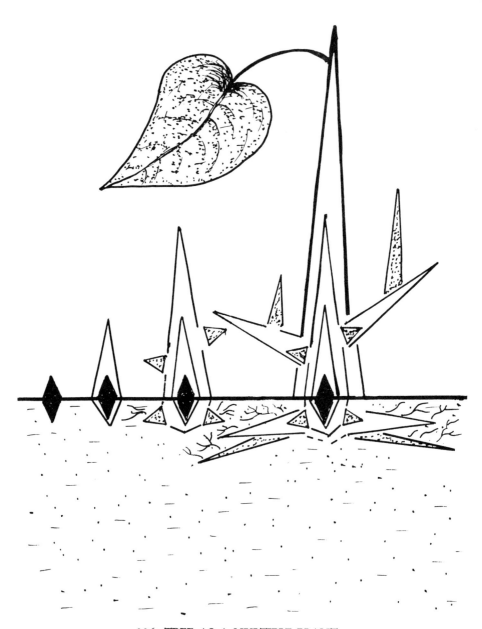

226. TREE AS A MULTIPLE PLANT

In a sense, a tree is a multiple plant, because every growth period a "new tree" grows over the older trees. A tree has 3 major organs—roots, stem, leaves. Flowers are modified leaves. An organ is a group of tissues that perform a specific function. A tissue is an orderly group of similar cells. Mycorrhizae (see diagrams 215–218) are, organs. And so are reproductive parts also, from flowers to fruit. Even though they are modified leaves, the changes are so great that they fit the definition of an organ. The practical importance of a tree as a multiple plant is that we get a new chance every growing season to help a tree.

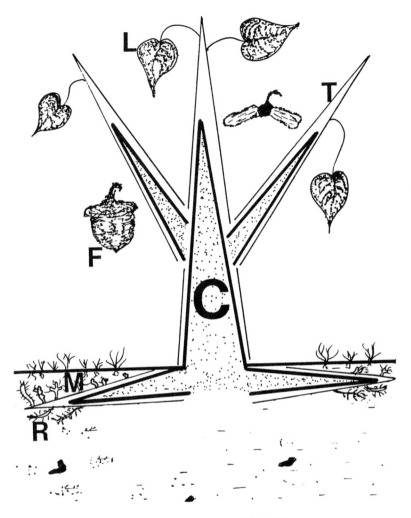

227. CORE-SKIN HYPOTHESIS

As new young trees grow over older aging trees, the young living trees become a "skin" over the aging "core". As the central core develops, nitrogen-based compounds are recycled out to the younger "skin" (226). A young tree is all dynamic mass — every place there can be a living cell, there is a living cell. As the central "trees" age and die, they become the static mass. The core-skin hypothesis is the basis for many of the concepts presented here and for many treatments. What you can do to a tree when it is young and 100% dynamic mass is different from what you should do to it when it has a large core of static mass and only a small skin of dynamic mass (127). Trees are generating systems (A,B,H). Every growing season new parts — leaves [L], twigs [T], non-woody roots that produce root hairs [R], mycorrhizae [M], and reproductive parts — are formed in new spatial positions. The core [C] will increase because the system is generating as long as it lives. Thus, the ratio of core to skin changes as the tree ages.

263

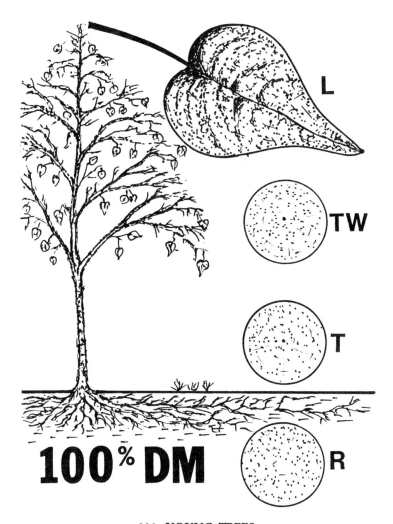

228. YOUNG TREES

A young tree is a tree that is 100% dynamic mass: leaves [L], twigs [TW], trunk [T], and roots [R]. The core-skin hypothesis (127) is supported by research on nitrogen recycling from aging cells to young cells (226). When a tree is young, the ratio of energy available—potential energy—to energy required—kinetic energy—to maintain order in the dynamic mass is far in favor of potential energy. As a tree ages, the ratio begins to change. When the ratio of potential energy to kinetic energy necessary to maintain order of the dynamic mass begins to get *NEAR* a 1 to 1 ratio, the tree begins to shed parts (136,276,364), or alters parts to form static mass (8,9,146). If the tree system, or its parts, do not regulate the ratio of potential energy to kinetic energy, the entire tree—decline—or parts of the tree—dieback—will go to a lower state of energy use to maintain order (384,385). And, when this lower state begins, the pathogens that can maintain order at that level of energy will take over. No systems can avoid these natural laws.

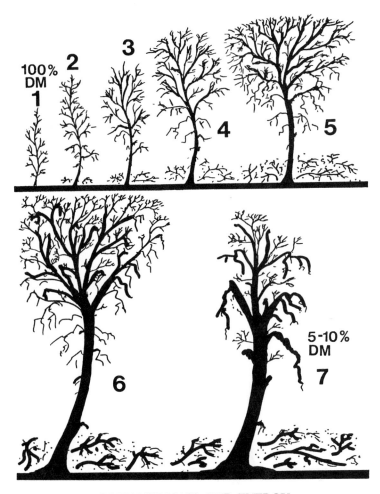

229. DYNAMIC MASS AND ENERGY

As a tree ages, the ratio of dynamic mass to static mass changes [1 to 7] The other natural ratio is potential energy to kinetic energy. The tree, being a generating system, is committed to increasing its mass. Yet, if all of the increase in mass was dynamic mass, the tree system would soon fail for lack of energy. Or the system would become an annual plant system. A unique feature of the long-lived trees is that they have developed ways to regulate their dynamic mass to static mass ratio so that the potential energy to kinetic energy does not approach a 1 to 1 ratio. As a compartmented system, parts are shed as the 1 to 1 ratio is approached. But, being a generating system, the tree grows new parts in new positions (A). As elegant as the system is, it does run out of time. As more and more parts fail, a threshold is reached where the entire system fails.

There are two ratios: potential to kinetic energy, and static to dynamic mass. To maintain order in the dynamic mass, potential energy is required to meet the demands of a living system that uses kinetic energy. As dynamic mass increases, the demand for potential energy also increases because more kinetic energy will be required to maintain order.

265

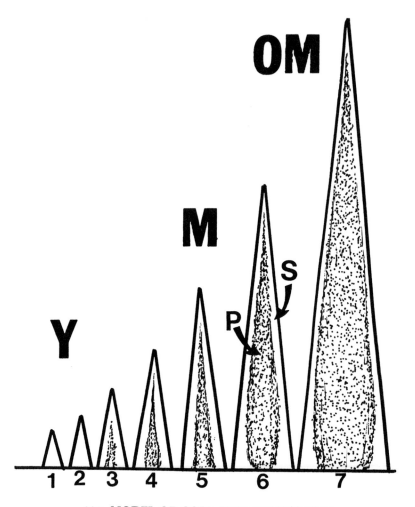

230. MODEL OF CORE-SKIN HYPOTHESIS

Here is a model that shows the changes in ratio of core [P] to skin [S] as trees age [1 to 7] from youth [Y] to maturity [M] to over maturity [OM]. How trees in the natural forest survive under the pressures of the potential to kinetic energy ratio, and dynamic to static mass ratio might give us some clues for treatments. Most twigs and branches that are shed die at the end of the growing season. The nitrogen reserves and other essential substances are recycled back to the tree first. Removing dead wood in winter, would take the food source away from organisms that would digest the dead branch. In nature many trees grow from seeds but very few reach maturity. There are two ways to survive; grow so fast that your crown is above others, or grow very slowly and keep your mass so small that you can survive on a very small energy budget. There are many dwarf trees in the natural forest. They do not reproduce and they receive very few wounds because they are small. The trees that die are those that "make a rush" for the top and increase their mass beyond the limits of available energy. I have seen this story many times in many places in my lifetime.

266

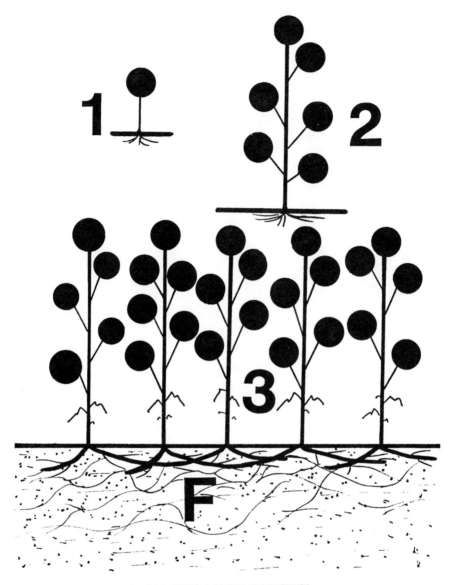

231. THE 3 TREE CONCEPT

Tree 1 is a young tree that is 100% dynamic mass. Tree 2 is a group of tree 1's on an enlarging core or static mass. Each major "branch" of tree 2 is a tree 1, and the top portion or portions on older tree 2's are tree 1's. Tree 3 is a group of trees that is made up of many tree 2's of the same species. The tree 2's are connected by root grafts and by the mycorrhizal fungi [F]. You can overprune tree 1, tree 2, and tree 3. Trees in natural forests grew in groups. They had group defense and group protection. When we take them out of the group, we take away these features. As tree 2's are removed from tree 3, the entire tree may decline or be so weakened that it does not take much to kill it. Then we blame some bug, some fungus, or some pollutant!

232. PHENOLOGY

Phenology [P] is the timing of natural processes. We have five major periods in our day: wake up [1], get dressed [2], eat [3], work [4], and rest [5]. Trees also have five basic periods: onset of growth [1], formation of new leaves and needles [2], high photosynthetic period [3], formation of new bark and wood, and storage of energy [4], and dormancy [5]. Insects and microorganisms also have five periods: onset of growth [1], intense utilization of available energy source [2], rapid reproduction [3], movement of new individuals to new potential growth sites [4], dormancy [5].

The variations of the five part theme are almost endless. Every living system must rest (103,104,268,274), must start again after rest, must take in energy, must grow and defend itself, and must reproduce to survive.

The more we understand the phenological periods of trees, their beneficial associates, and their pathogens, the more we will be able to do to time our treatments to the advantage of the trees and their associates and to the disadvantage of the pathogens. Every system has its strong times and its weak times (203). Every system has an Achilles' heel; a time when it is vulnerable to attack.

Phenology: 54,72,77,85,236,269,287,301,344,345.
Review basic plant biology (292).

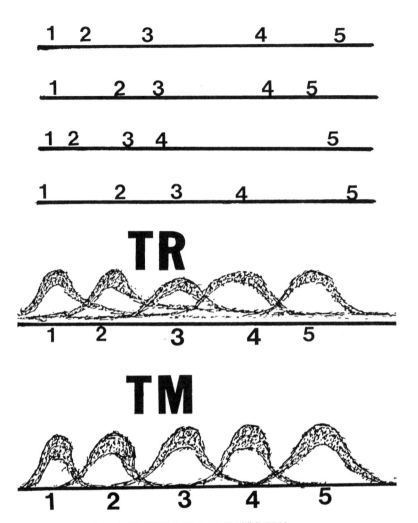

233. PHENOLOGICAL PATTERNS

A year has the same number of days in the tropics as in the temperate zones. However, the patterns of phenological periods will differ from the coldest to the warmest regions of the world. Each horizontal line is one year. The time spent in each phenological period is different for different climatic regions. In the cold regions, period 5 or dormancy is very long [numbers indicate phenological periods]. In the tropical areas period 5 is short; but in some hot, dry areas some trees have a midsummer dormancy. In tropical trees [TR] the bell-shaped curve for each period seldom touches the base line. This means that some trees of the same species will always have a few new leaves, or a few new flowers, regardless of the time of year. However, most of the phenological activities of the trees will fit the middle of the bell-shaped curve. In temperate climate trees [TM] the phenological periods do touch the base lines. When flowering is done, it is done most of the time.

269

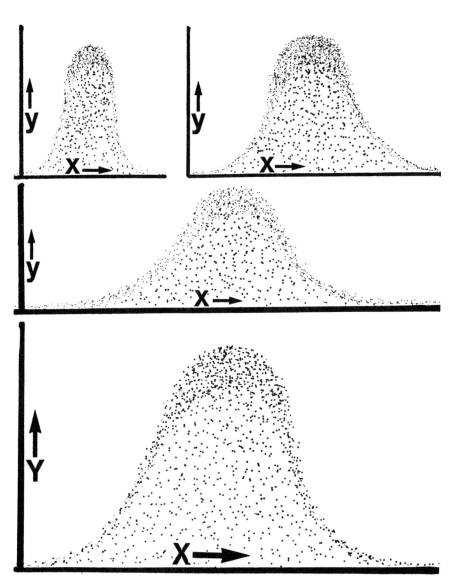

234. BELL-SHAPED CURVES

Bell-shaped curves mean that most of a group or most of the events in a series will cluster about a midpoint. There will usually be some events or individuals that act before most of the group, and some that act after. In large populations some individuals are misfits as they favor one extreme or the other of some characteristic. Even the shapes of the bell-shaped curves can be different. Some have abrupt turns and others have very broad turns. You can never squeeze "Mother Nature" into one neat box. Some "part" will always protrude. And, when you exert pressure to squeeze "her" totally into a box, "she" usually flies out in all directions. So it is with natural systems. Aim for 100%; but be happy when you can get 80 ± 10%. When you get 90%; run with it!

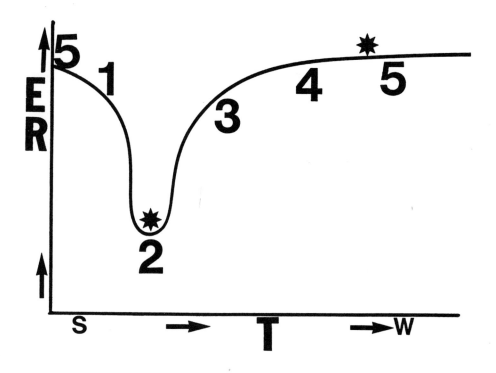

235. THE ASKENASY POTENTIAL ENERGY CURVE

Askenasy was a Russian fruit tree researcher. Priestly gives an account of his work on changes in potential energy during a year (288). On the horizontal X axis is shown time [T] from spring [S] to winter [W]. On the Y axis is shown the relative amount of stored or potential energy [ER]. I have superimposed the 5 phenological periods over the curve. Of course the position of each period will differ in different climatic areas. Also, each period should be seen as a bell-shaped curve; all curves overlapping. There are two critical periods in the tree system; period 2 when leaves have completed their formation, and at the end of period 4 before dormancy. Period 2 is the time energy reserves are at their lowest. I do not understand completely why the other period is critical. It could be because the electrical state of the system is changing before dormancy. It could be because the many leaf abscission zones take so much energy from the system. It could be because many new mycorrhizae are forming. There is so much we do not understand.

271

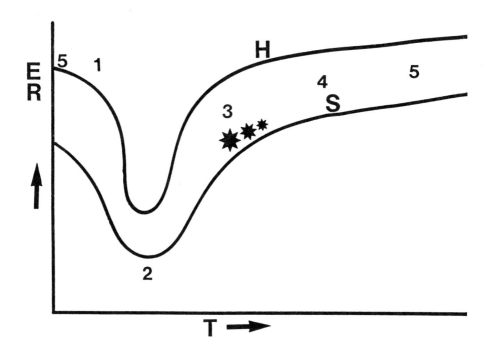

236. FERTILIZER TIMING FOR HEALTHY AND UNHEALTHY TREES

The first question that *should* be asked before any fertilizer treatment is: is the tree healthy and are you treating to maintain health; or, is the tree sick or stressed and are you treating to help the tree regain health? I define stress as a condition of low energy reserves where the system begins to operate near its limits for survival. Stress is a reversible condition. The system or its parts or processes begin to wobble. If the agent of stress continues, stress will go to strain; something breaks, or the entire system stops. A healthy tree [H curve] can be safely fertilized almost any time, any way, without causing problems, so long as the elements, and especially nitrogen, are in low amounts (204,205). Fertilizers should not be added to stimulate additional growth at the end of period 4 in cold climates. Stressed trees [S] can be fertilized with very low amounts of elements, except nitrogen, also at almost any time except for late period 4 in cold climates. I believe it best to add very very low amounts of nitrogen at several times (stars) in period 3. A fast release fertilizer would be best for this treatment.

Stress: 92,200,309,381,384,385; S: 191.

272

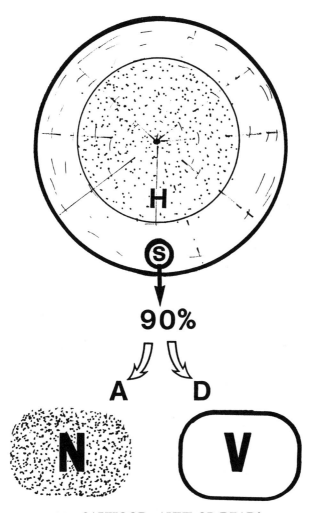

237. SAPWOOD: ALIVE OR DEAD?

If a plug of sapwood were cut from a tree [S is sapwood, H is heartwood], what percentage of the wood is alive [A] and what percentage is dead [D]? On a volume basis [V], about 90% of the sapwood in most trees will be made up of dead cells. However, on a number of cells basis [N], about 90% of the sapwood in most trees will be made up of living parenchyma cells. Then, is the wood dead or alive? The answer is yes! Wood is a highly ordered arrangement of cells, with walls of cellulose and lignin, in all gradations of aging. All wood cells are "born" alive. Vessels, tracheid, and fibers live for only a few weeks, and then die and become functional for transport. They are very large cells. [Some fibers do live for over a year (87,88). The living parenchyma — axial and radial — may live for over a hundred years (199).] The parenchyma cells are very small compared to the large transport cells and fibers. A major myth is that wood is dead. This is one of the major myths that has confused the understanding of trees.

273

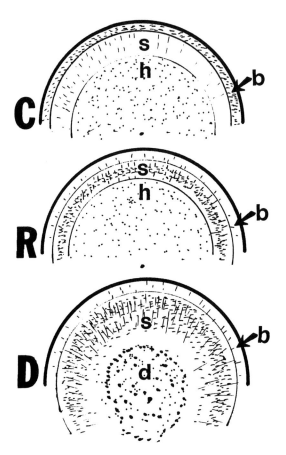

238. SAPWOOD STORAGE VOLUMES IN CONIFERS, AND RING AND DIFFUSE POROUS HARDWOODS

Living cells in wood can only be in sapwood. Here are some typical sapwood volumes in conifers [C] and ring [R] and diffuse [D] porous hardwoods. Heartwood is h, bark b, and discolored wood d.

As sapwood width decreases, the energy storage capacity of the tree decreases (S: 158,159,194). After severe wounding, white oaks produced more sapwood, and heartwood formation was stalled (S:68). The width of sapwood is a good indicator of the health of a tree. The width of sapwood can be determined by taking a small core out of the tree. Yes, this is a wound; but it may be necessary to determine the health of the tree. The sapwood width can also be determined by the electrical resistance pattern of the wood. The Shigometer, or other similar meters can be used to do this (S: 51,67,189). Usually a small hole — 2 or 3mm in diameter — is drilled into the wood. A probe is inserted that sends and receives a pulsed electric current. The resistance to the current is measured on an ohmmeter. There is an abrupt increase in electrical resistance as the tip of the probe is moved from sapwood into heartwood. First, base lines of patterns must be established from known samples of the same species. Then other trees can be sampled. (For more details, see the section on Shigometry.)

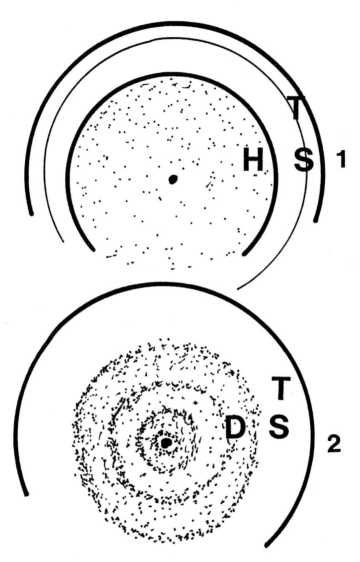

239. SAPWOOD STORAGE AND TRANSPORT

The width of sapwood [S] is an indicator of energy storage capacity. But, storage and transport are different. In some trees, only the most current growth increments transport [T] even when the sapwood width [S] is wide [1] (407,408). Species of *Robinia, Ulmus, Maclura,* and *Aesculus* have very narrow bands of transport tissues. Species of *Acer, Betula,* and *Fraxinus* usually have wide bands of transport tissues [2]. White oak, *Quercus alba,* plugs its vessels in the third growth increment inward with tyloses. *Quercus rubra* does not form tyloses unless the wood is wounded or when heartwood forms. The European white oak, *Querus robur* has a broad sapwood band, and a broad band of sapwood transport tissues. [D is discolored wood and H is heartwood.]

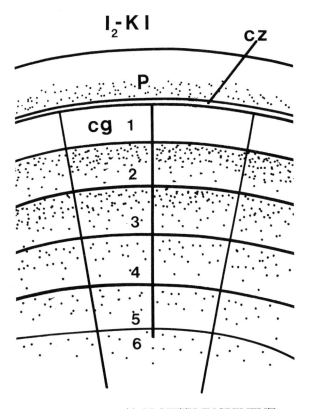

240. CURRENT GROWTH INCREMENT

As leaves and needles begin to form, the vascular cambium or cambial zone [CZ] begins to enlarge (348). [Numbers indicate growth increments.] The formation of leaves is an energy draining process. In young twigs or on young stems, chlorophyll cells in the cortex may begin to photosynthesize before the leaf buds open (270,273). This little added energy is like a small engine to help the starter of a larger engine. In some tree species, xylem and phloem cells do not begin to form until the leaves are halfway through their development (58,194). When the leaves are fully formed the xylem begins to become lignified. The first xylem cells have no lignin and the cells are like jelly. This is why bark can be removed easily in spring when leaves are forming. After the formation of the leaves more xylem and more lignification of xylem to form wood takes place. In most trees, about 90% of the growth increment will be formed in about 6 to 8 weeks after leaf formation. There will always be exceptions. The current growth increment (cg) does not store starch until near the end of the growth period (386,387; S: 194). Starch can be shown in most species by applying I_2-KI (iodine in potassium iodide) to the wood and bark [P]. The chemical stains starch granules in living cells purple.

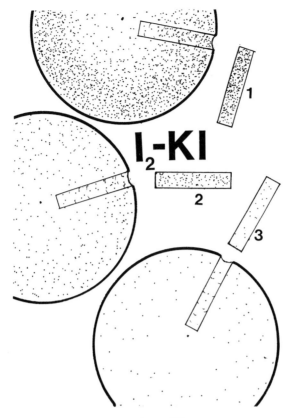

241. I₂-KI

I$_2$-KI is made by adding 0.3 grams of iodine crystals and 1.5 grams of potassium iodide crystals to 100 ml of water. A 2% solution of iodine in potassium iodide will result after a long period of shaking. The stain should be kept in a dark bottle. (Note: Iodine is a poison. Avoid skin contact, ingestion, or inhalation of fumes.)

For best results, a few drops of the stain should be put on a fresh, well shaved wood surface. Cores can be removed from trees and stained easily. The wood core is dipped in I$_2$-KI. A dark purple core [I] indicates high amounts of starch. A light purple core indicates a moderate amount of starch [2]. A yellow core indicates no starch. If the wood surface contains small bits and pieces of wood, the stain will give a false reading. Small bits of wood debris in large vessels will stain and give a false reading. Do not apply the stain to sanded surfaces. Cut the wood surface with a sharp knife or razor blade first for best results. Then you should begin making your own starch charts for the major species you treat in your work. Learn how dark the purple stain can be on the best trees and compare the intensity of the stain to the still living but very poor trees (382). The stain can be used at different times of the year to show the starch reserves in a tree (387). Starch will only be in living cells, so the stain will also show the width of living cells in your tree. The method can be used on roots also. The correct use of this stain can be one of the major diagnostic techniques to help you determine the best treatment for a tree.

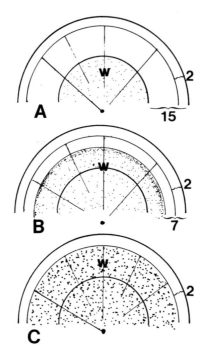

242. DUTCH ELM DISEASE

American elms *(Ulmus americana)* and other species of elms usually have about 15 growth increments that contain living cells and about 2 growth increments that function for about 90% of transport in wood [A] (407,408; S: 194). Most elms have cores of wetwood [W]. As the elms compartmentalize the infections, the volume of wood that normally stores energy reserves is decreased [B, 7 increments sapwood, 2 increments transport]. When energy storage is so decreased that compartmentalization no longer functions, the tree will die (S: 159,194) [C, 2 increments for storage and transport.] Starch tests on elm wood in the fall can be a reliable way to determine the amount of reserves in a tree. The width of the purple zone and the intensity of the purple can be seen easily on small cores removed from the tree. The coring causes wounds, and great caution should be taken when using this technique. A few small wounds must be weighed against the information gained. It is like a biopsy in humans. They hurt! Also, remember, taking the core does wound the tree, but nothing is being put into the wound. Problems start when all types of chemicals are forced under pressure into drill-type wounds in trees. When many drill-type wounds with chemicals are inflicted on trees, the tree will compartmentalize the columns of wood killed by the chemicals. And, every time the wood is compartmentalized, the volume of healthy wood required for energy storage is decreased (S: 132,159,181). Yes, some trees have survived these treatments for many years; but many have not. In the end Dutch elm disease was always blamed. I believe many trees were weakened greatly by the treatments. We must do better!

Dutch elm disease: 10,11,32,44,45,132,153,162,187,215,230,248,249,338,344, 345,350,399; S: 132,159,181,194.

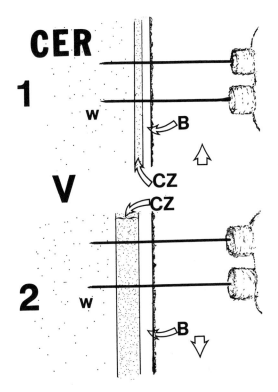

243. TREE VITALITY AND THE CAMBIAL ZONE: CAMBIAL ELECTRICAL RESISTANCE

The thicker the cambial zone [CZ], the more vital [V] the tree (32,48,55,101,173,244,280,284,301,348). A thin cambial zone [1] will have lower moisture and fewer cations than a thicker zone [2]. When the double needle electrodes of the Shigometer are pushed through the bark [B] and slightly into the wood [W] the pulsed electric current from the meter passes through one needle, through the tree tissues, and back through the other needle to the ohmmeter in the Shigometer where resistance in kilohms is measured. Because the cambial zone is so moist and because it contains high amounts of cations, most of the current flows through this zone. The higher the electrical resistance, the less vital [V] the tree. You can develop CER (cambial electrical resistance) records for your major trees in a very short time. Select 20 trees of a species at random in any area. Take two readings per tree; 40 readings. Divide the sum of all readings by 40. Now you have your CER mean for that species. To work with many species, first establish their means. Then use each mean as the denominator for each new reading. For example with four different species: 5/5, 6/6, 7/7, 8/8 etc. all equal 1; and 10/5, 12/6, 14/7, 16/8, all equal 2. You then record each new reading as a ratio of its mean. All trees with a 1 will indicate they are the same as the mean. All trees with a fraction below 1 will be better than the mean; and all trees with numbers higher than 1 will be worse than the mean. All of this information can be easily stored in a computer for comparison later.

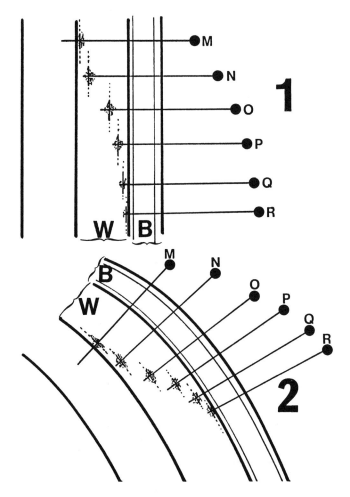

244. TROPICAL TREES AND GROWTH RATES

It is very difficult to measure the development of growth increments in most tropical trees. A simple pinning technique can help you determine the growth rate. On known calendar dates and at the time of phenological events, force small pins into the wood [W] through the bark [B] fissures. In some trees a hammer may be necessary to force the pin into the wood. Repeat the pinning and record the date and any obvious phenological event such as buds swelling, flowers starting to bloom, etc. After a year the experimental tree is cut, and the wood examined where the pins were set. If the pins were set in a vertical plane, the sample will appear as diagram 1; and if they are set in a circumferential pattern, they will appear as diagram 2. There will be a small area of discolored wood at the position of the wood at the time the pin was set. If an experimental tree is not available, the pins can be widely spaced and removed within a small increment core. The core should then be shaved to show the position of the wood at the time of pinning. This needs to be done only one time to learn how wood development coincides with obvious phenological events.

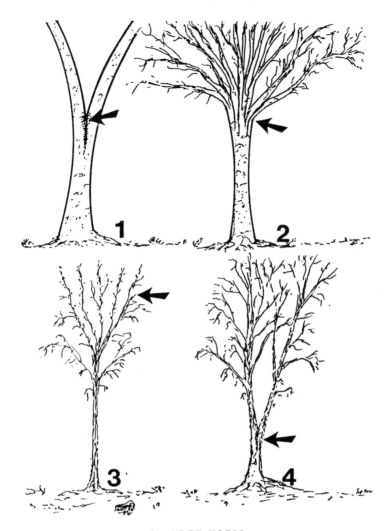

245. POOR FORM

Many trees that should not leave the nursery, do; in great numbers. Problems are planted: included bark between two major stems [1], multiple stems with included bark [2], multiple leaders [3], low stem unions with included bark [4]. Specifications should be written to avoid these common poor forms. Modern arborists should work with landscape designers and developers, and cities, and with the best trees for the correct sites. Some defects may be corrected by early pruning (373). Most of the time, the poor forms cannot be corrected. Included bark appears to be under moderate to strong genetic control in some trees. Do not buy or sell trees that have flush cut branches, tops removed, pruning cuts that leave long branch stubs or leader stubs, painted wounds, trunk covered with some wrapping, cracks, cankers, and wounds. Would you buy a car or any product that had obvious defects? Then, why do we buy trees that have them? (And, let the nursery know why you won't buy them!)

281

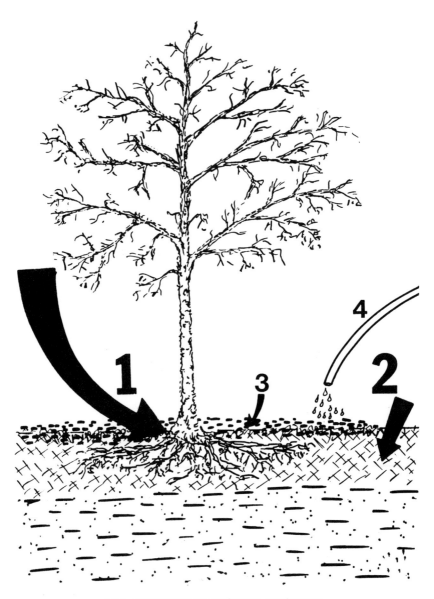

246. CORRECT PLANTING OF TREES

Planting trees too deeply is a worldwide problem. The soil line should be at the base where roots begin to branch [1]. Prepare a planting site by loosening the soil far beyond the drip line of the tree [2]. Do not "just dig a hole". Never tell people to dig a hole or that is exactly what they will do. Do not add stones or gravel below the roots. Water will fill in the area and cause problems. Add some mulch material [3]. Do not fertilize with nitrogen. Do water the tree beyond the drip line [4]. Add soil amendments *only* if the soil is very poor, or if there is no soil (building rubble). If amendments are added, incorporate them into the soil far beyond the drip line. (For more see 91,93,235,271,272,389.)

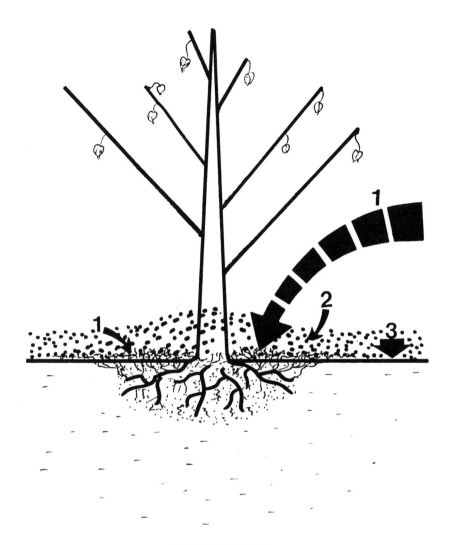

247. MULCHING

Mulching is a beneficial treatment. Many materials can be used, but composted leaf and twig litter are very good because they will support growth of mycorrhizae. Mulch should be incorporated into the top layer of soil. How much is too much? If tree roots are growing up into the mulch [1], the mulch is too thick [2]. Mulch should go beyond the drip line [3]. Chips that have been composted are fine for mulching.

Hard to believe, but asphalt and concrete act as mulches for some city trees. This is so, only when small trees have been planted near asphalt or concrete. Never put asphalt or concrete about the base of established trees. When small trees grow near asphalt or concrete the materials protect the roots. And, there is water and air under the asphalt and concrete. Sidewalk and road cracking often starts when trees are planted too deep and the tree roots are not given enough space to grow. More on this later.

248. PLANTING ON A MOUND

Planting on a mound is an old English method that has great merit, especially where there are heavy clay soils, or wet soils [1]. The mound should be a diameter that will accomodate the growing roots [2] for small trees. The height at center should be about one half meter. The parent soil should be incorporated into the mound [3 and 4]. Never make a mound of loam or topsoil on top of solid unbroken soil! The tree should be planted at the correct depth [1]. Planting on a mound will reduce sidewalk cracking. The mounds should be larger, of course, if larger trees are to be planted.

1 **2**

249. TO BRACE OR NOT TO BRACE TREES AFTER PLANTING

If the tree is small, and able to sway and stay stable in the soil, then do not brace the tree. If the tree roots are not stable in the soil, brace the trunk as low as possible to keep it stable while the top is able to sway (130). Never brace trees so tightly that they cannot sway slightly [1]. There are many methods and materials for bracing trees. The point is: let the tree sway [2], and do not girdle it to death [1].

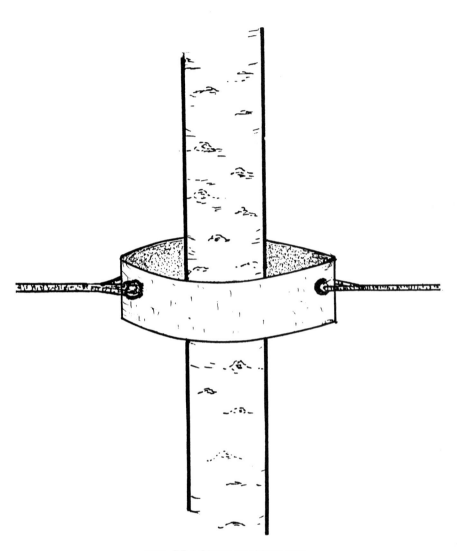

250. BRACING MATERIALS

Broad bands of soft materials are best for bracing. Rubber products, and belt webbing materials are very good. Never use wires or cables, or a wire in a hose. Many trees have died because of girdling by wire in a hose. The pressure of the wire is the same, in or out of the hose. Avoid using lag screws in larger trees. Use large bands at trunk-branch unions. Make certain the braces are removed after a year, or two at the most. If you do find a tree with wire embedded in the bark and wood, do not try to pull it out. Take away only the wire that is not embedded in the tree. So simple, yet many trees are injured and killed worldwide because of incorrect bracing.

286

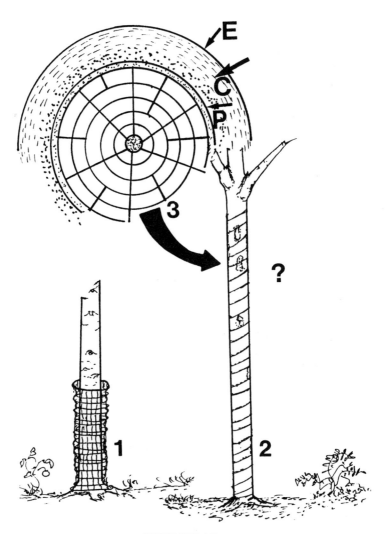

251. TREE WRAP

Tree wrap, like wound dressings and flush cuts will take some time to go away. Young trees have a cortex under their epidermis. The cortex is a soft tissue with living cells that have chlorophyll (119,238,270,349). Young trees require all the energy they can get. Covering the cortex of a young tree reduces a source of the energy for the tree. Many people believe the wraps prevent sun or frost injury. Results of our studies showed no difference between wrapped and unwrapped trees. Trees may require wire mesh or other strong materials to prevent rodent injury [1]. This is fine. Tree wrap does hide wounds, flush cuts, cankers, and other defects [2]. The arrow [3] shows a transverse section of a young tree: P, phloem; C, Cortex; E, epidermis. I know of no experiments *with controls* to show that tree wrap prevents sun and cold injury. I do know that wounds, flush cuts, dead spots from included bark, injured roots, and planting too deep will start trunk cracks and death of bark.

287

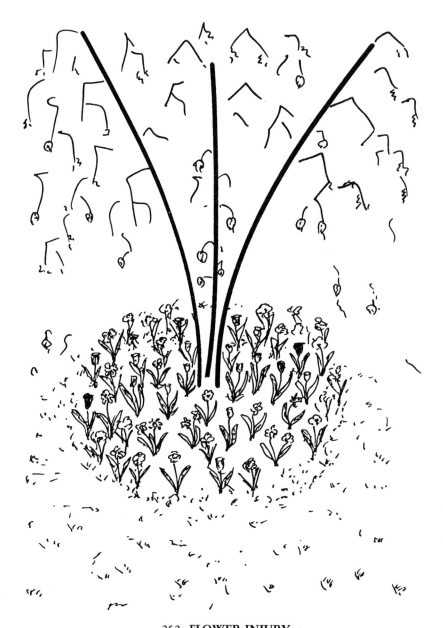

252. FLOWER INJURY

Young trees, and especially young birch trees, often suffer from what I call flower "disease". The tree is the perfect site for a spring garden. I have seen hundreds of bulbs and annuals planted about young trees. The tree usually dies; or before that it will have insect borers or twig dieback, or even "sun scald" or "frost cracks". The tree roots are injured during the planting of the flowers or bulbs, and the plants are usually fertilized heavily. Annual cultivation of the soil at the tree base injures more roots. Be on guard! The only treatment is to keep the tree well watered, and remove dying wood correctly.

253. GRASS AND TREE ROOTS

Trees have woody roots that support the tree and store energy reserves; and non-woody roots that absorb water and elements. Most nonwoody roots are very shallow. In natural forests where there is decaying leaf litter, the nonwoody roots, and especially mycorrhizae, will be abundant in the highly organic top layer of soil. Grass roots will compete with tree roots for water and elements. A common "new" tree problem is tree decline in lush lawns that have no weeds. Start young trees within a grass free area of at least one meter in diameter. If trees are planted too deep, and if the roots survive, they will grow upward and compete all the more with the grass. I have seen "forests" cut so heavily that grass was the major understory plant. The trees were declining. Roots of many grasses will grow deeper than non-woody roots of most species of trees.

Review roots: 37,41,59,85,99,100,136,140,207,271,272,275,276,277,352,364, 381,382,387.

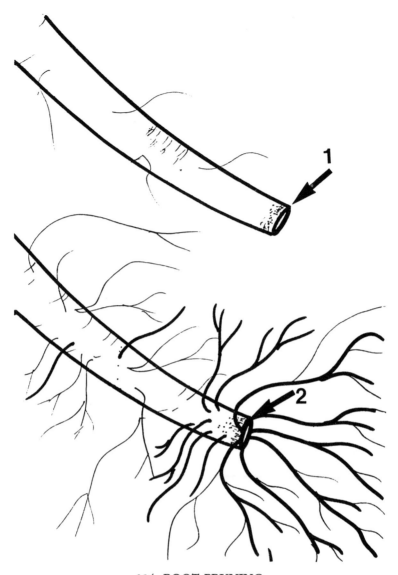

254. ROOT PRUNING

When it is necessary to cut roots, make cuts with a sharp tool and do not slant the cuts [1]. Callus will form about the cut and new roots will generate (not regenerate) from the callus [2]. Some new roots will form on the old root also. When roots are crushed during construction, when possible cut the roots to remove the crushed ends. When pruning crushed or dead roots at planting time, do not remove small diameter tips; instead move up the root until a cut is made at a root diameter of at least 1 or 2 cm. If root pruning is done prior to transplanting, make certain all cuts are made with sharp tools. Do not leave crushed roots. There is no need to treat root cuts with wound dressings. I think it is sad when the wrong tree is planted in the wrong place with no space to grow, and then roots are cut. (See 389 for details on roots and plants in containers.)

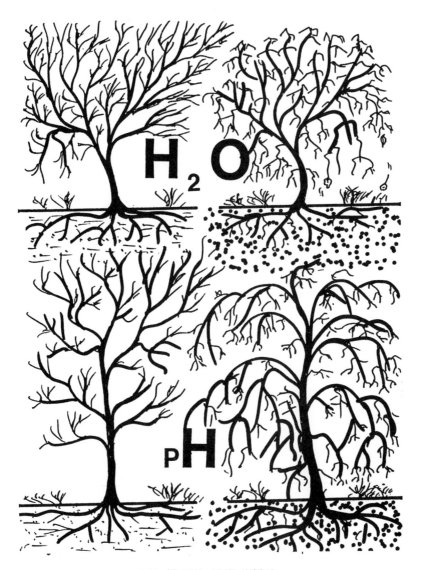

255. TREES AND SITES

Modern arborists will know the tree, the site, and the desires of the people who want trees (235). That is a large order. Some trees grow well on dry sites and others grow best on wet sites. Some trees grow best in low pH soils and others grow best in high pH soils. Knowing that a tree grows best in low pH soil and then planting the tree in high pH soil is not professional. I have heard the pin oak story many times. The customer buys what the nursery has. And, the nursery grows what the customer asks for. Time to break some circles!

Without a doubt, most of our tree problems are caused by people and their activities. Then, if this is our major problem, we must treat it by trying to inform people about trees. So many of the answers are so simple it is uncomfortable to write about them. Yet, the problems keep happening, so the messages are not getting out.

256. **TREE ROOTS**

Roots on most trees grow far beyond the drip line. Most tree roots are very shallow (272). There are some exceptions of course where roots grow down 20 meters or more. The jarrah tree in Australia has sinker roots than can go to 20 meters downward. Roots of mesquite have been found in mine shafts over 30 and 40 meters into the ground. Pines in sandy soils may have deep roots. The common textbook diagram of roots going downward to equal the height of the tree is a sad example of where we are with old arboriculture.

292

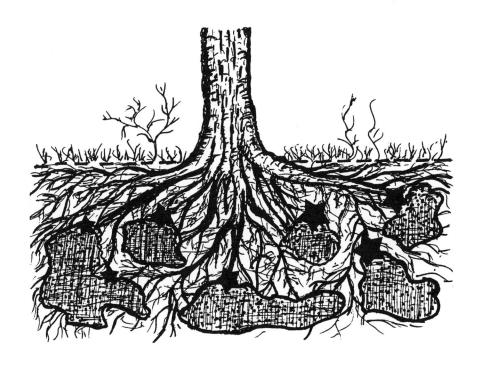

257. ROOTS AND ROCKS

In rocky soils roots often grow to a rock and stop. A branch root may then grow off to the side. Root stubs are common, just as branch stubs are. The pathogens do not "need to look" for openings into roots. Roots require stored energy not only for growth but for defense. Roots wound themselves as one root squeezes against another. Roots do compartmentalize very effectively (S: 131,142,146). I have dug roots of mature trees in natural forests where there never were any machines, and many root stubs and wounds were found. When tops of trees are removed, the defense system of roots is weakened. So simple. So difficult to make this point.

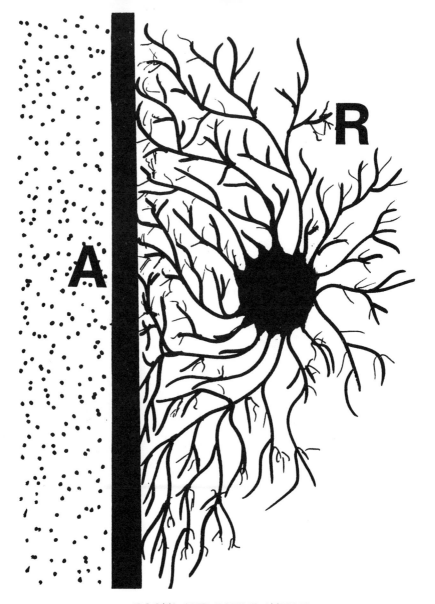

258. ROOTS AND FOUNDATIONS

When trees are planted close to buildings, usually most of the roots [R] will grow toward the building [A]. When the soil has shrinking clays, the tree is often blamed for cracks in the foundation.

It is surprising to some people that tree roots will also grow toward roads, or under roads more than into lawns on the other side. Roots grow where roots grow is an old statement that is indeed so (271,272). Roots will grow in one place until the requirements for growth are exhausted. If the roots are in a drain pipe or sewer pipe, they may grow until large mats of roots form. And the pipe will be plugged. Watering, aerating, and fertilizing soil away from the trunk is a way to stimulate growth away from the tree base.

294

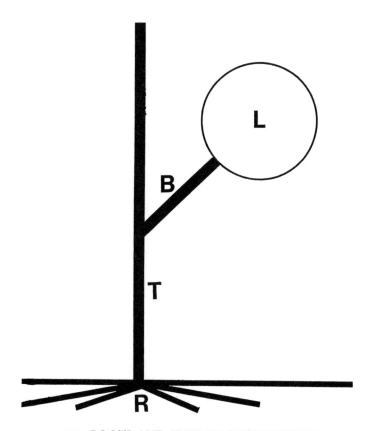

259. ROOTS AND ENERGY DISTRIBUTION

Roots get energy from leaves [L]. Cortex with chlorophyll can also provide energy in young trees and in twigs and branches on old trees. The leaves provide energy for the living cells in branches [B] and the trunk [T]. In turn, the leaves and cortex receive water and elements from the roots. It appears that roots get first priority for energy. If they did not, the system would stop. Next in priority is the trunk, and then the branches and leaves. When there is not enough energy to support the branch, it sheds parts and becomes smaller. As parts are shed, essential elements such as nitrogen are recycled to the still living parts. The same recycling takes place as wood ages (225). When there are so many dead twigs on a branch that the remaining twigs and leaves do not support the living cells in the branch, the branch is shed. A protection boundary forms within the branch collar. The shedding process takes time, and recycling of essential materials takes place. This is part of the aging and dying process. It is done in a way that best serves the survival of the tree system. When living branches on mature trees are cut or when the tree is topped, the parts are killed suddenly. There is a difference between dying and killing. Killing prevents recycling of materials. The roots are the first to suffer. (Be careful with data on this subject from tree seedlings and from current nonwoody growth on trees. Transport in seedlings and current growth is similar to that in annual plants. In annual plants, xylem and phloem may transport in either direction.)

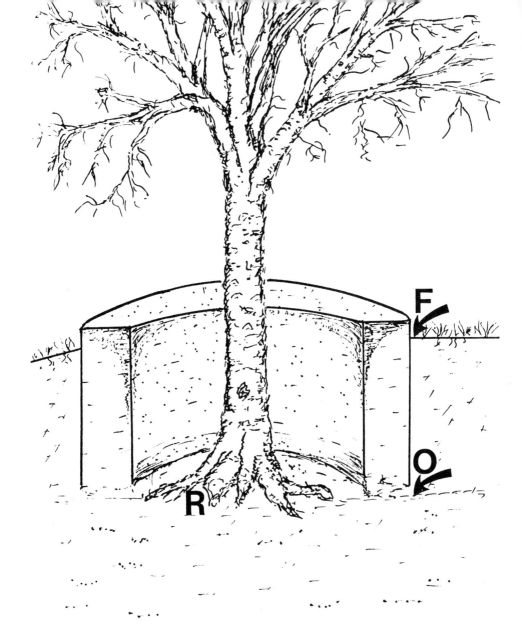

260. TREE WELLS

Tree wells can be effective when soil grade [0] must be increased [F] so long as the well is made before the roots [R] are injured by construction activities. The larger the tree, the larger the diameter of the well. Of course, the larger the well diameter, the better for the tree. Wells built after construction seldom help the tree to survive. Do not remove living branches in attempts to "balance top with bottom" at the time of well construction. I have seen many healthy trees in wells. Some have had grates over the wells where the tree base was 2 meters below present grade. (See page 4.)

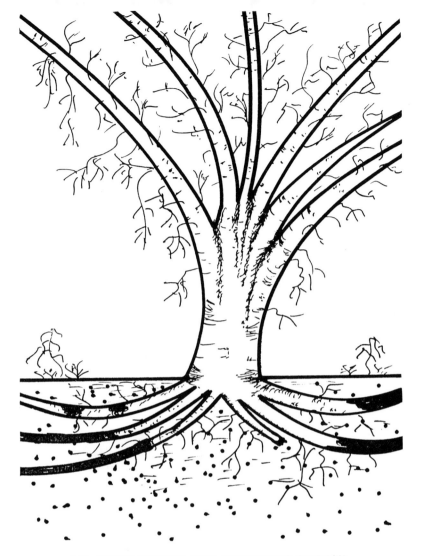

261. ROOT INJURY AND EPICORMIC SHOOTS

When roots are injured by construction or by other activities, many epicormic shoots often grow on the trunk and branches as branch tips die. Extensive growth of epicormic shoots is a sign of stress, which means low energy reserves. Removing living wood will stress the roots all the more. Application of high amounts of nitrogen will also cause more stress as the already low amounts of energy reserves are lowered further because the nitrogen will stimulate more growth. What can you do? First, make certain the tree or its parts are not high risks for failure. Remove potentially high risk branches, or the entire tree. If no potential hazard risk is evident, then keep the tree watered, where possible, make sharp cuts to remove crushed roots, remove dead wood only, and fertilize very lightly after new leaves form. Do not remove the sprouts. Wait for at least three years, and then, if economically feasible, remove only the dying suppressed sprouts. Great care must be taken not to remove the swollen base of the sprouts, or more sprouts will grow.

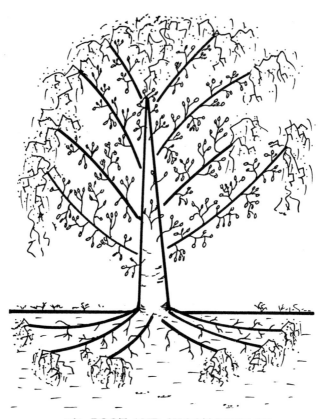

262. ROOT AND SHOOT DIEBACK

Trees do maintain a dynamic equilibrium between roots and shoots. Dynamic equilibrium is constantly confused with static balance. Balance is the equalization of opposing forces. Everything stops when balance is reached. If nature ever became balanced, it would cease to be! DYNAMIC EQUILIBRIUM IS A SITUATION WHERE TWO OPPOSING PROCESSES ARE MOVING BACK AND FORTH AT A STEADY RATE. Tree life starts with a seed or a cutting. Let us look at the seed. The seed is mainly stored energy with the beginning parts for root and shoot. When a seed germinates, in a sense, an oscillating seesaw system starts. The energy in the seed gives one half of the seesaw a push. As the one side goes up from the push—growth of shoot—the other side goes down—growth of the root. The shoot captures new energy and "sends" it to the root. The root side now goes upward. The two sides are horizontal for a short time. Then the shoot side continues downward. When it nears the bottom it may remain there for a time—dormancy— before another stored energy push starts it upward again. And, as the season continues, it gets bigger. The amount of push required to start it increases. The seesaw goes up and down at a steady rate. It is a moving process that makes energy, uses energy, and requires stored energy to give it that push to keep it moving. Is it balanced? As roots die, shoots die back. As shoots die back, roots die. As parts die, recycling takes place into the remaining system. When shoots or roots are cut suddenly, there is no recycling, only wobble. Wobble is stress. This is when other people jump on your seesaw. And they can break it!

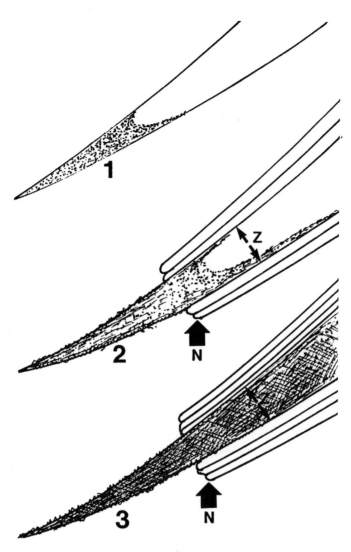

263. ROOT INFECTIONS

Roots can be infected through mechanical wounds, animal and insect wounds, wounds from two roots squeezing together, root stubs that form weak boundaries, and openings that do not close after mycorrhizae die. Most of the time the root compartmentalizes the infected tissues [1] (S: 131,142,146). The pathogens may continue to invade the root tissues present at the time of infection [2]. The new root tissues [N] formed after infection remain free of infection (unless the root pathogens grow from bark to wood, or from wood to bark—canker rots, perennial canker, *Armillaria* species). Z is the root present at the time of infection. If the root boundaries are weak, the pathogens will continue to spread up the root [3]. When energy reserves in roots are low, weak boundaries form, and pathogens have the advantage (173,174,184,381; S: 14,146). And, they take it.

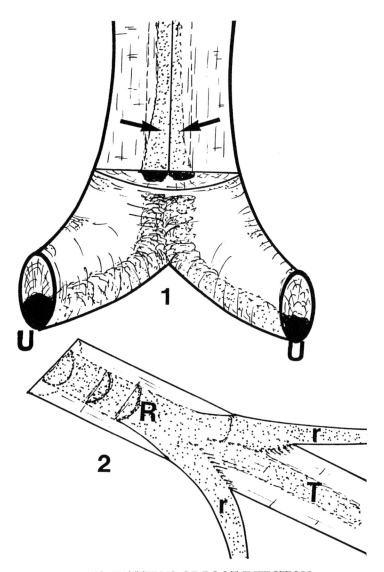

264. PATTERNS OF ROOT INFECTION

Roots may appear round or spherical, but their centers are near the bottom of the root [1]. (Remember roots do not have a central pith as branches do.) As root branches die, the infections spread [r] into the connecting root [2]. As infections coalesce in the larger root [R], the infections [U] then spread upward toward the trunk [arrows, 1]. Columns of infection toward the smaller end of the root [T] may be smaller in diameter than columns closer to the tree (R). The root bottom infections often come together at the tree base. Cracks may start at this point (S: 14,176,183). This is the place where root-rotting fungi often form fruit bodies. Always examine suspect root rot trees for dead spots or cracks where two roots join the tree base (S: 146).

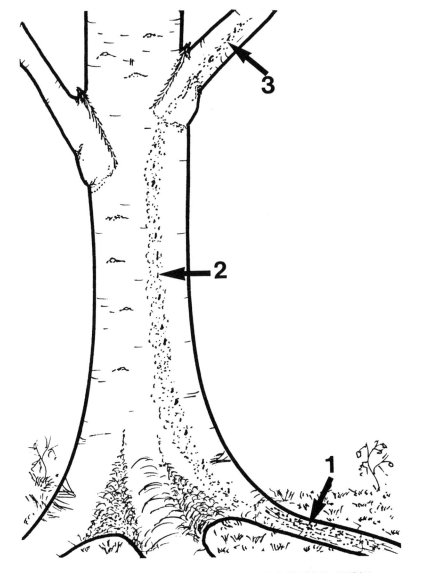

265. TRUNK CAMBIAL DIEBACK ASSOCIATED WITH
ROOT INFECTION

Strips of dead bark, or cracks may develop above dead roots [1] or more often between two dead roots. Long before we can notice the dead strips [2 and 3] insects "know" the tissues are weak and they may bore into the tree or deposit eggs in the weakened tissues. "Blood spots", "bleeding" cankers, or resin pitching in conifers often form when the oviposition wounds are infected. Some fungi, such as species of *Hypoxylon*, infect the still living but defenseless tissues (S: 1). Then *Hypoxylon* species are cited as the cause of the problem. Very few fungi and insects invade healthy tissues, even when minor wounds are present. The wound will be infected — establishment of an energy relationship — but the pathogens usually are compartmentalized rapidly and invasion or spread is stalled. Root infections or root problems commonly predispose trunks to borer injury, cracks, and cankers.

301

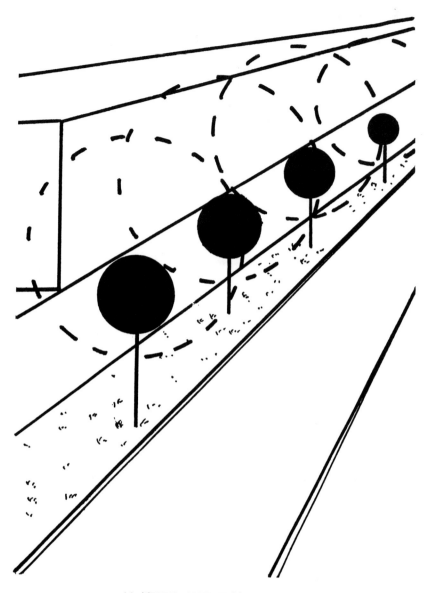

266. TREES AND FUTURE SPACE

Little trees do grow to become big trees. Little trees planted close to buildings and close to roads and sidewalks, and directly under power lines are major starting points for later mutilation (156,317). How wonderful it would be if people realized and recognized the mature size of a tree at the time of planting. I know the problem. People want instant green, instant tree effect; no empty spaces. When trees are planted with room to grow, very few problems will occur later. Here is a place where arborists must talk to city engineers. If space is limited, consider short rotation planting (see diagram 270) dwarf species, or varieties that have shapes, sizes, and growth rates that will not cause problems later. It seems that tree selection is seldom the first factor.

8'

267. TREES, SIDEWALKS, AND STREETS

Give trees at least 8 feet (2.46m) between sidewalk and street and you will have very few sidewalk cracking problems. The trees should be planted at the correct depth. If the soils are heavy clay or very wet, plant on a mound. The modern arborist must work with the "non-plant" people. Many of the mistakes are made because the "non-plant" people just do not understand plants. We say trees are big and tough, and grow for thousands of years, so the "non-plant" people believe the trees must be able to withstand a large amount of abuse. Maybe we should adjust our statements about trees. Yes, trees are big and tough, *however*, they will wane and die when their simple requirements for healthy growth are not provided.

303

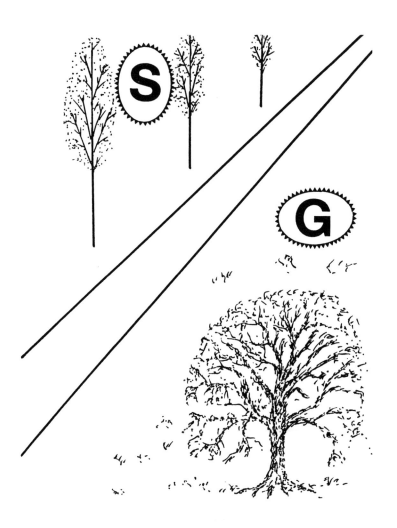

268. TREES AND CITY AND PARK DESIGNS

Street trees [S] should be in a space at least 8 feet wide (2.46m) between the sidewalk and street. The trees should be of a form that would make it possible to prune the lowest branches to a height of at least 3 meters (10 feet) above the ground. Specimen trees in large grassy areas [G] could have low branches with spreading crowns. A specimen tree is any tree that is considered worthy of occupying a focal point in a landscape. The worthiness can be based on size, form, species, beauty, historical significance or any other feature that is considered significant. The worthiness can be determined by an arborist, historian, landscape architect, or any other person who can show that the tree is worthy of special recognition. We need all the specimen trees we can get in our cities and parks. (See 21,22,231, 235,357,373,402,403.)

304

269. CLUSTER PLANTING

Consider planting clusters of trees, shrubs, vines, and all other plants you would find in the forest type nearest your area. Cluster planting works well in parks, golf courses, and on college and university campuses. The cluster has many advantages over formal designs or widely spaced trees. Walkways can be made away from the clusters. This makes it safer for people walking by because there are no large trees near paths where other people could hide. The cluster greatly decreases the compaction problem and the lawnmower wounding problem. The clusters also can be used as educational demonstrations. The cluster would represent a small part of a natural area. The cluster could be surrounded by wild flowers. The possibilities are endless. Think about it! Try it.

305

270. SHORT ROTATION PLANTING

In many places, space is limiting. But, people still want trees. One way to solve this problem is to design a short rotation planting. There are many species that grow very fast when young—hybrid poplars, elms, birches, and a great number of tropical trees. Some fast growing species are not planted in cities because they do grow too fast. The plantings must be designed so that the older trees are constantly being removed and the new ones planted in their place. No empty spots will be seen. The short rotation concept deserves some attention. I believe it is economically sound also.

271. NEW PLANTINGS BEFORE REMOVAL OF OLDER TREES

Before older trees are removed, new trees should be planted if space is available. The older tree should be pruned to keep it safe. If the tree is growing in a low risk area, and if it is being used by wildlife, it should not be removed. Always consider wildlife when making decisions on removal. Always try to convince a customer that it is best to plant some new trees before the old tree is removed.

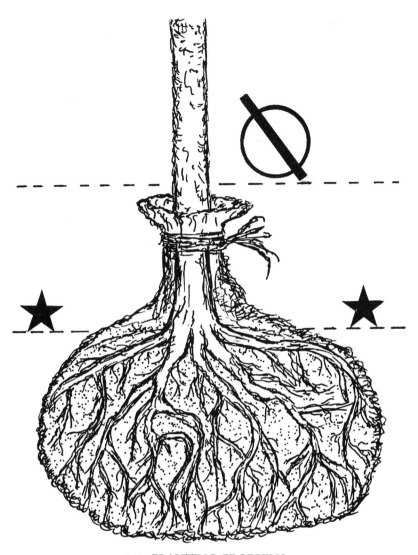

272. **PLANTING PROBLEMS**

It would be a grand day for young trees worldwide if people learned to plant trees at the correct depth [stars]. Trees in bags are often tied high on the trunk. It is really sad to see the use of non-biodegradeable strings and other materials. I hope this will change. A homeowner or even many "professionals" plant the tree above the point where it is tied. It is best to remove the string and to pull back the burlap. It is also wise to remove the burlap to examine the roots, or to see if there are roots! Broken roots should be removed with a sharp tool. Do not let the soil in the ball dry out. Keep it moist. Keep it out of the sun. Very, very simple actions. I have seen hundreds of trees committed to an early death because these very simple, common sense actions were not taken. (See 389.) (Maybe nursery people should spray the base of trees with a nontoxic colored liquid that will wash away in a short time. The colored base will show the planting depth for the tree.)

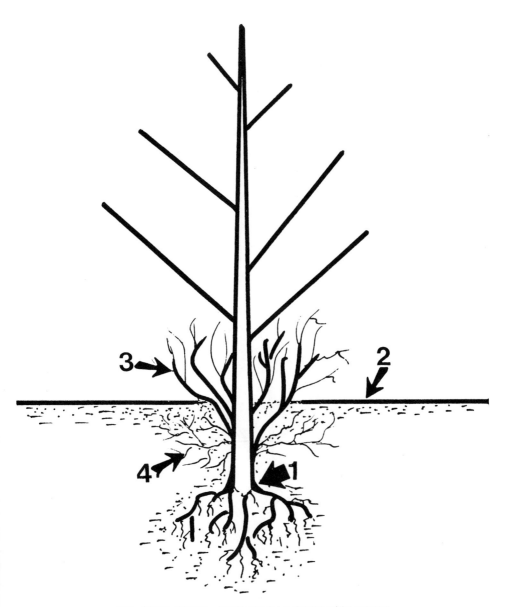

273. TOO DEEP, AND BASAL SPROUTS FORM

When many tree species are planted too deep, basal epicormic buds produce sprouts. The proper depth [1], and the planted depth [2] often vary greatly. Once the sprouts start to grow [3], it is almost impossible to eliminate them. Some smaller roots may grow [4] from the trunk below ground. Many trees remain alive, but in a weakened state because new roots do grow at the 4 position. If a newly planted tree is declining because it has been planted too deep, it is best to start over again with a new healthy tree that is planted correctly.

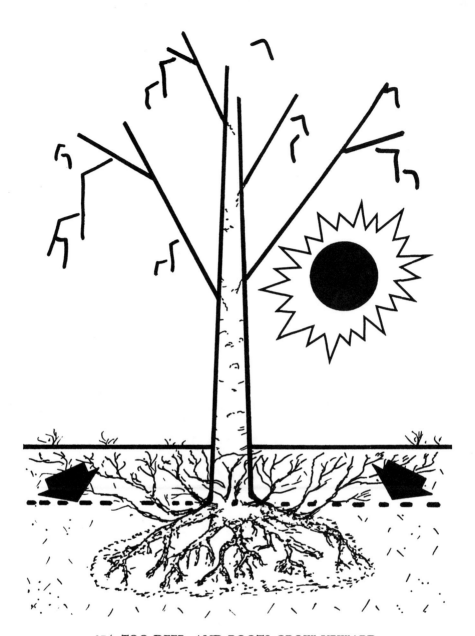

274. TOO DEEP, AND ROOTS GROW UPWARD

Some trees planted too deep survive because they form new roots that grow upward. (Green ash is a good example.) Arrows show the correct planting depth. The tree may live for a hundred or more years, and the roots will grow larger, but still near the surface, or even on the surface. The surface roots make it very difficult to cut the grass, if grass grows. I know of no way to correct this problem without injuring the tree. The best answer is to carefully remove the grass and add a mulch. Trees planted too deep do not have a flare at the base. Trees tolerate a great amount of abuse.

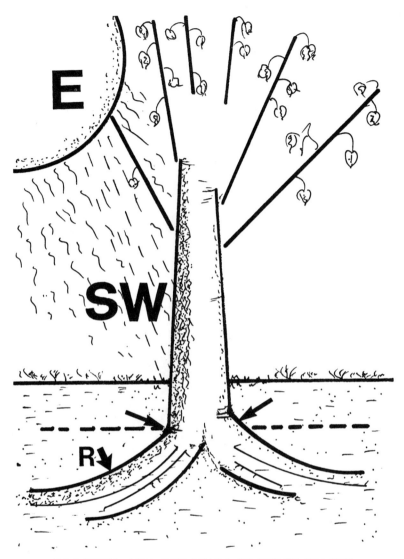

275. TOO DEEP, AND SUN SCALD OR FROST CRACKS
MAY OCCUR

When trees are planted too deep, (arrows, proper depth) especially larger trees with longer roots [R], the roots may become weakened or even infected. The trunk tissues above the weakened root will also be weak—weak in the sense of reduced growth and low amounts of energy reserves. If the weakened root and trunk portion face the southwest [SW], the likelihood of sun [E] injury increases. If the weakened area is subject to extreme temperature changes from warm sun in the afternoon to a sudden decrease at night, the trunk may crack to form a frost crack in the bark and may kill some wood. The important point is that the killing starts from the outside and develops inward. The other type of sun scald and frost cracks start from the inside and develop outward, (S: 14,148,200).

311

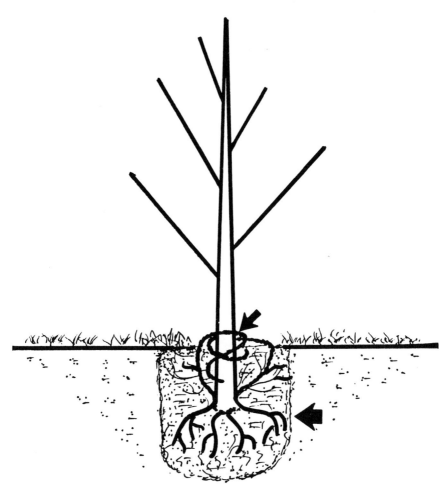

276. TOO DEEP, AND GIRDLING ROOTS MAY FORM

Planting too deeply is one possible cause of girdling roots. The roots may circle the trunk or other roots. There are other causes for girdling roots: spiraling roots in container grown trees, squeezing roots into small planting holes, adding amendments and fertilizers to small planting holes, and probably other causes that we do not understand (159). Rapid growth rate and sun at the tree base have been cited as possible causes also. Girdling roots on young trees should be cut. As the tree gets older, removal of the girdling root must be weighed against the injury caused by the root removal. If a tree has lived for over a hundred years with the girdling root, maybe it is best to leave it. There are no set rules. You must look at every tree as an individual case and use your understanding of tree biology and common sense. And, yes, there are girdling roots in natural forests. I have seen some very strange cases where "it appears" that a tree of one species "sends out" a root to girdle a neighboring tree of another species. Under the soil there are many girdling roots. There is so much we do not understand. (There is a concept of mass tropisms where roots will grow toward objects of high mass. I have cut roots of many forest trees that had engulfed large stones, as an amoeba would.)

277. COMPACTED SOILS

How long can you hold your breath? When you think about compacted soils [1], think about this question. Roots must respire — burn glucose to release energy. Oxygen is required for this process. The mycorrhizae are aerobic microorganisms [M]. Again, this means they require free, gaseous oxygen [O_2] for their growth. You can live for days or weeks without water [H_2O] or food, but not very long without oxygen. Learn the type of soil present where a species of tree grows naturally. Then plant that species where the soil is similar to its natural soil [2]. There are many machines that fracture and loosen soil (346). In theory, the techniques appear sound. When done along with watering and fertilizing, the trees may benefit. We need experiments with controls on these new methods. We must keep an open mind.

313

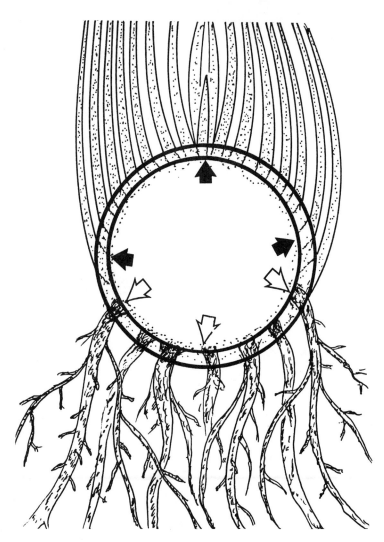

278. PALMS

Palms are monocots — they start life with one cotyledon or seed leaf. Other trees are dicots — they start life with two cotyledons. The anatomy of palms is different from the dicots. Monocots do not have a vascular cambium that provides trunk thickening. Some monocots do have trunk thickening, but not from a vascular cambium — *Cordyline* is a good example. Monocots have bundles of xylem and phloem in living cells called ground tissue. The living cells store great amounts of starch. Most palms do not branch; a few do. Palms have fronds, and some fronds can be many meters long. Palms start life with a meristem like a cover over a ball. The upper portion of the meristem produces fronds that build a stem along with the ground tissues [dark arrows], and the lower portion of the meristem produces long tube-like roots that do branch [open arrows]. The roots do not have secondary thickening. The roots can grow many meters away from the tree. You can top a palm, but only once! Then it is dead.

314

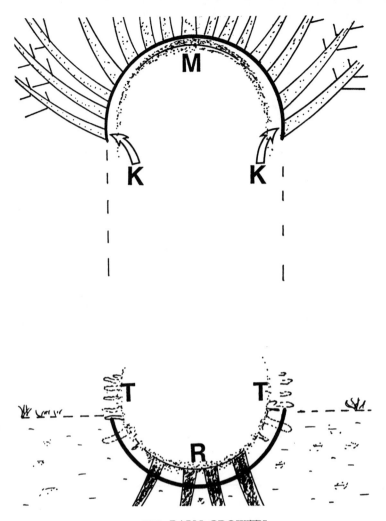

279. PALM GROWTH

As fronds grow and die, they build an elongated stem along with the ground tissues—the "ball" begins to pull outward. The top of the "ball" still remains meristematic [M], and the extent of the meristem downward from the top will vary greatly in different species of palms. The natural death of fronds is a good indicator where the meristems end [K]. Because fronds are produced in a vertical position, the center meristem [M] may be a meter or more downward from the tip of the fronds. Thickening of the trunk below the meristem does take place as the cells produced by the meristem mature and enlarge. The lower portion of the palm meristem stays in the same position and continuously produces new roots [R]. On some palms, the root meristem continues to expand upward [T] and small rootlets form. Palms that have this capacity are those that will tolerate deep planting. Many palms will tolerate deep planting, but this does not mean they benefit from it. Soils deficient in manganese cause a problem called "frizzle top". Young fronds and the meristem may be infected by a mycoplasma-like organism that kills quickly—lethal yellowing.

315

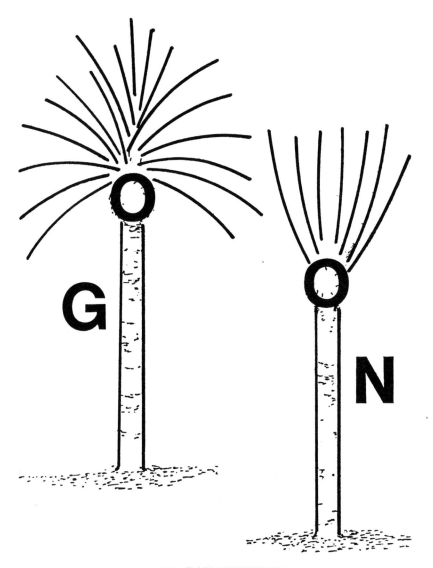

280. PALM PRUNING

Fronds should be removed as they die [G]. Because this could mean repeat visits over a few years, customers ask for "one good job" that will last for a longer time [N]. Now the problems start. Overpruning is to palms as topping is to dicot trees. The meristem is the first to suffer. Stem thickening is disrupted. Then later, problems start that are blamed on pathogens other than the ones that did the primary injury. Whether it is palms or dicot trees, over and over again so many of the problems are started by people. I know why dicot trees are topped and palms are overpruned; because that is what the customer wants and to stay in business you must provide this service. Remember, a drug pusher gives a customer what he wants. A professional medical doctor gives customers what they need!

Palms: 40,41,202,217,221,361,366.

316

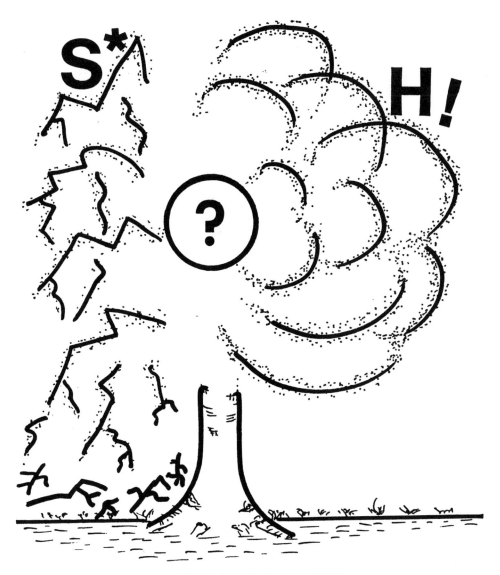

281. TREE: HEALTHY OR SICK?

A common question is whether a tree is healthy [H] or sick [S]. The answer many times is yes! Some parts of a tree may be very sick and other parts very healthy. Watch this one if you ever go to court. If a tree is in decline, then the entire tree is sick. If a tree has some dieback it may be dying back to survive, and the tree may really be healthy although to the untrained person it would appear very sick. Be alert for early signs of stress—smaller than normal leaves, early leaf fall, insect borers (S: 23), small wet spots at the base of the trunk (S: 14), fungus fruit bodies on roots (147), excessive sprouting, insect oviposit wounds, many dying twigs (137,304), premature leaf color, slow formation of woundwood about mechanical and pruning wounds. (See 337.)

317

282. & 283. TREE HAZARDS. 13 QUESTIONS THAT COULD SAVE A LIFE: MAYBE YOURS

Tree Hazards. Your trees can kill! (And you may go to court.)

13 Questions lay people need to ask, and to discuss the results with a tree professional—arborist.

You could help the trees, and save a life: maybe yours.

1. **Target**
   If the tree falls, will it hit cars, houses, power lines, or people?

2. **Architecture**
   Has the tree grown beyond its normal form into a dangerous form?

3. **History**
   Has the tree lost large branches recently?

4. **Edge Tree**
   Were neighboring trees cut away recently leaving tall trees at the edge?

5. **Dead Branches**
   Are there dead tops or branches? Is the tree dead?

6. **Cracks**
   Are there deep, open cracks in the trunk and branches?

7. **Crotch Cracks**
   Are there deep, open cracks below joining stems?

8. **Living Branches**
   Do living branches bend abruptly upward or downward where tips of large branches were cut off—tipping?

9. **Topping**

Are large branches growing rapidly from topping cuts on big trees?

10. **Storm Injury**

Are there broken branches, split trunks, or injured roots? Are branches close to power lines?

11. **Root Rot**

Are there fungus fruit bodies — mushrooms — on roots? Were roots injured by construction?

12. **Rots and Cankers**

Are there hollows or cankers — dead spots — some with fungus fruit bodies? Is the tree leaning?

13. **Construction Injury**

Have roots, trunk, or branches been injured? Is there a new lawn or garden over injured roots?

Warning! Hazardous trees are unpredictable. If clients think they have a tree problem, discuss it with them.

Lay people should not try to remedy the problem.

To remedy a problem it may be necessary to remove the target, remove parts of the tree or the entire tree, or cable and brace the weak parts of the tree. Again, these are jobs only for trained arborists who are insured! Lay people should work with arborists to keep their trees beautiful, healthy, and hazard free.

(From *Tree Hazards* by Shigo and Trees, Associates)

Tree hazards: 160,233,257,298,326,376,377.

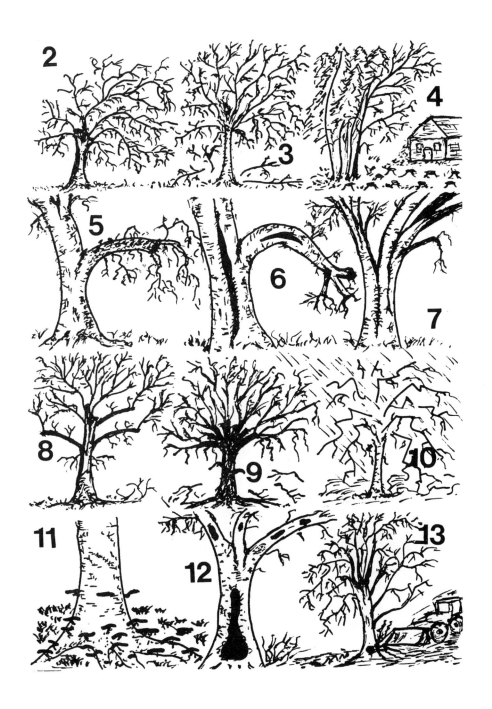

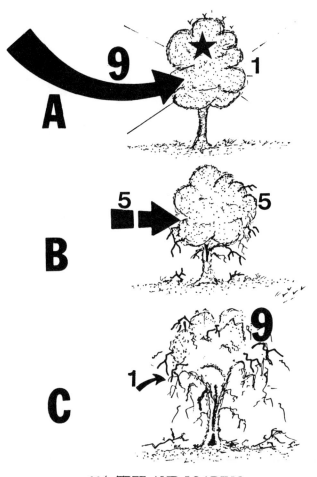

284. TREE AND LOADING

You cannot separate tree condition from loading. You can have the most healthy, strongest, best formed and positioned tree in the world; but if the loading—wind, mechanical impact, explosives, earthquakes, volcanic eruptions, tidal wave, storm— is strong enough, the tree or its parts will fail [A] (S: 176,183). On a scale of 10, the tree being in the best condition would be a 1, and the loading would be a 9. On the other hand, a tree could have every possible problem, and it would be a 9 that would take only a loading of 1 to cause failure [C]. The difficulty with risk is that the 2 factors often have a rating of 5 each [B], or 4 to 5 either direction. In my rating scale, both factors must always equal 10 when a branch or tree fails. In this way you must weigh the loading force as well as the potential failure risk of the tree or its parts. The diagrams 282 and 283 show signs of factors 8 and 9 when loading is 1 or 2. My point with this scale is that loading must be determined *first*. If loading is 8 or 9, then it matters not the condition of the tree. In an 8 or 9 loading situation strong and weak trees will fail. And, remember, heat is a loading force when it dries the wetwood in branch cracks (S: 200). (See 208,209,210.)

322

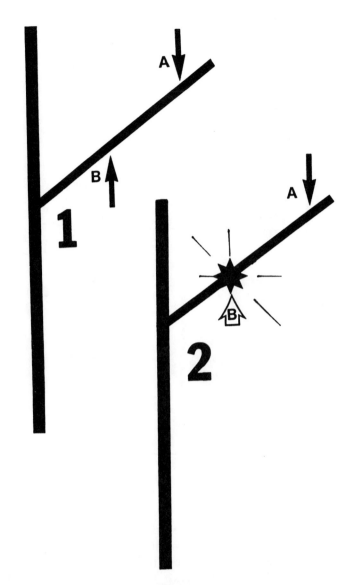

285. BRANCH LOADING

There are two major ways to fracture a branch: 1, Force A exceeds resistance B. 2, Some point along the branch gets weaker [open arrow B] until the constant force of A exceeds the resisting force of B. Do not confuse branch failure with branch pull out (see diagram 287). A point on a branch can be weakened by flush cuts, cankers, cracks, mechanical wounds and wounds made by birds, insects, and gnawing animals. When branches are frozen and loaded with snow, fracture is usually farther from the trunk or the branch pulls out of the trunk. When snow loads a branch that is not frozen, the fracture is closer to the trunk because the branch is supple and bends as far as possible.

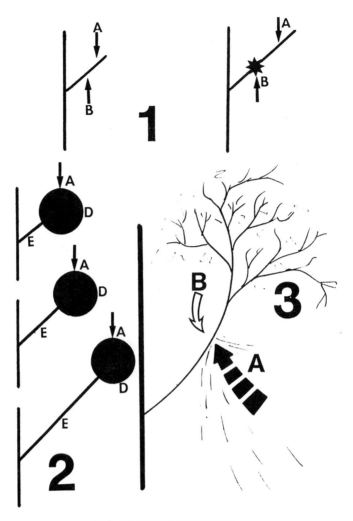

286. BRANCH FAILURES

Here are some additional details on loading and branch fracture. Diagram 1 shows the general principles. Diagram 2 shows that loading [A] and amount of foliage [D] can remain constant, but as branch length increases [E], the resisting power of the branch usually decreases. Some trees, such as deodar cedars, have very long branches with needles only at the ends. The branches are very pliable, but they do fracture, especially when they are blown upward. Diagram 3 shows that an upward loading by wind is a common cause of branch fracture. Branches, even long ones, are well constructed for downward loading, but branches are not well constructed for upward loading. Microbursts are sharp, forceful updrafts resulting from wind hitting the ground and bouncing upward. Microbursts have caused aircraft landing problems and crashes. I believe microbursts are major causes of branch fractures. Look at the splinters on the branch portion still on the tree. If they point upward, the branch fractured from upward loading.

324

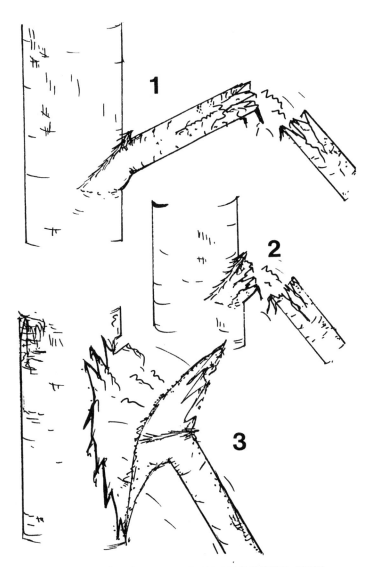

287. BRANCH FRACTURE AND BRANCH PULL OUT

Branches may fracture far from the trunk [1], close to the trunk [2], or they may pull out of the trunk [3]. Branch pull out is common where large vital branches are growing on highly defective trunks (H, diagram 289). The trunk defects are often associated with root injuries or with large topping cuts. Be alert for large, fast-growing branches on trunks that are obviously rotted. Or where branches are near large cracks on the trunk. Branch pull out is also common on low branches that have included bark. Roots growing between the trunk and branch act as a wedge that forces the branch off. Branch pull out is common on trees that have many branches growing from the same portion of the trunk — Bradford pear. Trees that have a history of branch pull out should be considered high risk for more similar failures.

288. TOPPING

Topping destroys tree dignity [H]. I believe it is kinder to remove a tree than to top it. Topping is wanted by most people to reduce the hazard risk, or to remove growth that blocks a view. The irony of topping is that it makes trees more hazardous most of the time and the new sprouts may grow taller than the old growth. Species in some genera—*Tilia, Salix, Platanus, Catalpa*—tolerate the treatment. This is why London plane and lime or linden trees are so common in the cities of the world in temperate climates. When a customer requests topping, that is the time to talk to them about planting some new trees of smaller maturing species. How to deal with trees that have already been topped is discussed in other parts of this book.

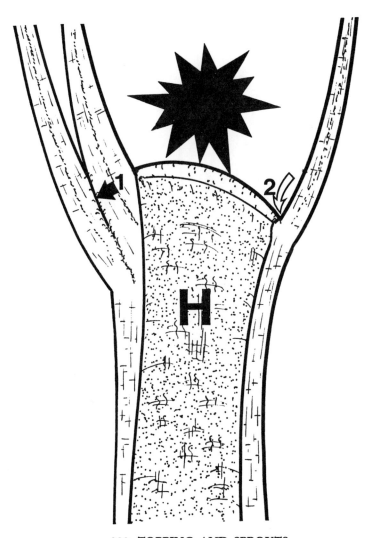

289. TOPPING AND SPROUTS

Sprouts grow from dormant or adventitious buds after a stem is topped. Dormant buds are cone-shaped points of meristematic tissue under the bark. The points can be seen easily when bark is peeled in the spring. Adventitious sprouts come from callus tissue, which is meristematic—can divide and form a new structure. When 2 or more sprouts grow from the same position, they may squeeze together at their bases and kill the cambial zones [1]. A dead spot results that weakens the sprout attachment. Sprouts that grow near the cut—mostly adventitious sprouts—often curl inward at the base [2]. The sprout may weaken its attachment as the curl of wood increases. Sprouts have weak attachments because it takes at least 3 years before a strong trunk collar begins to hold the sprout. Be alert to large dead and dying sprouts on topped trees, especially on tropical trees where sprouts can grow many meters in one year. H was the size of the stem at the time of topping. Decay spreads rapidly and forms hollows in many topped stems. Sprouts on decayed stems often fail.

327

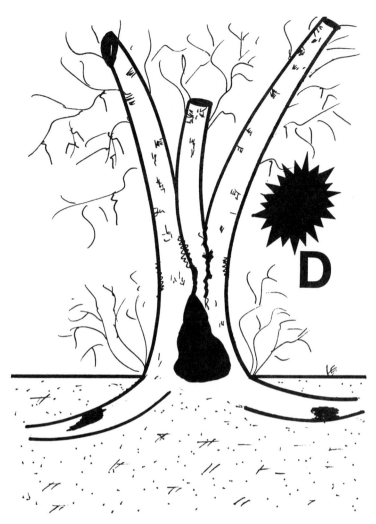

290. TOPPING AND THE DEMONS OF D

Topping is the same as removing weight from the raised side of a seesaw. This definitely will not balance the seesaw! Yet, this attempt to balance top with bottom is another major reason why young and old trees are topped, or crowns are reduced, which is the same most of the time. I cannot emphasize this subject enough because the treatments present a glaring example of not understanding how trees function. Again, there is no perfect machine, no perpetual motion machine, no absolutes. No machine will "balance" itself by the *REMOVAL* of energy. Even the best of machines—living things—require a continuing supply of energy. When the energy producing parts of a tree are removed, the other parts dependant on the energy will go to a lower state of energy potential. And, when that lower state cannot maintain order, the Demons of D that can live at that lower state will take over. I often wonder if I will see this understood in my lifetime! This belief hangs on the myth that trees get food from the soil, and from fertilizers. And that the removal of the top will decrease the demands on the roots to "feed" the top!

328

291. CONSTRUCTION INJURY

"Dozer" blight is a major member of the Demons of D. Dozers (bulldozers) can cause at least 6 types of injury: 1, Soil compaction. 2, Root wounds and disruption of mycorrhizae and other beneficial tree associates. 3, Butt wounds. 4, Trunk wounds. 5, Branch wounds. 6, Leaf injury from heat, and fumes from gasoline and oil. Prevention is the best medicine. Talk to the operator. Talk to the developer. Talk to city officials about tree protection before construction starts. Injury hurts the tree. Injury is a physiological disruption. Damage hurts the pocketbook. Damage is an economic disruption. The best way to prevent tree injury is to increase the price tag on tree damage. This is the only way some people will listen. Modern arborists need to be involved in helping to enforce ordinances. When trees are injured, scribe the wound, remove dead and dying branches, water the tree, apply a light coating of mulch, and keep all traffic away from the tree. The next growing season, continue to remove deadwood and fertilize very lightly after the leaves form. Do not remove living branches!

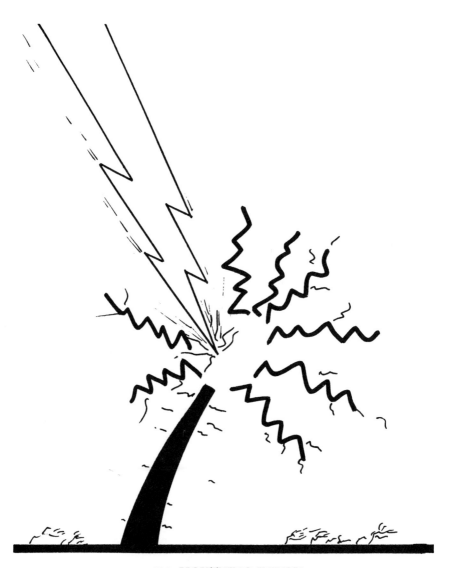

292. **LIGHTNING INJURY**

About 80% of what has been shown to me as lightning injury was caused by Joe Lightning tree service! Topping and multiple flush cuts in vertical alignment commonly start long vertical cracks and dead spots that are often called lightning injury. Lightning does strike trees! It may kill the tree instantly, blow it apart, or cause only minor injury. It is very difficult to assess the amount of injury when trees are struck and little mechanical disruption is evident. The only answer is to remove obviously injured branches and to wait and watch the tree. If a long strip of bark has been killed, remove the dead bark, but do not cut into the wood. Follow normal scribing techniques of shallow cuts and do not enlarge the wound. Some people say lightning rods help and others say they do not. I know of no experimental data on this subject. It depends on who you talk to.

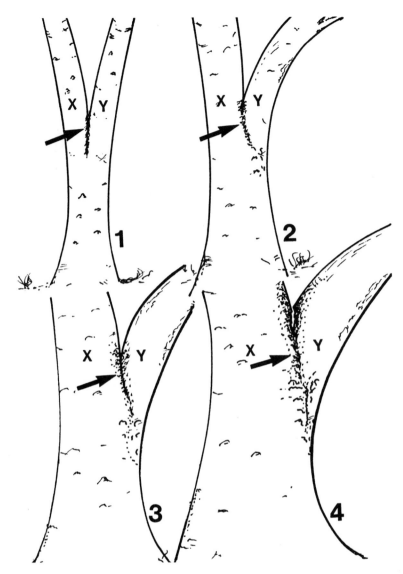

293. LARGE LIMB FAILURE

Large limbs may fall when loading is very light. The problem starts with forked stems [1], or codominant stems. So long as both stems grow upward, risk of failure is low, even when included bark forms. When one stem [Y,2] begins to grow toward a horizontal position, the risk of failure begins to increase. As stem Y grows outward [3] a crack may begin to form between the stems. The attachment of Y to X continues to weaken as the crack opens and as roots grow in the crack [4]. Be alert for large branches growing over sidewalks and roads. Examine the union of the stems to determine whether cracks are present. Stems will often grow over roads because of bright sunlight and the protection the road affords the roots on that side of the tree. Water runoff from rain and irrigation systems seeps through the cracks in the pavement and provides ample water for fast growth.

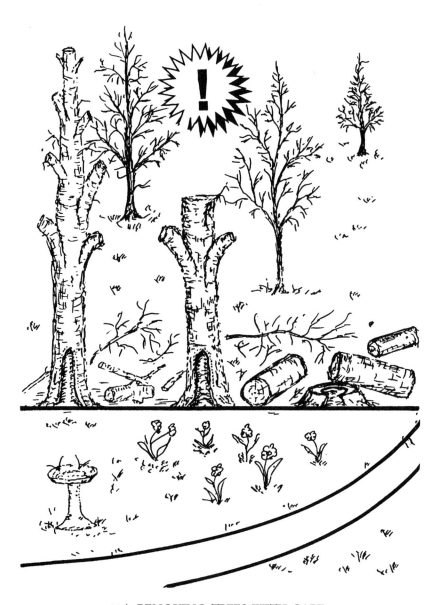

294. REMOVING TREES WITH CARE

Most of the time trees to be removed must be cut piece by piece from the top downward. When trees are near lawns, streets, and gardens, each tree section must be lowered with a rope. It takes a great amount of skill to remove a tree without injuring yourself, or neighboring trees and plants. Yet, I have seen large sections of trees dropped on lawns and gardens. Much can be done to decrease injury to the other plants. Customers rate arborists not so much on what they do, but how they leave the grounds. With small amounts of planning, much can be done to reduce injury to residual plants.

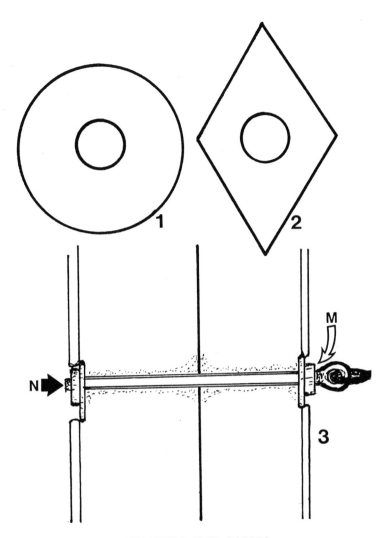

295. WASHERS AND CABLES

Cabling and bracing requires a great amount of experience and skill. At best, there are guidelines, but every tree will be different (S: 106,136). When done correctly, cables and braces can extend greatly the safe period of a tree or its parts. Done incorrectly, the technique will shorten the safe period. To put a cable between two members of a tree, it is best to use a bolt through the members—branch to branch, branch to trunk, branch or trunk to a holding member other than the tree. After drilling the hole with a sharp drill bit, place a round washer [1], not a diamond washer [2], and nut on each side [3,N and M]. The washers should not be on the bark or deep into the wood. Countersink the washers as shallow as possible in the wood so that they are flat against the wood. An amon nut should be placed on the cable end [M]. Cut the rod as short as possible on the opposite end [N].

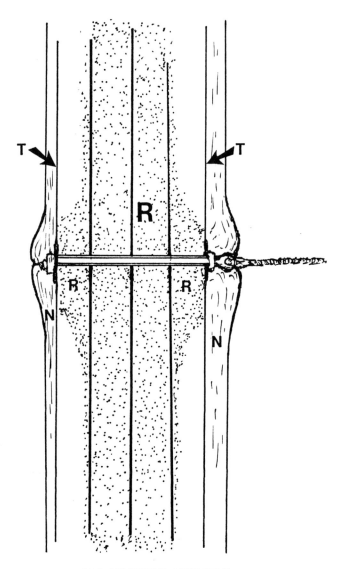

296. CABLING AND ROT

The wood that forms after installation of a rod will provide most of the holding power [N]. Rot may develop about the rod [R], but it will be walled off by the barrier zones [T]. In many trees, reaction zones resist the spread of decay in the wood about the rod (A). Some arborists like to let the rod with the amon nut protrude so that early closure will not envelop the cable. If the cable is enveloped in the woundwood, movement of the cable may wound the wood and weaken the holding power. Arborists provided me with many tree sections that had hardware. I dissected the sections to determine why so many old installations had failed. I found that washers on the end opposite the cables were often pulled into the rot, and I noted that large cracks and dead spots were associated with the diamond washers. Experiments were done and the adjustments came.

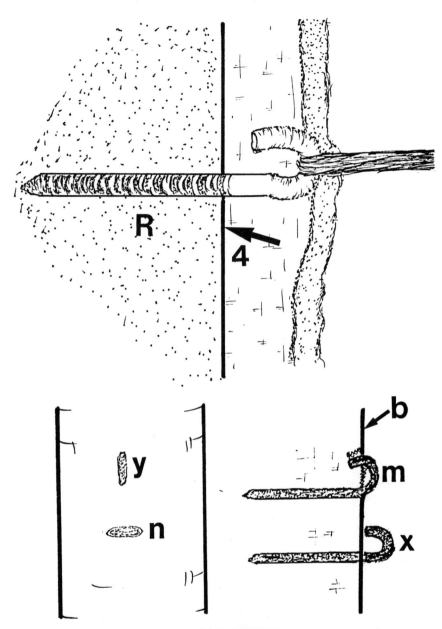

297. LAG SCREWS

Lag screws can be used on small branches and trunks, especially when there is no decay present. A barrier zone [4)] will wall off the rot [R] that may form. The wood formed after installation will provide the holding power. Do not screw [M] open ended lags into the bark [b]; always leave a space [x]. The lag end should be vertical [y], not horizontal [n]. Of course, always predrill holes for lags or the wood will split. Always check hardware installed in trees. Remember, cabling and bracing do not strengthen the branch or trunk. The technique can reduce the risk of failure of branches and trunks.

335

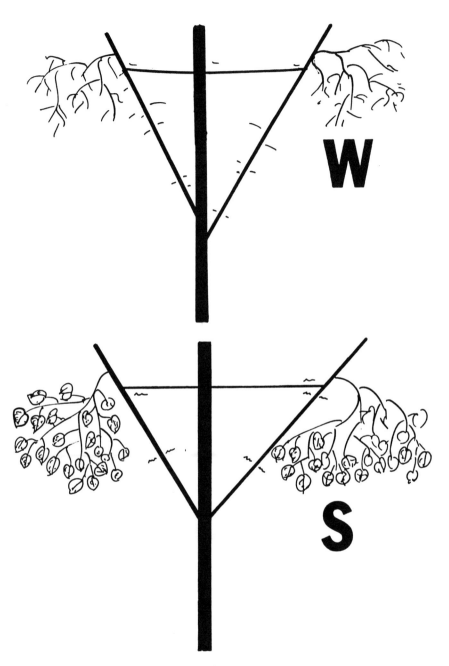

298. CABLES

Placement of cables in trees that have no leaves in winter [W] should be slightly slack. Cables should never be so taut that they are pulling the branches together [S]. The cable should be a static, or a nonholding device when there is no loading on the branches. (See 340.)

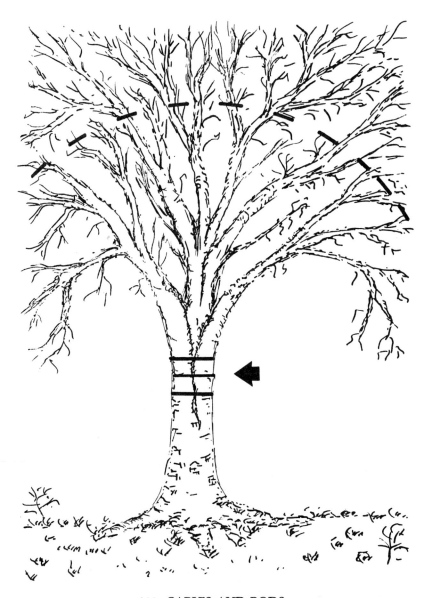

299. CABLES AND RODS

Placement of rods and cables is a very controversial subject. There are no set rules, only guidelines that must be adjusted for every tree. Rods should be placed below weak crotches [arrow] and cables should be approximately two thirds the distance from the tree crotches to the top of the crown. Again, I emphasize, these are guidelines, not rules. In conifers or other trees with excurrent branching, these guidelines do not fit. The arborist must have an understanding of the architecture of the tree and where cables and rods could be placed to help prevent failures during moderate loading. It is not easy. Record keeping on successes and failures are needed so that more arborists can use these important techniques.

337

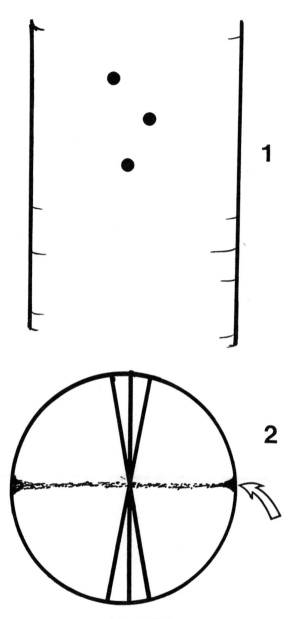

300. RODS

When holes must be drilled into a tree, always stagger them [1]. Diagram 2 shows a transverse view of diagram 1. The arrow shows the crack between two stems. All holes drilled to hold rods for cables should be in a straight line with the cables.

If possible, avoid drilling for rod and cable installation in spring when leaves are expanding and in fall when leaves are falling. These periods are from 3 to 8 days. The best time to drill trees is immediately after the leaves have expanded. Do not place rods near wounds or old open branch stubs.

Always check cables and braces later.

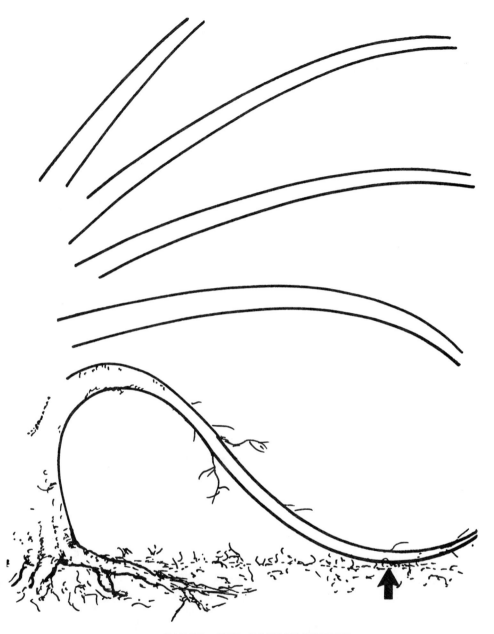

301. LARGE, OLD, LOW BRANCHES

As some trees get old, large branches will rest on the ground. I have seen these branches pulled upward by near vertical cables attached to the trunk. The vertical cabling can put such pressure on the trunk that it may split. I believe the old, low branches should be left alone. Let them rest. If they must be kept slightly above ground, then some block of stone or concrete can be put under them. If this is done, put a bolt through the stem so that the metal bolt rests on the block.

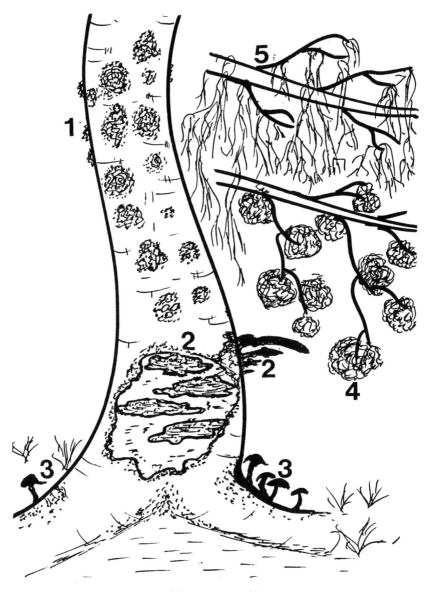

302. THINGS ON TREES

Trees support more communities of life than any other organism on earth; mosses, lichens, algae, ball moss, Spanish moss, orchids, ferns, and a long list of epiphytes — plants that grow on other plants. It is sad when some people tell customers that these plants are harmful and should be removed. I know of cases where people paid to have lichens removed [1], fungus fruit bodies removed [2 and 3] to stop rot, ball moss [4] and Spanish moss [5] removed because it was harmful. Dwarf mistletoe (135; S: 133,134) and mistletoes are parasitic plants that do harm trees. Branches with dwarf mistletoes should be removed on small trees. Removing mistletoes on large trees is a difficult job. I am not aware of any easy way to do this with chemicals.

340

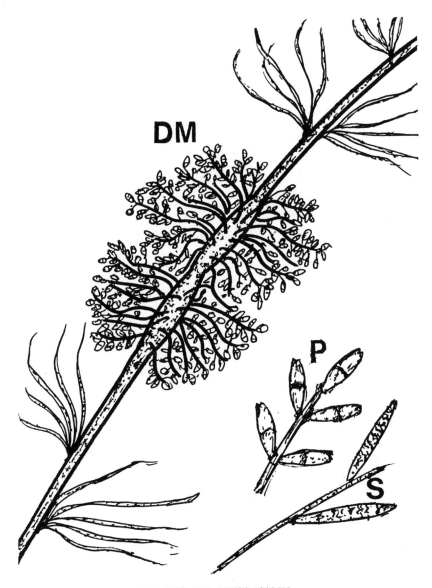

303. DWARF MISTLETOES

The dwarf mistletoes belong to the genus *Arceuthobium*. They are aerial dicotyledonous parasites that grow on trees in the pine family (*Pinaceae*) and cypress family (*Cupressaceae*). Dwarf mistletoes have no leaves [DM]. When the fruits are ripe, they are propelled out of the plant by an explosive mechanism. P is pistillate flower and S is staminate flower.

The fruits are sticky and adhere to needles, insects, birds, and animals. Infections often lead to stem swellings and witchesbrooms. Heavy infections can lead to tree death. On young trees that have only a few branches infected, the infected branches should be removed. Maintaining high vigor of the trees is the best way to prevent injury by dwarf mistletoes (135).

341

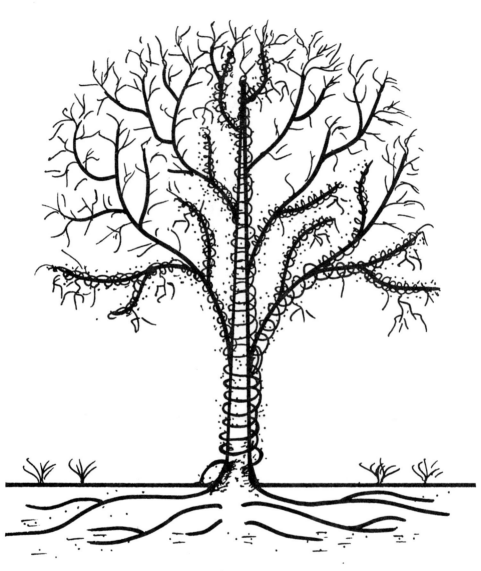

304. VINES

Ivy and other vines often grow on and over trees. The vine growth can be so heavy that small branches may break under the weight of the vines. Or, the vines may so shade the tree's leaves that photosynthesis is decreased. Some vines will girdle small trunks and branches. Heavy growth of vines may also compete with tree roots for water and elements. Other than the allelopathic effect of ivy on Boxwood (see diagram on allelopathy), I am not aware of any biological injury to trees caused by ivy. Vines also make homesites for rodents.

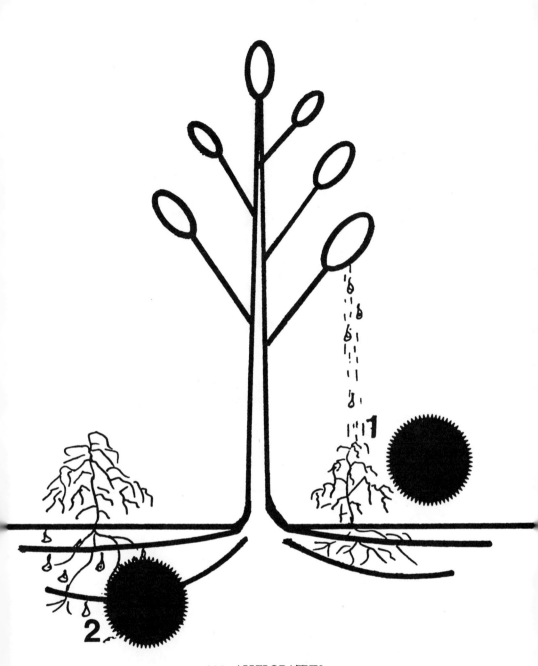

305. **ALLELOPATHY**

Allelopathy is the production of substances by one plant that adversely affect other plants nearby. Roots of black walnut produce substances — juglonines — that inhibit growth of tomatoes and other plants near the tree roots. Ivy *(Hedera sp.)* may cause a decline of boxwood *(Buxus* spp.*)* (Personal Communication; Klaus Vollbrecht, Sweden). The substances may leach from leaves [1], or from the roots [2]. Be alert for allelopathic problems.

343

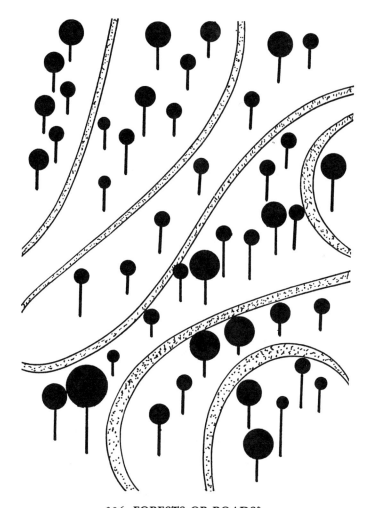

306. FORESTS OR ROADS?

When I walk in some forests, and when I fly over them, I often ask myself; are we "growing" roads with trees here and there, or are we growing trees with roads everywhere? I once told the supervisor of a world famous "forest" that he did not have a forest, but a beautiful network of roads. He was not so pleased. As we build more roads or fire ditches, we prune tree 3 (see diagram 231). You can overprune tree 1, and tree 2, and also tree 3. I believe we are seeing this in our time. What is the solution? Close most of the roads! One of the biggest parks in Europe is doing just that! So it can be done. It is a sound treatment for health of a forest or park. Roads change the pathways of water, allow grass to compete with trees, and disrupt the mycorrhizae and other tree associates. And when trees get sick, all the associates of trees also get sick. Ask a koala! (See S: 184,187,191,H.)

Acid rain: 34,38,39,94,333.

Air pollution: 89,250,311,313,314.

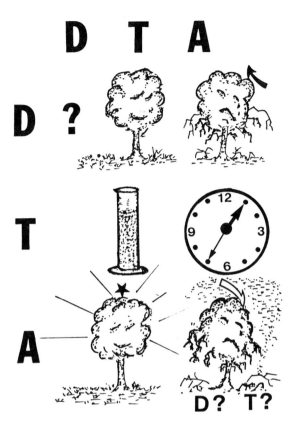

307. DIAGNOSE, TREAT, ASSESS: DTA

Now it is time to pull together the many parts given in the many diagrams. Help will come to our trees when we follow the same procedures used by modern medical doctors. They have developed a very effective scheme and it is there for our use. We do not have to reinvent the wheel! Start by asking what you want. Do you have a healthy tree and do you want to keep it healthy? Do you have a sick tree and do you want to help it regain health? Do you want to kill the tree? (Not so strange when you consider that herbicides are not being allowed on some power line rights-of-way.) Regardless, we must start with a diagnosis [D]. A diagnosis depends on a keen understanding of the many parts and processes of the entire tree system. Then you must formulate a treatment [T]. The treatment or treatments must be tied to phenological events, not to calendar dates. You must know timing and concentrations, or dose. You must keep records. You must know what you measured and how. Then you must assess or analyze [A] the results. What happened? What did you get? Did you get what you aimed for? If so, fine. If not, you must go back and determine why. Did you miss some important point? Was the dose too high or too low? Was the timing not right? Then you try again and again until you get what you aimed for. Adjustments, adjustments, and more adjustments may be necessary. That is the road to modern arboriculture. It is a road travelled by professionals.

308. RECORDS, RECORDS, RECORDS!

Until records are kept, old arboriculture will still be in effect. Recipes and dump-it-on methods will still be used in old arboriculture. Modern arboriculture starts with the DTA's and record keeping. Our computer world lends itself to this approach. The tree system approach and phenology lend themselves to this approach (54). Develop your own simple record file. Develop it so only a very short time is needed to complete each record. Then you will have a data base for your treatments. Believe me, this is the only way we will move out of old arboriculture and into modern arboriculture. We must begin by understanding the tree system, how it grows, how it defends itself, and how it eventually dies. We need to record our successes and failures. And, as we do this, we can increase the successes and greatly reduce the failures.

346

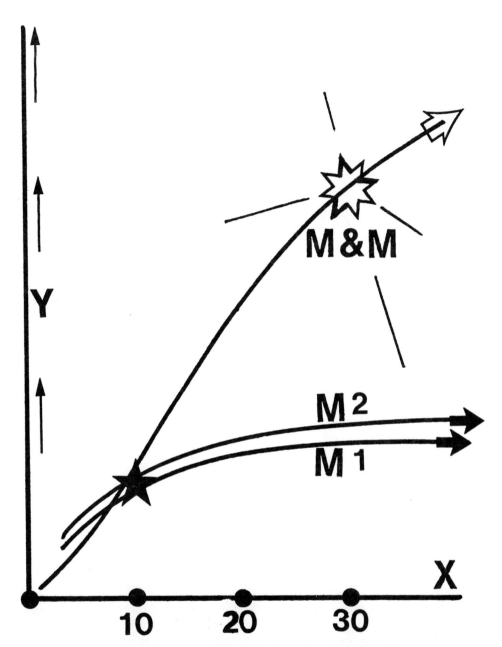

309. THE MIX OF MIND AND MUSCLE AND MONEY
   The average tree worker in his or her own business, using mostly muscles (M-1) can expect to earn approximately the same as the average college biology teacher, using mostly mind (M-2) after the 10th career year. (X axis is career years.) The average tree worker using mind and muscles (M&M) starts earning at a rate slightly below the M-1 and M-2 person, but after the 10th career year the M&M person's earning rate continues to climb far beyond the M-1 or M-2 person. (Y axis is earning power.)

347

310. COLLECTIONS AND CONNECTIONS

Research focuses on collections. Development focuses on connections. We need both.

The greater the collection of ideas, measurements, facts, parts, and other items, the greater the chances are for connections that serve a specific need.

Children often play the dot game. Numbered dots are connected until some recognized thing "jumps" out of the maze of dots. The game gets boring as children get older because they no longer need to connect all the numbered dots to perceive the connected image. As some people look at the dots, they can see the picture without going through the tedium of connecting the numbered dots.

This dot game is not so different from similar "games" played long into adulthood. Some people must connect every dot before they can "see" an image. Others can see an image without connecting the dots, or by connecting only a few.

Indeed, looking and seeing are two different things.

Be a collector. But, also, be a connector. Learn to see, fast. It takes practice. When you go on a potential client's property, connect dots. See things, fast.

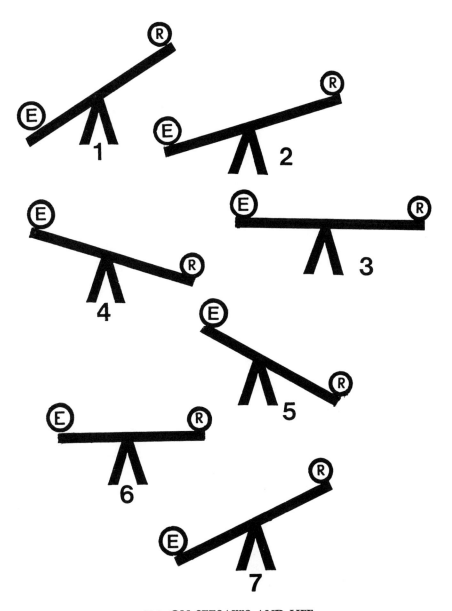

311. ON SEESAWS AND LIFE

When a seed germinates, a living seesaw gets its first push. It begins to move; to grow. The power that provided the first push was stored in the seed as potential energy. **As the plant grows, kinetic energy is being used. New life always starts on energy provided by another organism.**

As the living seesaw moves upward on the side that provided the push (we will call it the E side for energy), the other side (we will call it the R side that provides water and essential elements) moves downward. Dynamic oscillation is the equal movement upward and downward. The seesaw is an example of dynamic oscilla-

349

tion. Two parts are moving. As the parts get bigger, more energy will be required to move them. Dynamic oscillation speaks to the crown and roots.

As E moves upward, and R moves downward, there is a moment when they are in the same plane horizontal to the ground. At this moment balance is perceived. **Dynamic equilibrium is the equal rate of processes going on in opposite directions.**

Oscillation deals with parts, and equilibrium deals with processes. The processes are those that move energy-yielding substances, water, essential elements, and other substances essential for life.

If the seesaw were really balanced, it would stop at the horizontal plane.

The living seesaw is always slightly out of balance but always in dynamic oscillation and equilibrium. The E side must be slightly "heavier" than the R side because the push power can only come from a source of potential energy. The growth of the seesaw — tree — depends on the energy and water and elements. Therefore, one side cannot be more important than the other side. Both sides are important. If both sides are not present, there is no seesaw. The really important part is to understand how the seesaw is constructed and how it works. As it goes up and down it gets bigger. (In philosophy this subject is called dualism: good and evil, reality and appearance, order and chaos, simple and complex, mind and matter, harmony and strife, war and peace.) The seesaw concept is not new. It dates back to the beginning of philosophy 500 or 600 BC. See any philosophy book for details. I suggest 299 and 354. It is fascinating reading!

When the seesaw is young, the E side contains so much potential energy that the push power for rapid movement upward and downward is there. Weight can be removed from either side with little effect on the movement because the E side has so much potential energy.

As the seesaw gets bigger and older, the E side begins to approach the same weight as the R side. Adjustments must come because if the E side begins to equal the R side, the seesaw will stop. Balance. Death.

Shedding begins. Dynamic mass is reduced. However, before parts die, essential elements are recycled from the dying parts back to the still living seesaw.

As age increases and shedding continues to decrease the size of the living seesaw, the E side forms sprouts that help keep the E side still slightly heavier than the R side. When the time comes that E and R do approach balance and further adjustments cannot be made, the pathogens enter and do what they have been designed to do.

The seesaw analogy also fits well for topping, construction injury, and removal of living wood in the crown of maturing trees, and many other man-made mistreatments.

When some situation causes the seesaw to approach balance, or when the E side suddenly has less weight than the R side, something must be done or the seesaw will stop.

The usual practice is to take even more weight off the E side. This makes a bad situation worse. The E side cannot move downward. Instead it produces sprouts with the remaining potential energy. If the sprouts produce enough energy fast enough, the E side will move downward. With some trees—linden, plane tree— this often does happen. With other trees, the R side begins to deteriorate all the more.

The other choice is to lighten the R side. Will this not bring down the E side? It will; but where will the E side get the power to push upward again? And, again, the usual response from the E side is to form sprouts. If the sprouts return enough energy fast enough, the E side may push upward again. If not, the pathogens enter and do what they have been designed to do.

Another common practice is to add high amounts of fertilizer. Remember, fertilizers are not a source of energy. The result is that the already low energy reserves in the E side are decreased all the more. Indeed, growth may increase; but without a defense system. And, again, it is not long before the pathogens arrive to do their work.

What can be done? Learn to watch the seesaw. Try to keep it moving at its normal healthy speed. Keep it watered. Wait until parts have died and recycled their essential elements, and then remove the parts correctly. Keep watching the seesaw. As trees get older, remove fewer living branches. You can add small amounts of fertilizer after the motion of the seesaw begins. When is that? When you see that the tree is growing faster than it is shedding parts. Watch the rate of shedding.

I hope the next time you plan to top a tree, or to take a great amount of living wood out of the crown of a mature tree, or to "balance the top with the bottom" of a construction-injured tree, you think about the simple seesaw.

APPENDIX

SAFETY FIRST

Here are some safety rules professionals know and practice:

Plan your work, don't "just do it."
Do only what you have been trained to do.
Have proper training before working near power lines.
Wear safety gear at all times.
Know where your partners are at all times.
Do not work when you are sick or tired.
Do not ignore cuts and bruises.
Report all accidents.
Respect power tools and use them correctly and safely.
Check tools and equipment before you go into the tree.
Concentrate on your job.
Treat all electrical conductors as energized.
Do not force power tools and equipment beyond their limits.
Remove branches with care, using ropes when necessary.
Be alert to avoid chainsaw kickback.
Plan your cuts and do not bind your saw.
Stub cut branches before making the final cut.
Do not put climbing ropes over weak branches.
Have regular safety meetings.
Know first aid techniques.

DO NOT BREAK THE LAW

All persons pruning trees near electric lines must be qualified by training that includes correct pruning techniques, and an understanding of safety and line clearing requirements given by OSHA and ANSI Z 133.1-1988.

You must comply with these requirements.

Breaking the law is bad enough.

Breaking your body is worse.

The requirements are for your safety.
Know and practice them.

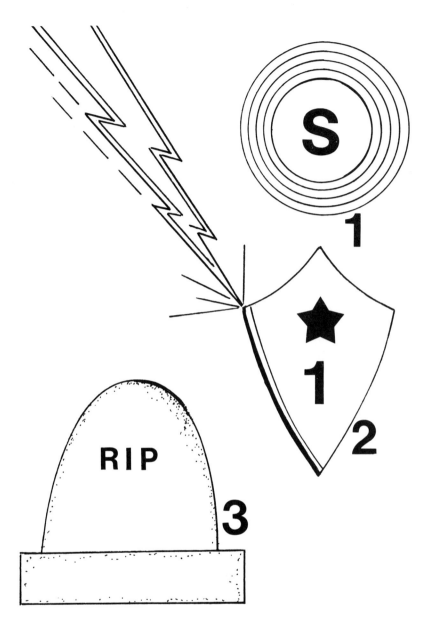

SAFETY FIRST

SAFETY FIRST OR LIFE WON'T LAST

Safety must be our target [1].
Safety must be our first concern [2].
Or else, we will not be here long [3].

COMMUNICATIONS

Communication is the transmission of a message.

Communication is a word many people use but few understand. That is why we have so much poor communications.

We will start by defining some words. Socrates said you know a person by the words he uses. Socrates went to his death because he felt so strongly about the definition of a single word. It is a fascinating story. For details see 354. Voltaire said if people defined their words, arguments would be less than three minutes.

Understanding words and their use is power!

Transmission is the orderly transfer of a message from sender to receiver with no loss in the content of the message. Dissemination is to spread any substance or idea. You can disseminate seeds or ideas. There is no assurance that either will grow. Dissemination is a random scattering of an item or idea. Random is the key word. Transmission is a highly ordered process.

A disease is transmitted when a second organism is infected by pathogens spread from another organism, and the second organism has symptoms identical to those of the first organism. The agents of disease are disseminated. The disease is transmitted. And so it is with other types of messages.

A message is a highly ordered arrangement of information. Because it is highly ordered, the likelihood of parts being altered is minimized. Information is the orderly connection of facts or any type of defined item. Connections are orderly for information. The reservoir of items or facts comes from collections that are random.

We cannot escape the concepts of order and disorder. The more highly ordered any idea or system becomes, the better the chances are for communications. **Order repeats, or can be repeated.** I believe this is truth. And, because our natural systems are constantly changing, the nature of truth is also constantly changing.

Enough of this!

Communication starts when you develop a message. What do you want the other person to know? If you cannot say it or write it clearly in a few words, it may mean that you do not have a message.

Now we can put our fingers on one of the major problems in communications. The sender, many times, does not have a highly ordered arrangement of information. When that happens, then noise is the result.

When bits and pieces are not sent in an orderly way, the result is noise. If you send noise, the receiver will get noise, and it is highly doubtful that your intended "message" will be acted upon. Then we wonder why we have problems with people and education.

Learn to develop clear messages. What are the facts? What do you want the other person to know? Use clear, simple words. Use photos, slides, diagrams, or any other type of item that will make your message orderly.

I have always said that a message should contain no more than 25 words. Tell me who you are. Tell me what you want to do. Why? If you cannot define yourself in 25 words or less, you are in trouble!

Who do you want to receive your message? Know your audience. Know what they want and need. **Give them what they need in a way they want it.** Never give them just what they want. This separates the dishonest and nonprofessional from the professional. Advertising by dishonest people sends messages that give the uneducated persons what they want — fast, easy, money, without using the mind!

Our responsibility as professionals is to communicate with homeowners, city managers, estate owners, park managers, developers, and a long list of others. We must perform in ways that can help our world, our environment, our trees and their associates, and to do it in ways that will return honest profits.

After you have tailored your message to your audience, how should you send it? We now have many ways to send messages: talks, videos, newsletters, personal letters, books, booklets, pamphlets, and the list goes on.

I believe the closer you can get to your audience, the better the chances are for transmitting your message.

You must get the attention of your audience. You get them to listen, to say "WOW!"

Here are examples of some messages I have developed and some ways I have tried to tailor them to different audiences:

1. There are no data to show that wound dressings stop rot.
2. Prune branches as close as possible to the branch collar.
3. Trees survive after wounding by compartmentalizing the infection.
4. Microorganisms infect tree wounds in successions.
5. Trees get energy from the sun and minerals from the soil.

You are familiar with these and many of my other messages. They are all very brief. They can be repeated many times during a presentation. I have repeated them so many times that the messages have become linked with me.

Do not be afraid to repeat. But make sure you repeat your message the same way every time.

Identify your service. Develop a message that states the type of service you provide for trees. Repeat it and repeat it until people identify you with the statement.

Identify the key words that define you and your service. Use these words over and over again. Do not try to be something you are not.

Some of my key words are: tree, health, education, rot, compartmentalization, defense, system, survival, associates, processes, boundaries, energy, order, mind, dose, communications, timing, definitions, and people.

The most successful communication adventure I have had was a publication called "A Tree Hurts, Too" (S: 59). Many of you know it. It had beautiful paintings by artist David Carroll. It was very brief. Full of bright color. Few words. Simple messages. How else could I "sell" rot, disease, and death?

Get a pen. Write your key words. Live with them. Polish them. Get comfortable with them. Repeat them. You will then begin to understand communications.

Communications: S: 81,89,102,128.

PRESENTATIONS

You are asked to talk to a group about your work or some other subject. What do you do? Panic? Many people do!

First. *It is not easy.* **People who tell you it is easy are probably poor speakers and poor communicators.** I do not want to frighten you. But, it does take a great amount of study, practice, preparation, skill, and "guts" to give a good presentation. And, sometimes no matter what you do, say, or how you do it or say it, your presentation may not be effective. Remember, the best actors, musicians, and athletes have bad days. Things that should never happen, often do!

However, there are ways to minimize all of this. I just wanted to make it clear first that this is not an easy subject.

I do not know of any easy way to tell you how to read your audience. You must find ways to connect with your audience as soon as possible when you get on stage. Once you connect with your audience and you move at *their* pace, you will have an effective presentation.

There are basic rules that you must follow:

Know your subject.

Do your homework.

Know your key words.

Practice.

Be your own critic.

Be yourself.

Never a naughty word or story.

Check room and equipment before your talk.

Thank your hosts; thank your audience.

Know your audience.

Start and end on time.

Allow questions.

Do not bluff.

Learn to say, "I do not know."

If wrong, admit it!

Do not use names on stage, unless for compliments or thanks.

Be well dressed, but not overdressed.

Maintain a strong but respectful posture.

Never point fingers.

Look your audience in the eye.

Smile.

Pause before major points.

Repeat key words.

Be courteous to your audience.

Do not read to them.

If you lose your trend of thought, say so, and try again.

If you are frightened, say so; and go on.

Watch your audience; not the wall or ceiling.

Know when to change the subject.

I do not believe in long notes, or reading a paper to a group. I believe that both insult your audience. I believe that it is better to make mistakes and be human on stage than it is to read to your audience and treat them as robots. **If you do not know your material well enough to talk about it for a short time, then you should not be on stage.**

There are ways to ease the pain of no notes or a written paper. The plan used by most speakers is to use color slides. The slides keep the person on track. Fine. If not overused! It is sad when most of our meetings are carried on in dark rooms. The speaker is often seen only for a few seconds before the signal is given to dim the lights. I would like to see some meetings with a time limit on color slides.

If you are going to use slides, make certain they are bright, clear, and in focus.

Overhead projections of charts and other materials is another way to keep on track. The room can be lighter than for slide projectors.

Flip charts, and boards—white, green, black—can be used to write key words. I like this method because it allows you to work best with your audience. If they want more on the subject, you give them more. If they are not interested, you leave the subject. You are not tied into subjects the way you are with slides and overhead material. How do you know if your audience wants more, or does not want more? You keep eye contact with them.

I always memorize my key words. I use them all as soon as I can at the start of the talk. Then I start with details. With this method, notes are not needed and you seldom lose your place.

I always critique my talks and think about what parts went well and what parts did not.

In summary; do your homework, respect your audience, and be yourself on stage.

Tell them what you're going to tell them.
  Tell them.
    Tell them what you told them.

Stand up with good posture to be seen.
Speak up with key words to be heard.
Sit down when your time is up to be appreciated.

NEWSLETTERS

Newsletters and small publications are excellent ways to communicate.

The wider your audience, the shorter the message. The major problem with most newsletters is overcrowding of content.

Get some popular magazines. Look through their advertisements. See how the large companies make their points. You may not be able to use large color prints; but you can use similar formats.

There are inexpensive ways to format your newsletter and to get the attention of your audience.

Use lots of bold headings and subheadings. Put your message in bold key words.

The best way to draw attention to your message is to surround it with white space. White space is powerful and not expensive.

Repeat your messages in photos or drawings.

Develop messages that will give your audience just enough so that they understand your point. But, not that much that they do not request more. You want them to ask for the details. Let them know you are eager to give details.

If you can afford to use color, it is very effective. Use a photo or drawing to make a point. Most photos show too much. If you are going to use photos or paintings, make certain that they are printed properly. There is nothing more detracting than a fuzzy photo, especially a fuzzy color photo. Remember, there is no magic in color! Poor color is worse than no color.

Be novel! Do something different. Experiment with format. Format is the key to reaching your audience. People will read large bold print. However, if you overdo large print, it looks like a kindergarten newsletter.

Use short sentences. Repeat key words. Use small powerful words. Key words should go first in a sentence.

Think of your newsletter as a wonderful gourmet meal. A real gourmet meal has many courses. The courses are small. There is space or time between the courses. They are attractive and served in an attractive way. And, when you leave, you can hardly wait to return. That's class!

EXPERT WITNESS

An expert witness is a person qualified to give information for legal matters. An expert witness is a person who has the ability to give detailed information on a subject or situation. To qualify as an expert witness a person should have proper credentials to show an understanding of the subject or situation, and experience with the subject or situation.

We live in a litigious country. We have only a fraction of the world's people; but we have the highest percentage of lawyers. I have heard figures such as 5% population and 75% of the world's lawyers. I have even heard higher percentages for lawyers. I do not have a factual basis for this but we do have many, that is for sure.

There is no doubt that lawyers know about trees; their value, and that trees fall and damage property and injure, or kill, people.

The modern arborist must understand liability and the legal machinery.

To have a legal case with tree failure, there must be somebody to sue who has money, some property must be damaged or a person must be injured, and there must be negligence.

The tree expert witness works with the last category—negligence. The key words now are reasonable and prudent. Did someone neglect to act in a reasonable way with the tree that failed? Were there signs of high risk? Were the signs of the type that could be recognized by the people responsible for the tree?

Then comes the subject of loading. Did the tree fail in a hurricane? Or during a mild, brief rain?

If you are going to be an expert witness, **never be influenced by other people.** Study the case without input from others. Make your own conclusions. And, stay with them.

INDIVIDUAL PROJECTS

1. Attend an arborist meeting and discuss what you considered the good and bad parts.
2. Interview 5 working arborists, landscape designers, or nursery people and discuss your views on their activities.
3. Spend the day with an urban forester, or city arborist, and discuss their problems and successes.
4. Visit two sites under development and critique what you saw. Give suggestions on improvements.
5. Locate two places in your area where you believe good tree work was done; and two places where poor tree work was done. Give reasons for your selections.
6. Discuss the characteristics of the 10 most common city trees in your area. Point out the good and bad features.
7. Discuss the major insect and disease problems of the 10 most common city trees in your area.
8. Identify 5 serious hazard trees in your area, and discuss why you think they are hazardous, and your recommendation to reduce risk of failure.
9. Develop a photo story of tree conditions in your area.
10. Discuss soil types in your area. Use photos, drawings, or collect soil profiles.
11. Rate the economic value of 5 trees, using the guides for tree values. Guides can be obtained from the I.S.A. and A.S.C.A.
12. If you are near a natural forest, compare the growth habits and conditions of the same tree species growing in the forest and in the city.
13. Develop a color slide story on the trees in your area. Give a twenty minute presentation on your project.
14. Observe and report on the phenological events on 10 trees of the same species. This can be done best in the spring and early fall. Observe when buds swell, when they open, when leaves or flowers start to grow, when fruit forms, when leaves are fully formed, when twigs start to grow, and as many other features as you can measure. If possible, take *small* core samples to determine starch content of trunk and roots at different phenological times. Also, from the cores, relate development of the growth increment with other features such as development of leaves and fruit, and the presence and amount of root hairs and mycorrhizae.

This project could be expanded for a graduate research project, or it could be done by selected employees in a private company. Until we know this type of information, we will have no baseline for timing our treatments.

15. Define the best sites and conditions for 10 individual trees of a species. If you are near a natural forest, do the project on a tree species found in the forest that is used as a city tree. Define soil type, pH, moisture conditions, amount of natural litter, light conditions, and other plants close by. Take soil samples and send off for elemental analysis. It is best to select trees that are growing very well and have not been treated by anyone. Again, this project can be expanded for a graduate research project. We need to know the trees' health profile in a natural forest or in an area in the city where no treatments—fertilizers, pruning—have been done. Once we get a tree health profile, then we will have baseline information for treating that species in a city site. For a long term project, the phenological information should be linked with the tree health profile. Then we would begin scientific tree care.

16. Demonstrate techniques for isolating microorganisms from wood. Have some isolates growing on agar in petri dishes. Show differences between bacteria and fungi. If you are in an area where Dutch elm disease or oak wilt are present, show how to isolate from twigs and small sections of trunk. (See references 12 and A for information on this subject; or if there is a microbiologist, mycologist, or plant pathologist in your college, or near by, ask for help on this very important project.)

17. Collect samples of tree defects and diseases. Name the problem and give a brief description. Make transverse and radial longitudinal cuts through internal defects. All cuts should show the pith. If not, they are artifacts and will confuse more than help. If you have access to a tree that has been cut, collect defect samples and give a defect autopsy report of the tree. If the tree had injections or implants, show the internal effects of the treatments. If there was hardware in the tree, split the sections to show the effects of the hardware on the trunk. The autopsy of a tree could be a class project.

18. Develop your own 8-page homeowners guide for proper tree care. You can use photos, drawings, or any other novel items.

19. Discuss OSHA and ANSI requirements for arborists.

20. Discuss safety and first aid.

21. Have a mock trial over a tree that has killed a person. Have one person act as an expert witness for the plaintiff and another person as the expert witness for the defense. The role of the expert witness is to give information on the tree and the reasons for the failure. The expert witness can give an opinion concerning negligence or not. Sad, but true; remember the questions are often directed more toward the credentials of the expert witness than to the facts of the case. (Get help from arborists who have gone to court as expert witnesses. Or, ask them to act as the judge for your mock trial.)

22. Read and discuss an essay from Scientific American. I suggest that you start with 201,291, and 370.

LONG TERM PROJECTS

1. Establish a demonstration area for good and bad tree treatments.

a. Planting depth: 15 small trees of the same species; 5 too deep, 5 correct, 5 too shallow.

b. Grass: 15 small trees of the same species; 5 with grass to the trunk, 5 no grass one meter diameter about the trunk, 5 no grass two meters diameter about the trunk.

c. Fertilization: 15 small trees of the same species; 5 trees receive one pound (.444 kg.) of 10-10-10 per caliper inch (2.5 cm) mixed in the soil at planting time; 5 trees receive one pound of 10-10-10 per caliper inch, spread over a 3 meter diameter area about the tree base, after leaves form in the second growth period; and 5 trees no fertilizer.

The fertilizer demonstration can be greatly varied to suit your trees, soil, and climate. You may want to have more than 3 treatments. This is fine as long as you have at least 5 trees in each treatment. Keep accurate phenological records and accurate records of the type of fertilizer and amounts.

d. Pruning: Start with small young trees and have at least 5 trees per treatment; strong central leader, single stem pollard, multiple stem pollard, round, low horizontal, and no pruning. As with fertilizers, the amount of pruning and types are almost endless. Develop your pruning treatment to suit the tree species in your area. Keep phenological records and records on amount of wood removed.

Other treatments that lend themselves to this project are soil compaction, mulches, soil aeration, "balancing" top and bottom at planting time, root pruning, watering, flush cuts and correct cuts, wound dressings and scribing.

Records must be kept. There must be control trees that receive no treatments. At least 5 trees must be in each treatment. Keep photo records of the trees as they grow. It would be wonderful if each chapter of the International Society of Arboriculture could establish a demonstration of treatment of trees in their areas.

e. Growing samples: Inflict wounds, flush cuts, injections, implants, wound dressings, and other insults on young trees for future autopsy work. The trees could be used for laboratory work or workshops. Use opposite branching trees for proper and improper pruning cut comparisons.

f. Phenology: Start long-term phenological observations on selected trees. Keep a photo record.

WORKSHOPS

Trees and their associates will never be understood until you touch all parts, inside and outside. Here is the workshop outline I have used in 27, 3½ day workshops. The workshops have been a great learning experience for me. As part of the workshop, I have dissected and studied the important trees—over 3000—in many parts of the world: New Zealand, Canada, Ireland, England, Germany, Switzerland, The Netherlands, Italy, and throughout the United States from the northeast, northwest, southwest, and to the tropical areas in Florida. Other shorter workshops have given me opportunities to dissect and study trees in Australia, South Korea, France, Sweden, Denmark, Norway, and Spain.

In every workshop, I not only had an opportunity to see *their trees* from the inside and outside, but I had good opportunities to see *their problems* and *their successes.* I listened when they talked. I went to their cities, parks, nurseries, campuses, estates, and forests.

My point is that the workshops have taught me a great deal. I want to pass along this wonderful experience to you.

MATERIALS AND LOGISTICS

Whether you are going to follow this outline for yourself or use the outline for your class, some tools, materials, and other items are needed.

1. **Space to work.** A square meter of table space is needed for each student. It is best to have a room on ground level that has easy access to space outside where cut trees and samples can be kept. The space outside can be used for cutting large samples with a chainsaw.

2. **It is best to limit workshops to 15 people;** or 20 at the maximum.

3. **Tools:** chainsaws (2), handsaws (6), knives with 15 cm (6 inch) blades (one per person), single-edged razor blades (at least 20 per person), eye protection glasses, dissecting microscopes with 10 to 30 magnification (one per person), electric power hand plane, 2 work benches, shovels and picks (5 each) for digging roots, large plastic bags for collecting roots, petri dishes (1 per person), drawing pads and colored pencils for drawing the samples, wood-splitting tools, large trunk sections on which to split wood, discs of trunks for chopping and cutting small samples (2 cm thick and about 30 cm in diameter is best, 1 for each person), paper towels, water in small dropper bottles, I_2-KI in small dropper bottles, first aid kit.

4. **A place to cut and dig trees.** At least 50 small trees—5 to 20 cm in diamter—must be cut. It is best to go to an area that was logged about 10 to 20 years ago. Young, fast growing trees are best. If you have no access to such an area, you can use branches from large trees. We have collected samples from parks, arboreta, gardens, golf courses, estates, windbreaks, and campuses. If trees cannot be dug for root studies, small patches of sod can be removed from lawns, and roots can be collected from the soil below. Then the sod is replaced.

5. **Places to go for discussions.** If possible, start with a natural forest area. Then go to parks, golf courses, cities, or any place where trees are growing.

PROJECTS

1. **Ring porous wood anatomy.** The best trees are deciduous oaks, elms, black locust, and mulberry. Samples should be trunk sections 5 to 10 cm in diameter at the base. The samples should be as free of defects and branch stubs as possible. Try to select samples that have growth increments of at least 3 mm wide. Cut a disc 1 inch or 2½ cm wide. Shave the cut surface with the plane or shave it as best you can with a knife. The cut surface is the *transverse* view. With a sharp razor blade, shave one portion of the sample very clean. If you see debris in the vessels, the surface has not been shaved clean enough. Making clean cuts with the razor blade is extremely important. Make certain not to crush the bark. Under low power of the microscope, study the features as shown in the diagrams in this book.

Cut or split the sample to expose a radial view and then to expose a tangential view.

2. **Diffuse Porous Wood.** Best trees are maples, birches, poplars, plane trees, and lime or linden. Follow the same procedures as given for ring porous wood: transverse, radial, and tangential sections.

3. **Conifer Wood: Resinous and Nonresinous.** Best trees for resinous woods are pines; and for nonresinous woods; cedars, hemlocks, yews, and arborvitae. Again, follow the design for transverse, radial, and tangential views.

Radial and tangential surfaces can be seen very well without shaving the wood.

With the diffuse porous wood and the conifers it is necessary to slice a very thin small section of wood to view under the microscope. The slice must be so thin that you can see through it. (Palms should be dissected in areas where they grow.)

4. **Roots:** Dig out several small trees — 5 to 15 cm in diameter at trunk base. Determine the extent of the roots. Collect portions of fine roots with soil attached for study later of root hairs and mycorrhizae. Place the nonwoody roots with soil, and the woody roots with the lower 30 cm of trunk, into plastic bags to carry to the laboratory.

In the laboratory, take small portions of the nonwoody roots and place them into an open petri dish. Wash some of the soil away and transfer the washed sample to another petri dish. Add a small amount of water to keep the sample moist. Find and study the mycorrhizae and root hairs. Make certain that your nonwoody roots are attached to thin woody roots. Do not confuse your tree roots with roots of annual plants, especially grass.

5. **Anatomy with I₂-KI.** You can do the I_2-KI projects after the anatomy work, or you could space the projects by putting the root work between the continuation of anatomy work. (It is difficult for people not trained or experienced in microscope work to use the microsccope for long periods. This is why I space the microscope work with other projects, such as digging roots and discussions in the forest and city.)

When I_2-KI is added to a *freshly* cut and very smooth, clean wood surface, the starch in the parenchyma cells will turn purple. Start with the ring porous trees. If you see purple in vessels, you have a poorly-cleaned sample! The wood surface *must* be shaved with a sharp razor blade. The surface must not be sanded.

Continue by adding I_2-KI to the thin slices of wood.

CAUTION!

I_2-KI is poison. Use with great care. Avoid skin contact. Wash immediately after you get some on you. Keep I_2-KI away from children. Always label your bottle. Remember, a bottle *without* a label should be disposed of properly. Always use great care when working with any chemical. Clean up chemical spills immediately.

6. **Wounds:** Collect many wound samples from small and large trees. Start by dissecting wounds on small trunks — 5 to 15 cm in diameter at trunk base. Study the transverse and radial longitudinal faces. The radial longitudinal face should extend far beyond the column of discolored wood. Smooth and clean the surfaces and add I_2-KI. Observe the reaction zone and the barrier zone. Apply CODIT model terms and examine the walls 1,2,3, and 4.

Use the power plane on large samples.

7. **Wound Dating:** Find the barrier zone and date the wound to the year it was inflicted. Find a sample that has a barrier zone within the growth increment. Date the wound to a two week period when it was inflicted. To do this you must learn when the growth increment starts to develop in the species and area you are studying. In most species, the growth increment starts as the leaves are forming, and the growth continues for 6 to 8 weeks.

8. **Cracks:** Collect samples that have vertical cracks or seams. Make transverse cuts to study the internal anatomy of the stems. Smooth the large surfaces with a power plane.

On some smaller samples, the woundwood curls inward, and cracks start at the margins of the wound. Be on the alert for these cracks when viewing other samples.

Note where cracks start.

9. **Branches:** Collect young stems that have small branches and codominant stems. Pull the branches downward and out of the stems. Pull apart the codominant stems. Examine the collars.

10. **Branch Stubs:** Collect samples that have old and recently formed stubs. Split the samples through the pith of the inner branch core and the stem. Discard samples that do not show a split through the pith. It is often necessary to use several knives to make a clean split through the pith. The section will be a radial longitudinal one through the branch stub and stem. Study samples that show the A,B, and C protection zones at the branch base.

11. **Stem Stubs:** Repeat the dissections as given above for dead tops, or stem stubs, and sprouts.

12. **Included Bark:** Repeat the radial longitudinal splits of samples that have included bark.

13. **Cankers, Insect Wounds, and Other Wounds:** Dissect small and large wounds; transverse and radial longitudinal sections.

14. **Compare Roots and Trunk:** Compare anatomy of roots and trunk samples from the same tree. Use I_2-KI to show differences in starch.

15. **Starch Profile:** In spring when leaves are forming, cut a small tree—3 to 5 m tall, and collect wood samples from the top to the trunk base. Apply I_2-KI to see the color changes in discs collected from the top to the bottom.

16. **Bark Removal:** In the spring, remove the bark to see the jelly-like new xylem. Scrape away some of the new xylem with a knife or your finger nail. Pull the bark away from living branches to view the collars.

17. **Buds:** Collect twigs that have large buds. Make radial longitudinal sections through the bud and the small stem. Note that the pith of the stem does not meet the pith of the base of the bud. Add I_2-KI to view the position of the starch. The amount of starch will vary at different times of the year.

18. **Field Discussions:** Discuss forest trees and city trees.

When I do the 3½ day workshops, I keep the participants in the lab until 12:30 PM or 1:00 PM. Then after lunch we go outside. I summarize our work after lunch and at the end of the day when we return to the laboratory.

If you plan to do the workshop projects as part of a college course, you can mix the projects to suit your area and time of year.

It is very important to have the participants draw all of their samples. Each drawing should be large—at least 10x15 cm—and all parts labeled. Use colored pencils.

Make certain that the anatomy of the healthy tree is understood first. Do not select samples in the beginning that have wounds, cracks, stubs, or other features that will be studied later. The students must understand the healthy tree first. Great confusion will start if you do not follow this basic rule.

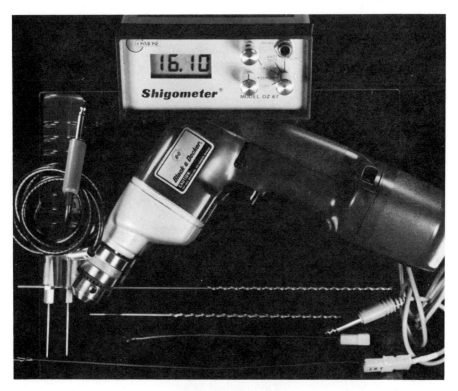

SHIGOMETRY

Shigometry is a procedure that helps determine relative vigor of trees and the condition of wood — sound or decayed — by interpreting patterns of electrical resistance (ER) given by a pulsed-current meter, the Shigometer.™ Double noninsulated needle electrodes are pushed into the bark to measure cambial electrical resistance (CER). A twisted-wire electrode is inserted into a hole drilled into a tree or wood product to measure the internal electrical resistance (IER). CER is used to help determine relative tree vigor. IER is used to help determine the condition of the wood in living trees and wood products.

Wood condition is reflected in its moisture and ion concentrations, which are fairly constant in healthy tissues; and although they may change over the year, they do follow regular patterns. When a pulsed current is passed through infected tissue, the current passes with either more or less resistance than it would through healthy tissue.

SHIGOMETER

The Shigometer is a battery-operated, lightweight field ohmmeter. It generates a pulsed direct electric current and registers in thousands of ohms (kΩ) the resistance to the current as it passes through wood or bark.

Three models are now in use: A meter with a dial ohmmeter, model 7950, that was manufactured by Northeast Electronics Co., Concord, NH, and two models with a digital ohmmeter, models OZ-67 and OZ-68, manufactured by the Osmose Wood Preserving Co., Inc., Buffalo, NY.

How Does the Shigometer Operate in Wood?

When the temperature is above freezing and a pulsed direct electric current is passed through wood that has a moisture coninuum, the resistance to the current will be directly affected by the concentration of positively charged ions, or cations, in the wood.

How Does the Shigometer Operate in the Cambial Zone?

As the cambial zone—cells formed by the cambium that have not yet differenciated—increases in thickness, it can hold more moisture, and more moisture can hold more ions. The thicker the cambial zone, the lower the electrical resistance. The thicker the cambial zone, the more vigorous the tree.

Decay in Trees

The electrical procedure helps to identify the stages of the decay process, not the results of the process.

Heartwood and Discolored Wood

Before wood begins to decay, it becomes wetter and contains more ions. Early stages of whiterot are associated with increasing potassium ion concentration; brownrot, with increasing hydrogen ion concentration (decreasing pH).

The important thing to remember is that rapid ionic changes are measured as substantial differences in ER of the wood and take place before wood becomes visibly decayed. This means that both decaying and decayed wood can be detected by electrical methods.

Decomposed Wood

In advanced stages of decay, the tips of the electrode may have intermittent contact with the wood and the ER will increase and decrease abruptly.

Wetwood

After boards are cut from logs, the wetwood retains moisture longer than sound wood. As wetwood dries in wood products, cracks and wood shrinkage will occur.

Wood Products

Many problems in wood products have their origin in the living tree. The sooner defects are detected, the better the chances are for making decisions on the best use of the wood.

In freshly cut logs, infected wood gives a much lower ER reading than that in contiguous sound wood. When the logs will be utilized for long-term products such as utility poles, use of the Shigometer can help detect unsound, but not visibly defective, wood. Low ER readings near large, open branch stubs or near the base of the tree may indicate extension of decay columns.

Factors Affecting Electrical Resistance

Electrical resistance of a pulsed current through wood or bark is affected greatly by moisture content, temperature, and concentration of cations or electrolytes. The physical condition of the substance may also play a part, together with distance between and type of electrodes and their degree of penetration into the wood.

Moisture

Wood in living trees will usually be above the fiber saturation point, or approximately 27 percent weight of water over weight of oven-dried wood when volume is constant.

The Shigometer functions avove the fiber saturation point. Regular moisture meters function below the fiber saturation point. Above fiber saturation, as free water increases, ions become the dominant variable in determining ER. When moisture content is near fiber saturation, moisture will be the major factor affecting ER. As moisture content exceeds 60 percent, increasing amounts of moisture will have very little effect on resistance readings.

Temperature

When the temperature is near freezing, small temperature changes will have a great effect on ER. After temperatures reach 40 °F (5 °C), additional increases will have little effect on resistance.

Ions

Concentration of ions will have the greatest effect on resistance when temperatures are above 40 °F and moisture content is above 60 percent. In living trees, moisture content is usually above 60 percent. As wood decomposition increases, concentrations of ions usually increase.

Electrode Spacing and Surface Contact

The spacing of the electrodes affects resistance readings, especially if the electrodes are very far apart—more than 6.5 ft (2 m)—or if they are very close together—less than four-fifths of an inch (2 cm). Operators should keep the spacing as constant as possible and well within these extremes.

The amount of electrode surface in contact with the wood or bark affects resistance readings. The operator should standardize the amount of contact that the needle electrodes have in the bark by pushing them in until the wood is touched.

Meter Misuse

The shigometry procedure will not function in wood below the fiber saturation point or where decayed wood is resin soaked or dry. The procedure will not work when wetwood fluids flood the drill hole. The needle electrodes will not measure CER when they are placed into dead wood. The procedure also will not work in frozen tissues.

How To Use Internal Electrical Resistance (IER) Readings

Shigometry can be used to determine the internal condition of living trees and some wood products, especially inservice utility poles. In trees and poles, the operator first drills a small hole into the wood. The diameter of the hole is seven sixty-fourths of an inch (2.8 mm). the depth may be 8 to 12 inches (20.3 to 32cm) or more, depending on the length of the drill bit. The operator next attaches a special twisted-wire electrode to the meter. The electrode has a tip that both sends and receives the electrical current.

As the operator slowly pushes the electrode into the predrilled hole, the changes in ER of the wood along the hole are shown in k   on the meter. In sound trees, the ER is lowest at the cambial zone and usually increases as the electrode is pushed inward. When the electrode tip touches heartwood, there is a sudden increase in ER. When the electrode tip touches wood that is wetter than normal and has concentrations of ions greater than that in normal wood (for example, wood in the early stage of decay), there is a drop in ER. How far the ER decreases depends on the ionic condition of thw wood.

Before one can use shigometry to assess wood conditions, the pattern of ER readings for healthy, sound trees must be determined on a species-by-species basis. For large groups of trees, the baseline ER pattern will be similar. For example, healthy beech, birch, maple, ash, poplar, and so on, will have similar readings. Oak, walnut, cherry, locust, and other heartwood-forming trees make up another pattern group. The pine group and the fir and spruce groups have still other patterns.

A sudden drop in ER below a typical reading of the species indicates wood with high moisture and high ion concentration. In species that usually have wetwood, a sudden ER drop confirms its presence, especially when the drilling torque does not decrease while the hole is being drilled. Wetwood fluids, which are generally darker than sap, usually flow out of such holes. To determine the internal boundary for columns of wetwood, the operator drills above the first hole in increments of two-fifths of an inch (1 cm) until the wetwood is reached.

Decreased drilling torque and changes in color of the drill shavings are good indicators of possible problems within wood or wood products.

How To Use Cambial Electrical Resistance (CER) Readings

Double, noninsulated needle electrodes are used to determine CER. The thicker the cambial zone, the lower the ER.

CER increases at the beginning of dormancy. In cold climates, CER readings from trees with high and low vigor are similar during midwinter. When temperatures are near freezing, however, temperature then becomes the major factor affecting resistance. When bark tissues are below freezing, shigometry will not work.

As with IER, operators must determine a mean CER of each species being evaluated. To determine the mean, CER is measured at two points on at least 20 healthy trees selected at random. CER readings on other trees of that species can then be compared to the mean. Trees with CER readings lower than the mean are more vigorous than those at the mean. Trees with CER readings higher than the mean are less vigorous than those at the mean.

There are two basic ways to use CER readings:

1. Accurately characterize the trees on the basis of objective measurements. For example, choose samples of trees that represent the extremes of the observed range of measurements. Measure the CER of the extremes to determine whether there is a statistically significant difference between the two extremes. Never concentrate on the middle readings in first-time studies. Over time, or space, you may find that the middle readings are moving toward one extreme or the other.

2. Take many CER readings from a large random sample. Next, select two groups that best fit each extreme CER set. Then study the measureable characteristics of the two sets of extremes to determine whether they are statistically significant. Again, stay away from the middle readings in your first studies. As you learn more about the extremes, you will be able to work toward the middle.

Ratio Method

In the ratio method, the reading is divided by the mean. Trees more vigorous than the mean will have ratios less than 1, and trees less vigorous than the mean will have ratios great than 1.

Utility Poles

Shigometry can be helpful in determining which living trees would make the best utility poles. It can detect resin-soaked zones that sometimes develop around old wounds and stubs. These zones do not accept preservatives readily. And wood preservatives usually have a shorter effective time in wood that was already infected in the living tree.

In utility poles already in place, the internal decay detection procedure can be used at groundline. If wood is decaying, the wood will be above the fiber saturation point. Basic patterns of ER must be determined first. Sudden drops in ER indicate higher moisture-ion content of the wood and therefore presence of decay.

Checklist

Here are some suggestions for operators using the Shigometer in the field.

Drilling and Drill Bits

- Make certain that drill bits are firmly held in drill chuck.
- Guide drill in by cupping hand around the drill bit.
- Do not make sudden moves. They will break drill bits.
- Drill at a comfortable position that will use your arm to best advantage to push straight inward on the drill.
- Make certain that reverse drill position has not been accidentally set.
- Do not touch hot drill bits.
- Keep tip of bit sharp.
- Keep flutes at drill tip free from wood shavings.
- Drill in and out several times before going inward the entire distance.
- Do not waste power. Pull the drill out quickly.
- Do not be afraid to push on the drill.
- Learn by the sound when pressure is too great.
- Recharge batteries after they have lost all power.

Do not recharge batteries that still have some power. Some rechargeable batteries seem to have a "memory". It is best to run batteries down completely by holding and operating the drill in the air before recharging. A small gasoline-powered generator is best for jobs that require many drillings.

Bending Wire Electrodes and Other Electrode Problems

The wire should fit tightly into the hole. Always clean the tips of the electrode with your fingernails and spread the tips slightly before performing each probe.

If the meter is registering k   below 500 when the electrode is in open air, the tips are dirty or stuck together. Be alert for this when working with pines and trees that have sticky or milky sap.

Look for worn insulation along the electrode shaft. This causes very erratic readings. Also, check for shorts at the plastic end of the electrode.

Meter Problems

Use care when changing batteries, especially in the older dial meter. Clean the terminals before inserting new batteries. It is also wise to apply some saliva on the terminals and then roll the batteries in the terminal sockets. This solves many problems when batteries must be changed.

Be alert for accidentally turned knobs, especially when moving through the forest or from one pole to another.

Double-Needle Electrodes

Older model double-needle electrodes may short. Shake wires to check for shorts in the handle and in the socket within the meter.

Needles suffer metal fatigue after heavy use. Move needles into bark and wood with a gentle up and down motion. Avoid abrupt changes in position when inserting or removing the needles.

Always carry extra needles. A plastic 35-mm film cartridge can be used as a container for the needles, and extra needles can be stuck into the ends of the container.

SOME SPECIFIC USES FOR THE SHIGOMETER

Permanent Inventory Plots

On a small sample of trees in permanent inventory plots, the internal condition of the trees and the relative vigor should be measured. Internal measurements show the width of sound wood in the sampled trees. The CER would show whether the trees are growing more or less vigorously than other groups of trees. The ratio method, with each reading divided by the mean reading for that species, should be used so the vigor of trees of different species can be compared in a mixed stand. This information could be put on a computer and the changes in internal defects and relative vigor could be followed over time.

Plantations

CER readings help identify at an early age the very vigorous trees. The CER method makes it possible to rank the relative vigor of particular trees. By entering such data into a computer, managers could compare, for example, the CER means for plantations. The CER method is also very rapid and can save valuable time.

CER of City Trees

The CER of city trees could also be put into a computer. Again, the ratio method (reading divided by mean) would be best so individual species could be observed over time.

The CER of recently planted trees can indicate early problems. One side of a tree may be very weak while the other side may be very strong. Knowledge of the weak and strong sides may help when pruning or fertilizing. A CER record of trees before and after fertilization or other treatments could also help field crews determine which trees should be treated.

The CER can be taken very quickly to determine the relative vigor of trees. This measurement can give valuable information, especially on trees that are extremely important, such as the cover photo of an American elm on the lawn of the U.S. Capitol.

Hazard Trees

When crews examine what looks like a high-hazard tree, they should check the base of the tree and exposed roots to determine their soundness. Areas that are suspect because of fungus fruiting bodies, cracks, dead bark, old wounds, insect holes, and other signs should be assessed with the meter.

When a large cavity is obvious, the operator should check the width of sound wood 1 ft (0.3m) above the top of the cavity and on the opposite side of the trunk. The measurement will reveal the amount of sound wood present behind and above the cavity. If the tree has a great amount of sound wood at this position, it usually will not be a hazard. Additional measurements should be made on suspect trees.

Cavity Work and Cabling and Bracing

Internal measurements indicate the width of sound wood in the trunk behind the cavity. If the cavity is a "stovepipe" or only a very short hole, then treatment will differ greatly.

Hardware should never be partially put into decayed wood. If wood is decayed, put hardware or rods and bolts entirely through the trunk. Check CER of the margins of the obvious cavity to determine whether bark is alive or dead.

Genetic Selections for "Tough" Trees

Some trees within a species can resist the spread of decay much better than others. In research studies, it is often necessary to bore many large holes into trees to determine the type of wound response for the individual tree. To determine length of defect associated with wounds, it is not necessary to cut the tree.

Drill a measurement hole 4 inches (10 cm) above the wound, and a second hole 2 inches (5 cm) to the right or left of the measurement hole. With the twisted-wire electrode, measure the ER above the original wound and the ER in the control wood to the side of the wound. If the wood above the original wound is discolored or decayed, the ER will be lower than the ER of the control wood. If both ER readings are the same, then the defect column is less than 4 inches (10 cm) above the original wound. In some trees, it may be necessary to bore the test holes higher than 4 inches (10 cm) above the original wound.

Dormancy

As trees go into dormancy, the cambial zone begins to decrease in thickness. As the zone decreases, CER increases. The patterns of CER may be helpful in determining the stage of dormancy. When trees start to grow in the spring, CER usually decreases.

ER Patterns

As the electrode tip moves into a sound tree, the ER readings increase (fig 1).

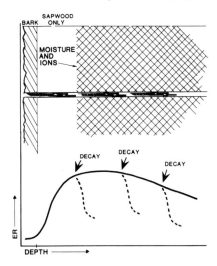

Figure 1—ER patterns in sound wood.

Figure 3 shows the typical pattern of ER in heartwood-forming trees. A 1-second abrupt increase in ER occurs as the tip moves from the sapwood into the heartwood.

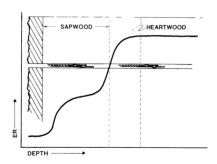

Figure 3—ER patterns in heartwood-forming trees.

Figure 2 illustrates the ER profile in altered wood. When the tips touch wood that has a higher concentration of moisture and ions, ER suddenly decreases. To determine the depth of the altered wood, as soon as ER decreases, hold the electrode by two fingers and pull it out of the pole. The length of the probe from your fingers to the bowed portion of the tips will be the depth of sound wood.

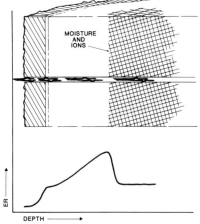

Figure 2—ER patterns in altered wood.

An abrupt decrease signals concentrations of moisture and ions, which may indicate discolored wood or decayed wood (fig. 4).

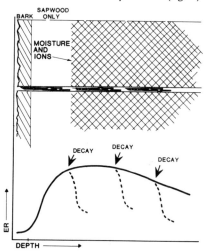

Figure 4—Patterns of ER in decayed wood.

374

The electrode tips may move from sound to decayed wood and back to sound wood. The ER will decrease in altered wood and increase in sound wood (fig. 5).

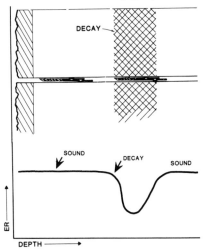

Figure 5—Multiple patterns.

When the electrode tip is pushed into resin-soaked wood, ER increases (fig. 7). Learn to recognize patterns indicating resin-soaked wood.

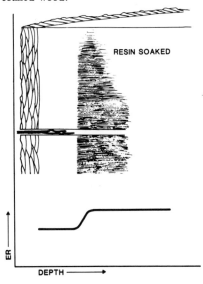

Figure 7—The ER pattern in resin-soaked wood.

When the electrode tip moves into dry, decayed wood (fig. 6), the ER increases. Dry, decayed wood is near old open wounds. When using the method in such areas, make the measurements at least 1 or 2 ft (0.3 or 0.6 m) above or below such wounds.

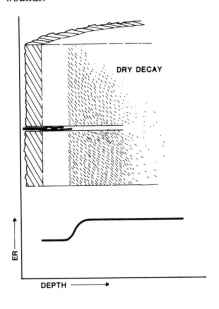

Figure 6—Dry, decayed wood.

In conifers, several types of root rots are characterized by bands of decayed wood and resin-soaked wood. When the electrode tip moves through the bands, ER increases and decreases. This pattern (fig. 8) of abrupt increases and decreases in ER is typical for root rots.

When wetwood is penetrated, the wetwood fluids flow out of the hole. The hole cannot be used for a measurement because the walls will be saturated with moisture. To determine the position of the wetwood, drill a hole two-fifths of an inch (1 cm) above the first hole and continue to drill in increments of two-fifths of an inch (1 cm) until the wetwood is reached (fig. 9).

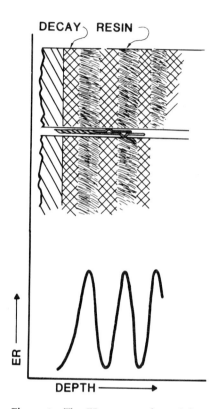

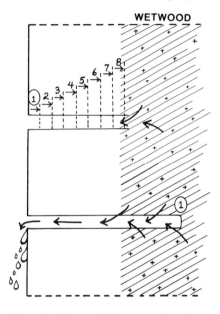

Figure 9—Proper drilling technique for a tree with wetwood requires several penetrations.

Figure 8—The ER pattern of wood from trees with root rot.

(Information given here on shigometry was taken from S189. For more details on the technique, see S189.)

ENERGY RESERVES AND STRESS, OR
THE STORY OF BILL AND JOE

Stress is a word used by many people, but rarely defined. We hear of water stress, wound stress, compaction stress, and many other types of stress. What do they mean? Are they *really* talking about stress? Let's give a closer look at stress.

I define stress as a reversible condition where a system begins to operate *near* the limits for which it was designed. Further, yes, too much or too little water, too high or too low temperature, many wounds, and other injurious agents are a part of the total picture. But are they really the stress factors? Do they really *start* stress? I believe that reduction in energy reserves is the major cause of stress.

Here is a story about Bill and Joe that might help to make my points.

Bill and Joe are the same age, they have worked in the same factory for the same time for the same salaries and they have the same size families. Bill has saved money over the years, and he has invested in sound health insurance. Joe and his family have spent their money as fast as it came in. Very little went for savings, and they have a very poor health insurance plan.

The factory was not doing well, and Bill and Joe lost their jobs at the same time. A week after they were out of work they both had a similar accident.

Bill had some health insurance, so he was able to pay the medical bills. Joe had to take a loan for his bills.

As weeks went by, Bill used his savings to maintain the SAME QUALITY of life that he always had. None of his neighbors or family recognized any difference in the way Bill and his family were living.

Joe had to take another and another loan to pay his bills. **His lifestyle changed drastically.** His friends and neighbors could see that he and his family were in trouble.

After a few months, Bill and Joe were able to find new jobs. They both earned the same salary again. Bill started putting money back into his savings. Joe had to pay back his many loans. Bill and Joe made the same amount of money but Bill's buying power was at least twice that of Joe's because Joe had to pay back the loans and Bill did not.

The story could go on, but I'm sure you are beginning to understand my point. If Bill and Joe were to have similar difficulties again, Bill would still be in the best position to survive. Because of his loan payments, Joe was under constant stress. Another accident or another lost job could cause Joe to go from stress to strain — serious trouble.

The question again: what starts stress? Both Bill and Joe lost their jobs and both had accidents. Can we say that job loss and accidents start stress? I don't think so. Remember, Bill had the same job loss and a similar accident, and he and his family *never changed their lifestyle*.

Why? Because Bill had savings; he had a sound defense plan ready to go.

So it is with trees. If a tree with high energy reserves is infested by gypsy moths, it will refoliate and survive. If a tree that has low energy reserves is infested by the same insects, the tree may die. Is the gypsy moth the stress agent?

Of course, repeated defoliation, very long periods of drought, excessive wounding, and other destructive agents that repeat their attacks with high severity will indeed kill even the healthiest individual with the highest amount of reserve energy. But even then the individuals with the highest amount of energy reserves will survive the longest.

A possible exception to this might be the rust fungi that often attack the most vital trees. (Do not confuse vital with vigorous, see B.) But, even then, I wonder if the most vital tree is one that has the highest energy reserves. Growing big, fast is no indication of energy reserves. Remember, Joe *looked* and *acted* more prosperous than Bill. Joe was "moving fast". So, I believe the concept still holds for energy reserves.

Another example is about water. Two trees look the same but one has high energy reserves and the other does not. Drought strikes and the tree that had low reserves dies. Did it die from water stress? Why did the other tree not die? Was it not faced with the same decrease in water? There are many accounts of trees that died from drought, insect defoliation, and other agents, But, again, the *real* stress starts when there is no energy to maintain the order of the tree system. If this is not so, then why did other trees that received the same "stress" continue to live? Bill did not change *his* lifestyle!

It is extremely important to know how problems START. As your savings decrease, secondary agents or events can threaten your survival. Other examples are frost cracks and sun cracks. So long as you believe they really are started by frost or the sun, there is nothing that can be done to stop the frost or sun. However, once you accept the fact that the cracks *start* from wounds, stubs, flush cuts, included bark, and branches and roots that wound themselves, then much can be done to prevent frost and sun injury. Do not lose sight of the primary cause.

Back to stress. *If we keep aiming at secondary agents we will never hit primary causes.* And, sad to say, that is where we are today with many problems.

Much can be done to prevent stress. Much can be done by starting with tough trees. Much can be done by treating them in ways that will help them store energy reserves. Much can be done by keeping them healthy by providing sound cultural practices.

Too often we force trees to be Joe types. All looks well until a problem strikes. And problems will always strike. Understanding these simple concepts will really make modern arboriculture work.

All will profit: the tree, the tree worker, and the tree owner.

CONCEPT OF SURVIVAL

Survival is to stay alive under conditions that have the potential to kill or to stop a system.

Natural systems are designed to survive. The system survives as a group; as a webwork. The system is ruthless. "Decisions" are made for the group and for the individuals that can best perpetuate the group. This is survival of the fittest, indeed, but more.

Survival of the fittest focuses more on the individual. And, of course, a group is made up of individuals. But, it's time to think beyond the individuals and to consider the survival of the system. Then it's also necessary to define the system.

The system is a collection of parts and processes—individuals—that have a predetermined design for survival, or to put it another way—to produce some product or service. Here I focus on survival because if the system does not survive there will be no product or service.

Now we look at the natural system as a collection; an orderly collection of individuals that are designed to perpetuate, or to maintain the webwork. Survival because of the product and the service.

Order is the key word. Order means designed in a way that all parts have little or no tolerance for failure, and thus the system can be easily repeated. It repeats or can be repeated. How easily the repeats come determines the degree of order.

To establish order requires energy. The laws of thermodynamics come to play. When order is not maintained by a sufficient amount of energy, the system will begin to go to increasing degrees of disorder. **When disorder increases, the energy still available in the system becomes available for others who can use it and pass it along.** The first law of thermodynamics is to conserve the order still remaining. In doing so the breakdown becomes an orderly process to dismantle the parts or processes while using all energy available.

When energy becomes limiting to the point where order cannot be maintained, some other system will take over.

Order and disorder are two faces on the card. Order is built into a system. Disorder cannot be defined as a system. It is an antisystem.

An antisystem is a collection of parts that act as a reservoir for future systems. **An antisystem is like a large bin or sack that collects everything.** But, in time when parts are needed for the orderly design of a system, the antisystem becomes the depository, or the place to look.

Breakdown. Build up. One requires energy. The other supplies energy. The concept of dualism comes to play. Both processes are required to maintain both of them—dynamic equilibrium.

The antisystem contains the parts. The developing system selectively chooses the parts to make a complete system.

When all the energy is "squeezed" out of a system, all that will be left is the antisystem.

A system has high energy demands. Limitations in energy require the system to discriminate ruthlessly. Only the parts that best fit the processes, that can assure survival, will be used. All others go back to the antisystem as soon as possible so that the developing system is not threatened. Systems develop as "big" as the energy will "allow".

The antisystem has no regard for order; it is disorder. It has no regard for energy. It takes what is left. It is a random collection, not an orderly collection.

The system and the antisystem "survive" because of each other.

Trying to treat a sick tree
that you do not understand
is the same as
trying to start a Rolls Royce
by hitting it
with a sledgehammer.

A. L. Shigo

This we know.
The earth does not belong to man;
man belongs to the earth.

This we know.
All things are connected like the blood
which unites one family.
All things are connected.
Whatever befalls the earth
befalls the sons of earth.

Man did not weave the web of life,
he is merely a strand in it.
Whatever he does to the web,
he does to himself.

Chief Seattle

ON THE INTELLIGENCE OF NATURAL SYSTEMS

Are trees and pathogens intelligent? Can they learn? Far fetched? I don't think so. Let's explore the subject. Not from a philosophical view, but, from a **common sense** view. Let's define our terms and see how the subject looks.

**Intelligence is the *capacity* to *acquire* information. *Knowledge* is the state of knowing. *Wisdom* is the understanding of what is true, right, or lasting; *common sense*. The above are from the dictionary. I believe these words need greater refinement in definitions if we are to pursue this subject. Here is how I understand, and define, the terms associated with intelligence.

Survival is the key word. If you, a tree, bug, or the natural systems do not survive then there is no discussion. So, we must focus on survival. Survival is the ability to stay alive, to keep going, to remain serviceable, under conditions that have the potential to kill, to stop, or to wear down the subject to the point of disruption or disorder.

A *system* is an orderly collection of parts and processes that have a predetermined design for survival. Survival depends on communications.

Communication is the *transmission* of a message. Transmission is the transfer of an idea, condition, or substance from one source to another. The receiver then has the same idea, condition, or substance that was sent by the sender. Information must be sent. *Information* is the orderly *collection* of facts or items that can be repeated in a message. A *message* is the orderly *connection* of information. A messenger sends the message.

Think about it. Information in our chromosomes or genes sends messages that result in a new being, a new life, a new survival force.

Feedback processes send out messages and receive them back again. If the message received was not the message sent,.then an adjustment is made in sending the message the second time. Then, it is checked or received back to assure accuracy. Natural systems depend on an active feedback process for survival. If what is being sent is not what is being received, the message could result in a different kind of product, being, or life form. But, is that all bad?

If the new product survives, then it is good. Survival is the key element.

Environmental conditions are chaotic. They do not fit a long or short design of high order. Yes, over a year you know that summer will be warmer than winter. But what about rain, storms, and sudden decreases or increases in temperature? Weather is not easy to predict. It doesn't follow a "nice" linear curve over short periods.

So, living things must be able to survive the great variations of the environment.

Think of a great table top. As a force comes from one direction, some pieces on the top fall off. When the force comes from the other direction, some others fall off. Soon, the "subjects" on the table "learn" that the "safest" position on the table is the center. Competition starts now for survival position. Those on the edges have little chance of surviving the slightest disruption.

So, the table bounces up and down, and the wind blows this direction and the other direction. The edge subjects are really in trouble. How do you get to the center where survival is assured? You begin to compete against your associates, and try to "move" to the safest position.

Then we have an earthquake or a volcano eruption. Or, an area that always had rain, has a drought.

Now the center subjects are in trouble. They have the same problem as the edge subjects. They die! So, now, everything rushes to the edges where it is safe! Dynamic equilibrium is against the disorder or nonliving forces. The messages change. Feedback processes speed up. What was survival yesterday spells death today! The center of the table is no longer the place to be. It has a hole in it! And, when you get to the center, you drop out!

So it is that the forces of living things depend on a chaotic nonliving environment.

So back to intelligence and what does all this table talk have to do with intelligence?

How do you "learn" that at one time an edge is the safe place. And, then later "learn" that the center is the safe place?

Intelligence. The systems learn to survive.

After millions or hundreds of millions of years of constant adjustments, the living systems have the intrinsic passive ability to adjust or adapt when survival is threatened. It is the ability to adjust or adapt that gives the system intelligence. (This does not mean that *a* tree can make *a* decision on *a* current problem. I do not believe plants have this type of ability.)

Life will persist against the forces of no life because life has the *capacity* to accumulate *information* that serves for survival. Messages are developed that are sent in the genes. Please note: Capacity is what you have; ability is what you do with what you have.

However, when any system no longer changes, or adjusts, or adapts, that system will be taken over by another system that can adjust, adapt, and change under the new conditions of the abiotic force. When you do not adjust, you will become extinct or die.

Trees and pathogens do have intelligence. They have the capacity to accumulate information that assures survival. They send the information in messages in their genes. They are constantly making adjustments and adapting to the changing abiotic forces. So, again, adjustments and adaptions are built into their programs. When survival is threatened the adjustment and adaption processes accelerate. The feedback process triggers the rate reaction. This may be why an injured tree produces more fruit.

Trees and pathogens exert constant pressures against each other. This exchange maintains the adjustment and adaption processes; it keeps the life forces at attention. Then, when abiotic forces affect either tree or pathogen, or both, the survival processes accelerate and increase the chances for survival.

In the end, why do you need to know this? You could say, so what!

We need to know that the survival processes are there for trees and pathogens. And, difficult to believe, or understand, they need each other. The constant vibration between the two maintains or keeps the survival processes in working order.

Let me give you an example with grass and some of our agriculture crops because they are very short-lived compared to trees.

Our cultural methods for food crops, and for grass as an ornamental plant are designed to get as much as possible from the plant in the shortest possible time. Reproduction, or growth to produce a crop, or growth in grass are the goals. Soil preparation, weed elimination, fertilization, irrigation, and constant spraying for pests make up the program.

The cultural methods to obtain a desired result is costly. Chemicals must be used because most of the plants have little or no energy reserves for a strong defense system. So, we "buy" a defense system for the plant. We spray. I'm sure you have seen beautiful, lush, green, weed-free lawns with sick trees. Why?

You can see the same sick trees along many golf courses, and near agriculture sites. The condition repeats too often to be coincidence.

The danger, as I see it, is that our insults and assaults are coming faster than the survival system can adjust or adapt. This is especially true where individual trees are concerned. And, in forests where the tree associates have been greatly weakened or destroyed by our "management" schemes—**roads, roads, roads! They are not forests. They are small parcels of tree crops laced with roads.** And we wonder why our trees have problems! Once the survival processes are stalled or destroyed, any pathogen, weak or strong, will attack. Why? **We are slowly but surely destroying defense processes of individual trees and groups of trees in forests.**

So, what can we do? First, let's use some of our "intelligence" to learn how "their" intelligence works. I believe the real issue here is whether *we* as humans really have the intelligence to survive in the environment we have created! **We have become the great environmental pathogen.**

Let's give natural systems a chance to change and adjust. Let's take some time to learn how they work and how we can work with them. Let's give them some respect. Let's drive out greed!

Not an easy task. No easy answers to put into practice.

But, if we do not start soon, we are going to find *ourselves*, not the trees, falling off the table!!

TREE DEFENSE: AN OVERVIEW

Tree defense is a nonspecific dynamic process in response to living and nonliving agents and events that threaten tree survival. Defense processes strengthen existing anatomical features, and alter development of normal features and processes to higher states of protection (A). How effectively defense processes function depends on the genetic programs of host and pathogens (196,300,302,303,323), energy reserves of the host (381,382,384,385), and environmental conditions (309).

Trees are highly compartmented, shedding, woody, perennial plants that have a central trunk (A,B,H). They grow normally as compartmented systems that regulate their mass to energy ratio by shedding parts and by altering aging wood to a state more protective than healthy sapwood (S:54). Trees are generating systems. New parts are formed in new spacial positions every growing period. Annual parts form in new spatial positions over an expanding woody framework or core (127). When trees are injured and infected, normal processes of compartmentalization and formation of protection wood are increased. This defense process that leads to higher states of protection is compartmentalization. (22,31,82,142,162,263,264, 265,300,302,310,323,325,327,328,330,338,351,A,H).

Compartmentalization is a tree defense process where protection features— boundaries, and protection wood—develop that resist, not stop, the spread of pathogens (319,320,321). The protection features defend the liquid transport, storage, and mechanical support systems by resisting the spread of the pathogens.

Defense is a dynamic process that leads to stronger protection features. Defense is the active state and protection is the static state. Protection means the chemical alteration of tissues already in place and the formation of new boundaries in new spatial positions.

Wood is altered to a higher state than healthy sapwood in several ways: 1, Genetically controlled aging process leading to impregnation of wood with extractives, gums, resins, and other similar substances—heartwood (8,9,108,131,146,166, 322,333). 2, The wood becomes dry, case hardened wood (142). 3, The wood becomes wetter with disruption of membranes that result in high concentrations of microelements, water, and high pH—wetwood (56,232,239,306,307,362,380, 397). 4, Exhaustion of all nutrient reserves—false heartwood (409). 5, Formation of anti-microbial substances—discolored wood in early stages (15,75,108,131,148, 189,195,196,327,328,330,332,375).

Heartwood is wood altered to a higher state of protection than the sapwood, as a result of normal, genetically controlled aging processes (S: 54,68,74,126). Heartwood is age-altered protection wood. Extractives, gums, and other protection substances impregnate cell walls, and in some cases, cell lumens. In a sense, the tree "embalms" the aging wood. Nitrogen-based substances move out to younger wood as heartwood forms (226).

Trees age in a radial direction as well as in a vertical direction (253,254). Transverse sections of the bole of a tree will reveal approximately the same number of sapwood growth increments before heartwood is reached. Radial views from the complete longitudinal dissection of a heartwood-forming tree will give a different view of sapwood as the base and top of the tree are reached. The core of heartwood attenuates at the tree base and there will be an increase in the number of sapwood growth rings. There will be great variations in these patterns with different species that form a "true" heartwood. (The reason I emphasize "true" heartwood is because researchers have often confused heartwood with other types of colored wood, especially discolored wood.)

When "true" heartwood is wounded, boundaries of discolored heartwood will form (S:126). This suggests that heartwood maintains some stored energy or that enzymes in heartwood can still react when oxygen becomes available. It is more correct to say that heartwood *reacts*, not responds. I reserve the word respond to describe actions of cells with living contents (320,321).

If false heartwood is wounded, or if discolored wood is wounded again, no new boundaries form (A). False heartwood and discolored wood have already changed to a state that has exhausted energy reserves or has "spent" the entire enzyme budget. They are the results of a defense process. They have reached the limits of further alteration.

You cannot break into a stone wall and have it rebuild itself. Remember, building a wall to keep out enemies is a defense process. It is dynamic. It is action. When the wall is built, it becomes a protection feature. So it is with tree defense processes and protection features.

I really do not understand how heartwood reacts to wounding, but it does. It may be also that chemicals produced by the pathogens play some role in the formation of the boundaries. Boundaries are just as important to the invading pathogens as they are to the invaded tree. The invading pathogens spread deeper and deeper into the tree against all types of obstacles. The pathogen must not only maintain its niche; but it must protect it from other organisms competing for the same wood (A:1,6,7,13,24,44,45). Maybe this is why approximately 80% of the ultimate column volume of discolored and decayed wood is invaded by microorganisms the first 8 years after injury and infection (111).

385

When wood is very dry or very wet (397), wood-rotting fungi seldom grow in it. When wood is dry, changes must occur to wet it before the fungi can attack. When wood is too wet, changes must occur to dry it slightly before the wood-rotting fungi can attack (330,332). Altering wood to a very dry or very wet state can increase its protection. Dry wood on wound surfaces is often called "case-hardened wood". White, "bone-faced" wounds seldom have large volumes of rot behind them (S:20). This is well known on old logging wounds. This is why I believe that prompt, proper scribing of wounds can decrease the threat of rot. I do not mean *digging* into the wound face! I mean cutting away the torn bark, and making very shallow cuts to make clean, rounded margins about the wound.

Wood that is very wet resists decay (397). Wetwood is a disease of wood. It is usually caused by bacteria (239) that live where there is little to no free oxygen. Wetwood is a type of biological protection wood. It is a disease, but wood-rotting fungi seldom grow in wetwood because of the high amount of water, low amounts of oxygen, high pH, and high amounts of microelements (397). It is better to have one fox in your chicken yard, and the fox eats one chicken a day, than having no fox in your chicken yard, and having the constant threat of hundreds of foxes attacking your yard and taking all the chickens (A). A little problem that is understood, or under control, is better than no problem at the present time, but the threat of complete disruption at any time. Trees in the genera *Ulmus* (350), and *Populus* seemed to have evolved with wetwood as a form of protection wood. When wetwood begins to decrease, rot begins to increase.

The old answer to wetwood was to drill a hole into the tree and insert a pipe to drain the fluids. Arborists have brought me sections of trees that had this treatment, and I always found decayed wood within the wood present when the pipe was inserted. Wetwood would often spread outward to the injured wood about the tube. Dieback about the drilled hole was common. The dieback was blamed on the wetwood pathogens killing the cambium. Further "proof" that wetwood fluids kill cambium was based on dead spots above and below branches that were pruned, especially dead branches that had a visible flow of wetwood liquids on the trunk below the cuts. When the pruning was done, it was considered correct to remove living collars at the bases of living and dead branches. It was the flush cut more than the wetwood fluids that killed the cambium, especially when we consider that the dieback areas developed *above* as well as below the cuts. Wetwood fluids may have some injurious effects on injured and defenseless bark and wood; but without the major injury of drilling big holes into the tree, and destroying defense boundaries within the collars, I doubt that the wetwood liquids would kill much cambium. If this were so, then why do we not find big dead spots *above* and *below* the many wetwood sites on elms and cottonwood?

False heartwood was studied intensively in European beech (409). It was often called red heart. Red heart in beech and in birch often has different chemical characteristics.

An understanding of branch anatomy and physiology (S: 186) is essential for understanding false heartwood. Branch collars form as branch tissues turn abruptly about the branch base and develop downward. Trunk collars form about the branch collars and secure the branch to the trunk. As branches die, a protection boundary forms within the collar tissues of the branch base. The boundaries could be very strong or very weak. Or, very aggressive microorganisms growing in a large dead branch may exert such a strong invasive force that the branch boundary may be breached.

When the branch dies, the trunk tissues connected to the branch deplete their energy reserves and die. The death of the trunk wood is determined by the death of branches. As branches die upward on the trunk, the columns of dying tissues develop downward.

In false heartwood wood cells die as energy reserves are depleted. The cells exhaust their reserves. The wood is usually lighter in color than the healthy sapwood. In time, the wood changes to pink or red in beeches and birches, and to tan in ashes. So long as the branch protection boundary resists the inward spread of microorganisms, the wood will be sound and free of wood-rotting fungi (374).

If the pathogens grow through the branch boundary, the false heartwood will begin to be altered. Because the false heartwood has so little nutrient value for pathogens, and because false heartwood is usually dry, the first pathogens must have the ability to alter the wood to a more moist state and to utilize some of the cell wall constituents as an energy source.

If bacteria are the pioneer invaders, the false heartwood takes on the characteristics of wetwood. If non decay-causing fungi are the pioneers, the wood discolors further, but does not become very moist. Wood-decay-causing fungi may follow.

The protection wood is the false heartwood. The false heartwood forms within the trunk tissues connected to the branches. The pathogens may invade the false heartwood. If they do, they follow the column of false heartwood as set by the death of branches. Such growth through false heartwood appears to defy the concept of compartmentalization. It does not. The compartments were first determined by the death of the branches.

The false heartwood, unlike "true" heartwood when wounded, does not form boundaries that resist spread of pathogens (A). The pathogens are resisted in their spread through false heartwood by the highly protective state of the false heartwood. Invasion of false heartwood is possible; but is usually very slow.

Trying to explain discolored wood in a few words is like trying to describe a rainbow with a few colors. The more the rainbow is expanded, the more the various colors and shades appear, and the more difficult it is to tell where one color ends and the next one starts. We then begin to understand gradations. This is the way we must approach the subject of discolored wood. The closer you get to it, and the more you want to know about it, the number of ingredients become greater, and the more difficult it gets to tell where one process ends and the other begins — gradations.

Let us start with a wound that injures the bark and wood. Immediately after wounding, the still living cells near the injured cells begin to respond to the injury. The response is a nonspecific one. This means that the cells will respond the same way regardless of the type of injury or the species of organisms that infect.

First there is an electrical change that can be measured as a change in voltage (64,237). Next, enzymes in the cells begin to act on energy reserves. Many chemical changes take place as anti-microbial substances are formed (327). In hardwoods these substances are usually phenol based and in conifers they are terpene based. The cells "discolor themselves" and then die. This is different from the "discolored wood" in false heartwood where the cells wane or decline as they exhaust food reserves and then they die. In "true" heartwood, the cells are colored as substances are impregnated into them as they age and eventually die. So, you see, discolored wood or wood colored from the sound sapwood can take place in several ways or through several pathways.

The first boundary of discolored wood defines the reaction zone (319,320,321,335). It surrounds the injured and non-infected wood. Wood, once injured, cannot prevent infection and that is why we must say injury *and* infection. As pioneer pathogens breach the first reaction zone, a new one forms deeper in the wood.

In the first stage of this defense process, the tree response is the major action. As pioneer pathogens invade, both tree and microorganisms make up the second stage of the process. And, after the first formed boundaries are breached, other microorganisms invade in an orderly sequence that is a succession (S: 24). And now we are into stage three. Again, Stage 1 is the tree alone, stage 2 is the tree and microorganism interacting, and stage 3 is microorganisms interacting with other microorganisms in a pattern of succession (S: 29).

Succession means an orderly sequence of microorganisms. It does not mean that organism A is always first, followed by organism B, and so on.

In some cases the decay-causing fungi may be the pioneers (332) but most of the time, not all the time, bacteria and non decay-causing fungi are usually the pioneers (A). This is so because some of the microorganisms have the ability to alter, or actually digest, the antimicrobial substances in the reaction zone.

Where decay-causing fungi may act as pioneers, their presence may stimulate the tree to produce even stronger boundaries. In this case, the pioneers may soon limit their own survival. But, remember, in nature, somebody is always waiting for your energy and space. So it is with successions in trees.

The discolored wood first formed is a protection wood. It sets the boundaries for the first compartments within the wood present at the time of injury and infection. As pioneers breach these boundaries, new boundaries are formed. The wood "left" between an old boundary and a new boundary is then left to easy invasion by the pioneers. The cells are trapped, and they die as they are starved and infected all at the same time.

It is important to understand the development of the column of discolored wood. The entire column is often called by one name, discolored wood. Yet, at the edge we have discolored wood as protection wood, behind that is trapped wood that is in a state of starvation and infection, and behind that is wood that has been invaded by the pioneers and may be invaded next by decay-causing fungi. So, the column of discolored wood is like a 3-dimensional rainbow that changes as it increases in size.

To help clarify these processes a model called CODIT (A) was developed. CODIT is an acronym for Compartmentalization Of Decay In Trees. CODIT is a model and should not be confused with the actual process by mixing model terms with biological terms. (The D could also mean defect. CODIT is a model.)

In the model, the reaction zone is represented by three walls that give dimension to the boundaries. Wall 1 resists vertical spread; wall 2 resists inward spread; and wall 3 resists lateral spread. After injury and infection the still living cambium begins to form a new boundary, the barrier zone. This boundary separates the wood present at the time of injury and infection from the new wood that will continue to form. The model representation of the barrier zone is wall 4 (191,193,263,264, 265,324,335,358).

The first part of CODIT; walls 1,2, and 3 are in wood present at the time of injury and infection. The second part of CODIT, wall 4, is a separating wall. The formation of boundaries in part 1, or the formation of the reaction zone, is under moderate to strong genetic control. Some individuals of a species compartmentalize more effectively than other individuals (196,300,302,303,323).

There are biochemical markers that indicate strong compartmentalization (323). Suberin is a part of some boundaries, especially the barrier zone (263,264,265). We do not understand how the tree "knows" how big to make the boundaries. It must be a difficult "trade off" for the tree. Because, when a tree walls off the pathogen, it also walls off spaces that would normally store energy reserves (S: 191). So, it is possible to compartmentalize yourself to death (S: 194). And that is the other side. As energy reserves are lowered, the building blocks for strong boundaries decrease, so weak boundaries form or at some point, no boundaries form. Then the tree or tree part is alive without a defense system.

When our treatments destroy boundaries — flush cuts — and reduce energy reserves, we begin to grow trees that have a weakened defense system.
Once we understand how tree defense works, then and only then will we begin to adjust our procedures to strengthen the tree's defense system.

This earth is precious to Him, and to harm the earth is to heap contempt on its Creator.

The Whites too shall pass; perhaps sooner than all other tribes.

Continue to contaminate your bed, and you will one night suffocate in your own waste.

Chief Seattle

REFERENCES

1 Adaskaveg, J.E. and J.M. Ogawa. 1990. Wood decay pathology of fruit and nut trees in California. Plant Disease 74: 341-352.

2 Altman, J. and C.L. Campbell. 1977. Effects of herbicides on plant diseases. Ann. Rev. Phytopathol. 15: 361-385.

3 Anderson, L.M. 1988. Legal liability for defective trees in the United States. Landscape and Urban Planning. 15: 173-184. Elsevier Science Publishers B.V., Amsterdam.

4 Ashton, F.M. and A.S. Crafts. 1981. Mode of Action of Herbicides. John Wiley & Sons, New York, 525 p.

5 Backhaus, R.A. 1985. Rubber formation in plants—A mini review. Israel J. Bot. 34: 283-293.

6 Backhaus, R.A. and S. Walsh. 1983. The ontogeny of rubber formation in Guayule, *Parthenium argentatum* Gray. Bot. Gaz. 144: 391-400.

7 Baker, W.L. 1972. Eastern forest insects. US Dept. Agric. Forest Service, Misc. Publ. No. 1175, 642 p.

8 Bamber, R.K. 1976. Heartwood, its function and formation. Wood Science and Technology 10: 1-8.

9 Bamber, R.K. and K. Fukazawa. 1985. Sapwood and heartwood: A review. Forestry Abstracts 46: 567-580.

10 Banfield, W.M. 1968. Dutch elm disease recurrence and recovery in American elm. Phytopathologische Zeitschrift 62: 21-60.

11 Barger, J.H. and W.N. Cannon, Jr. 1987. Response of smaller European elm bark beetles to primary wounds on American elm. J. Arboric. 13: 102-104.

12 Barnett, H.L. and B.B. Hunter. 1987. Illustrated genera of imperfect fungi. Macmillan Publ. Co., New York, and Collier Macmillan Publ., London, 218 p.

13 Barrett, D.K., D.A. Seaby, and I.D. Gourlay. 1987. Portable compression strength meter; a tool for the detection and quantification of decay in trees. Arboricultural Journal 11: 313-322.

14 Bassuk, N., B. Mayndard, and J. Creedon. 1986. Stockplant etiolation and banding for softwood cutting propagation: working towards commercial application. Proc. Inter. Plant Propagators Society. 599-601.

15 Bauch, J. and P. Baas (eds). 1984. Development and characteristics of discolored wood. IAWA Bull. n.s. 5: 91-154.

16 Bavendamm, W. 1974. Die Holzschäden und ihre Verhutung. Wissenschaftliche Verlagsgesellschaft MBH, Stuttgart. 136 p.

17 Beal, R.H., J.K. Mauldin, and S.C. Jones. 1983. Subterranean termites—Their prevention and control in buildings. US Dept. Agric. Forest Service, Home and Garden Bull. 64: 36 p.

18 Becker, G. and W. Liese (eds). 1965. Holz und Organismen, Heft 1, Duncker and Humblot, Berlin, 543 p.

19 Beckman, C.H. 1966. Cell irritability and localization of vascular infections in plants. Phytopathology 56: 821-824.

20 Beckman, C.H. 1987. The nature of wilt diseases of plants. Amer. Phytopath. Soc. Press. St. Paul, Minnesota. 175 p.

21 Bernatzky, A. 1982. The contribution of trees and green spaces to a town climate. Energy and Building 5: 1-10.

22 Bernatzky, A. 1983. Baumchirurgie und Baumpflege. Verlag Aloys Bernatzky, Frankfurt am Main. 178 p.

23 Bernatzky, A. 1988. Nachtrag zur 4. Auflange (1988), Baumchirurgie und Baumpflege. Verlag Aloys Bernatzky, Frankfurt am Main. 173-216.

24 Berry, F.H. 1982. Reducing decay losses in high-value hardwoods — A guide for woodland owners and managers. US Dept Agric. Forest Service, Agric. Handbook No. 595: 22 p.

25 Bier, J.E. 1964. The relation of some bark factors to canker susceptibility. Phytopathology 54: 250-278.

26 Bier, J.E. 1966. The possibility of microbiological types with different degrees of disease resistance within a tree species or clone. in, Breeding pest-resistant trees. Proc. of a NATO and NSF Advanced Study Institute. Gerhold, H.D., E.J. Schreiner, R.E. McDermott, and J.A. Winineski (eds). Pergamon Press, London. 257-270.

27 Biggs, A.R. 1984. Boundary-zone formation in peach bark in response to wounds and *Cytospora leucostoma* infection. Can. J. Bot. 62: 2814-2821.

28 Biggs, A.R. 1984. Intracellular suberin: occurrence and detection in tree bark. IAWA Bull. n.s. 5: 243-248.

29 Biggs, A.R. 1989. Effect of pruning technique on Leucostoma infection and callus formation over wounds on peach trees. Plant Disease 73: 771-773.

30 Biggs, A.R. 1989. Temporal changes in the infection court after wounding of peach bark and their association with cultivar variation in infection by *Leucostoma persoonii*. Phytopathology 79: 627-630.

31 Biggs, A.R., W. Merrill, and D.D. Davis. 1984. Discussion: Response of bark tissues to injury and infection. Can. J. For. Res. 14: 351-356.

32 Blanchard, R.O. and J.K. Carter. 1979. Electrical resistance measurements to detect Dutch elm disease prior to symptom expression. Can. J. For. Res. 10: 111-114.

33 Blanchette, R.A., J.R. Obst, J.I. Hedges, and K. Weliky. 1987. Resistance of hardwood vessels to degradation by white rot Basidiomycetes. Can. J. Bot. 66: 1841-1847.

34 Bondietti, E.A., N. Momoshima, W.C. Shortle, and K.T. Smith. 1990. An historical perspective on divalent cation trends in red spruce stemwood and the hypothetical relationship to acid deposition. Can. J. For. Res. 20: (in press).

35 Bonnemann, I. 1979. Untersuchungen über die Entstehung und Verhutung von "Wundfäulen" bei der Fichte. Dissertation zue Erlangung des Doctorgrades der Forstlichen Fakutät, der George-August-Universität zu Göttingen. 230 p.

36 Borgmann, G. 1987. Allgemeine Baumchirurgie Wenden, Richtiger Schnitt Aufzucht von Obstbäumen und Obststräuchern für den Praktiker. Verlag G. Borgmann, Georgemarienhitte, Germany. 42 p.

37 Bormann, F.H. 1966. The structure, function, and ecological significance of root grafts in *Pinus strobus* L. Ecological Monographs 36: 1-26.

38 Bosshard, W. 1986. Sanasilva. Kronenbilder. (Couronnes d'arbres, Le chiome delgi alberi). Eidgenössische Anstalt für das forstliche Versuchswesen Birmensdorf, Switzerland.

39 Bowden, R.D., G.T. Beballe, and W.B. Bowden. 1988. Foliar uptake of ^{15}N from simulated cloud water by red spruce (Picea rubens) seedlings. Can. J. For. Res. 19: 382-386.

40 Broschat, T.K. and H. Donselman. 1985. Causes of palm nutritional disorders. Proc. Fla. State Hort. Soc. 98: 101-102.

41 Broschat, T.K. and H.M. Donselman. 1984. Root regeneration in transplanted palms. Principles 28: 90-91, Florida Agric. Exp. Sta. J. Series No. 4694.

42 Butin, H. 1983. Krankheiten der Wald- und Parkbäume. Leitfaden zum Bestimmen von Baumkrankheiten. Georg Thieme Verlag Stuttgart, New York. 172 p.

43 Butin, H. and H. Zycha. 1973. Forstpathologie für Studium und Praxis. Georg Thieme Verlag Stuttgart. 177 p.

44 Campana, R.J. 1977. Limitations of chemical injection to control Dutch elm disease. J. Arboric. 3: 127-129.

45 Campana, R.J. and B.L. Schafer. 1977. Tolerance of the Dutch elm disease fungus *Ceratocystis ulmi* to solubilized benomyl. J. Arboric. 3: 108-113.

46 Campbell, J. 1982. Grammatical man, information, entropy, language, and life. Simon and Schuster, New York. 319 p.

47 Carey, A.B. and H. Reed. 1981. Routing to accelerate tree-cavity formation. The Wildlife Soc. Bull. 9: 14-21.

48 Cha, B. 1984. Vitality measurements in street trees by electrical resistance. Master's Thesis, The Graduate School, Seoul Nat. Univ. 38 p.

49 Chadwick, L.C., R.R. Miller, and D. Erskine. 1952. Prevention of undesirable fruit on flowering trees. Plants and Gardens, n.s. 8: 10-13.

50 Chalmers, D.J. and B. van den Ende. 1975. Productivity of peach trees: Factors affecting dry-weight distribution during tree growth. Annals of Botany 39: 423-432.

51 Childress, J.J., H. Felbeck, and G.N. Somero. 1987. Symbiosis in the deep sea. Scientific American 256: 114-120.

52 Chudnoff, M. 1971. Tissue regeneration of debarked eucalypts. Forest Sci. 17: 300-305.

53 Clark, F.B. 1966. Increment borers cause serious degrade in black walnut. J. For. 64; 1.

54 Clark, J.R., N. Matheny, and J. McNeil. 1990. Developing a species profile. J. Arboric. 16: 101-107.

55 Cole, D.M. and C.E. Jensen. 1980. Estimating phloem thickness in lodgepole pine stands using electrical resistance measurements. Can. J. For. Res. 10: 102-106.

56 Coleman, J.S., C.W. Murdock, R.J. Campana, and W.H. Smith. 1985. Decay resistance of elm wetwood. Can. J. Plant Pathol. 7: 151-154.

57 Courtois, H. and P. Risse. 1979. Kiefernstockfäule auf grundwasserbeeinflusstem, kiesigem Sand. I. Bodenkundlichabiotische Einflüsse auf die Erkrankung von kiefernwurzeln. Allgemeine Forst und Jagdzeitung 150: 185-190.

58 Craighead, F.C. 1950. Insect enemies of Eastern forests. 1950. US Dept. Agric. Misc. Publ. No. 657, 697 p.

59 d'Ambrosio, R.P. 1990. Crown density and its correlation to girdling root syndrome. J. Arboric. 16: 153-157.

60 Darnell, J., H. Lodish, and D. Baltimore. 1986. Molecular cell biology. Scientific American Books, Div. of Scientific American Inc. Distributed by W.H. Freeman and Co. New York, 1192 p.

61 Davey Tree Expert Co., The. 1909. Our wounded friends, the trees. The Davey Tree Expert Co. Kent, Ohio. 20 p.

62 Davey, J. 1909. The salvation of our trees. The Davey Tree Expert Co. Kent, Ohio. 8 p.

63 Davey, M. 1931. The unseen army of science. The Davey Tree Expert Co. Kent, Ohio. 30 p.

64 Davies, E. and A. Schuster. 1981. Intercellular communication in plants: Evidence for a rapidly generated, bidirectionally transmitted wound signal. Proc. Natl. Acad. Sci. USA 78: 2422-2426.

65 DeHaeck, A. and P. Geeroms. 1985. Nieuwe inzichten in verband met boomverzoring. RMLZ-Documentatie map landschapsonderzoek 13: 3-31.

66 Derr, J.F. and B.L. Appleton. 1988. Herbicide injury to trees and shrubs. A pictorial guide to symptom diagnosis. Blue Crab Press, Virginia Beach, Virginia. 72 p.

67 DesCars, A. 1983. Pruning. Translated from the 7th French edition by C.S. Sargent. William Rider and Sons, London. 67 p.

68 Dessureault, M. and A.E. Rich. 1976. Effects of dressings containing growth substances on healing of tree wounds. Ph.D. Thesis, New Hampshire Univ. Library, Durham, New Hampshire.

69 Dilley, M.A. and R.P. Covey, Jr. 1980. Survey of wood decay and associated Hymenomycetes in central Washington apple orchards. Plant Disease 64: 560-561.

70 Dilley, M.A. and R.P. Covey, Jr. 1981. Association of Coriolus versicolor with a dieback disease of apple trees in Washington state. Plant Disease 65: 77-78.

71 Doepel, R.F., G.D. McLean, and O.M. Goss. 1979. Canning peach decline in Western Australia. I. Association between trunk cankers, trunk pruning wounds, and crotch angles of scaffold limbs. Aust. J. Agric. Res. 30: 1089-1100.

72 Dowler, W.M. and F.D. King. 1967. Seasonal changes in starch and soluble contents of dormant peach tissues. Proc. Amer. Soc. Hort. Sci. 89: 80-84.

73 Duchesne, L.C. and D.W. Larson. 1989. Cellulose and the evolution of plant life. BioScience 39: 238-241.

74 Dujesiefken, D. 1989. Baumpflege: Untersuchung der Methoden. Erste Folgerungen fur die Praxis. Taspo Magazine, October 21-23.

75 Dujesiefken, D. and J. Bauch. 1987. Biolgishe Charakterisierung von Eichenholz mit Mondring. Holz als Roh-und-Werkstott 45: 365-370.

76 Dujesiefken, D. and W. Liese. 1988. Holzbiologisches Untersuchungsprogramm zu Methoden der Baumpflege. Das Gartenamt 37: 618-622.

77 Dujesiefken, D. and W. Liese. 1990. Einfluss der Verletzungszeit auf die Wundheilung bei Buch (Fagus sylvatica L.). Holz als Roh-und-Werkstoff 48: 95-99.

78 Dujesiefken, D., E. Ebenritter, und W. Liese. 1989. Wundreaktion im Holzgewebe bei Birke, Buche und Linde. Holz als Roh-und-Werkstoff 47: 495-500.

79 Dujesiefken, D., T. Kowol, and W. Liese. 1988. Verleich der Schnittführung bei der Astung von Linde und Rosskastanie. Allgemeine Forstzeitschrift 43: 331-332, 336.

80 Duval, M. 1982. The king's garden. Univ. Press of Virginia, Charlottesville, 214 p. (Originally published in 1977 as La Plante des fleurs, Editions Robert Laffont, S.A.)

81 East Bay Municipal Utility District. 1986. Water-conserving plants and landscapes for the bay area. East Bay Municipal Utility District. EBMUD. California. 107 p.

82 Eckstein, D., W. Liese, and A.L. Shigo. 1979. Relationship of wood structure to compartmentalization of discolored wood in hybrid poplar. Can J. For. Res. 9: 205-210.

83 Enebok, S.A. and R.A. Blanchette. 1988. Canker formation and decay in sugar maple and paper birch infected by *Cerrena unicolor*. Can J. For. Res. 19: 225-231.

84 Engelhard, W. (ed). 1989. Soilborne plant pathogens: Management of diseases with macro- and microelements. Amer. Phytopath. Soc. Press. St. Paul, Minnesota. 217 p.

85 Ericsson, A. and H. Persson. 1980. Seasonal changes in starch reserves and growth of fine roots of 20-year-old Scots pines. Ecol. Bull. (Stockholm), 32: 239-250, in T. Persson (ed) 1980. Structure and Function of Northern Coniferous Forests — An Ecosystem Study. Uppsala, Sweden.

86 Esau, K. 1965. Plant anatomy. 2nd ed. John Wiley & Sons, New York, London, and Sydney.

87 Fahn, A. and B. Leshem. 1962. Wood fibres with living protoplasts. New Phytol. 62: 91-98.

88 Fahn, A. and N. Arnon. 1962. The living wood fibres of *Tamarix aphylla* and the changes occurring in them in transition from sapwood to heartwood. New Phytol. 62: 99-104.

89 Fenn, M.E. and P.H. Dunn. 1990. Black stain root disease in ozone-stressed ponderosa pine. Plant Disease 74: 426-430.

90 Ferris, M.A., J.D. Castello, and W.A. Sinclair. 1989. Effects of virus and mycoplasmalike organisms infection on green and white ash. Phytopathology 79: 579-583.

91 Feucht, J.R. 1982. Urban plant management. Dept. of Hort. Colorado State Univ. 171 p.

92 Feucht, J.R. 1987. Urban stress in trees. The Green Thumb. 44: 38-43. Denver Botanic Gardens, Inc. Denver.

93 Feucht, J.R. and J.D. Butler. 1988. Landscape management. Planting and maintaining of trees, shrubs, and turfgrasses. Van Nostrand Reinhold Co. New York. 179 p.

94 Fink, S. and H.J. Braun. 1978. Zur epidemischen Erkrankung der Weisstanne Abies alba Mill. (,,Tannensterben"). II Vergleichende Literaturbetrachtungen hinsichtlich anderer,, Baumsterben." Allgemeine Forst und Jagdzeitung 149: 184-195.

95 Fisher, J.B. 1981. Wound healing by exposed secondary xylem in Adansonia (Bombacaceae). IAWA Bull. n.s. 2: 193-199.

96 Floris, P. 1987. Bomen laten sich lezen. Tuin and Landschap 10: 25-30.

97 Forest Service, US Dept. Agric. Forest Fertilization Symp. Proc. US Dept. Agric. Forest Service Gen. Tech. Report NE-3, 246 p.

98 Foster, A.A. 1968. Damage to forests by fungi and insects as affected by fertilizers. in, Forest Fertilization — Theory and practice: 42-46. TVA, Muscle Shoals, Alabama.

99 Foster, R.C. 1986. The ultrastructure of the rhizoplane and rhizosphere. Ann. Rev. Phytopath. 24: 211-234.

100 Foster, R.C., A.D. Rovira, and T.W. Cock. 1983. Ultrastructure of the root-soil interface. The Amer. Phytopath. Soc., St. Paul, Minnesota. 157 p.

101 Gagnon, R.R., E. Bauce and M. Pineau. 1986. Relation between the water potential and cambial electrical resistance of balsam fir and white spruce after budbreak. Can. J. For. Res. 17: 105-108.

102 Gendle, P., D.R. Clifford, P.C. Mercer, and S.A. Kirk. 1983. Movement, persistence and performance of fungitoxicants applied as pruning wound treatments on apple trees. Ann. Applied Biol. 102: 281-291.

103 George, M.F. and M.J. Burke. 1976. The occurrence of deep supercooling in cold hardy plants. Current Advances in Plant Science 22: 349-359.

104 George, M.F. and M.J. Burke. 1977. Cold hardiness and deep supercooling in xylem of shagbark hickory. Plant Physiol. 59: 319-325.

105 Gibbs, J.N. and D.W. French. 1980. The transmission of oak wilt. US Dept. Agric. Forest Service Res. Paper. NC-185. 17 p.

106 Gillespie, R.J., D.A. Humphreys, N.C. Baird, and E.A. Robinson. 1989. Chemistry. Allyn and Bacon, Inc., A Div. of Simon & Schuster, Needham Heights, Massachusetts, 1132 p.

107 Gleick, J. 1987. Chaos: making a new science. Penguin Books, New York, 354 p.

108 Good, H.M., Murray, P.M., and H.M. Dale. 1955. Studies on heartwood formation and staining in sugar maple. Can. J. Bot. 33: 31-41.

109 Götze, H., G. Schultze-Dewitz, and W. Liese. 1989. Zum 150. Geburtstag von Robert Hartig. Beiträge für die Forstwirtschaft 23: 92-97.

110 Gramss, G. 1985. Invasion of wood by basidiomycetous fungi. I. Pathosism and saprophytism as determined by certain experimentally accessible virulence properties. J. Basic Microbiol. 25: 305-324.

111 Gramss, G. 1985. Invasion of wood by basidiomycetous fungi. II. Obliterated differences between pathosism and saprophytism on pre-degraded wood substrates in monoxenic culture. J. Basic Microbiol. 25: 355-364.

112 Gramss, G. 1987. Invasion of wood by basidiomycetous fungi. IV. Microbiological approach to the role of kratovirulence in the expression of pathovirulence. J. Basic Microbiol. 27: 241-251.

113 Gramss, G. 1987. The influence of the concomitant microflora on establishment and dieback of decay fungi in standing timber. J. Phytopathology 120: 205-215.

114 Gramss, G. 1989. Bioassay for the mechanisms of decay resistance in stemwood of European beech (*Fagus sylvatica* L.). Eur. J. For. Path. 19: 263-273.

115 Gregory, R.A. 1978. Living elements of the conducting secondary xylem of sugar maple (Acer saccharum Marsh.). IAWA Bull. 4: 65-69.

116 Gregory, R.A. 1982. Release of sap sugar and control of sap pressure in Sugar Maple Research: Sap production, processing and marketing of maple syrup. US Dept. Agric. Forest Service, Gen. Tech. Report NE-72: 1-7.

117 Grosser, D., H. Schulz, und H. Utschig. 1985. Mögliche anatomische Veränderungen in erkrankten Nadelbäumen. Holz als Roh-und-Werkstoff 43: 315-323.

118 Grothaus, R., G. Hard, and H. Zumbansen. 1988. Baumchirugie als Baumzerstörung — auf den Spuren eines lukrativen, Unsinns. Der Gartenbau L'Horticulture suisse. 43: 1987-1991.

119 Grozdits, G.A., S.E. Godkin, and C.T. Keith. 1982. The periderms of three North American conifers. Part 1: Anatomy. Wood Sci. Technol. 16: 305-316.

120 Hacskaylo, E. (ed). 1971. Mycorrhizae. Proc. First N. Amer. Conf. on Mycorrhizae. US Dept. Agric. Forest Service Misc. Publ. 1189. 255.

121 Hailey, J.R. and P.I. Morris. 1987. Application of scanning and imaging techniques to assess decay and wood quality in logs and standing trees. Forestry Canada and Alberta Dept. For., Lands, and Wildlife. Project 1432-43: 48 p.

122 Haissig, B.E. and R.E. Dickson. 1979. Starch measurement in plant tissues using enzymatic hydrolysis. Physiol. Plant. 47: 151-157.

123 Halliday, D. and R. Resnick. 1988. Fundamentals of physics. John Wiley & Sons, New York. 975 p.

124 Hamakawa, Y. 1987. Photovoltaic power. Scientific American 256: 76-82.

125 Hanger, B.C. 1988. Mineral nutrition of woody plants: Nutrient uptake distribution, storage, function, and disorders. Aust. J. Arboric. 1: 12-18.

126 Hanover, J. 1966. Studies on the nature of resistance of *Pinus monticola* Dougl. to infection by *Cronartium ribicola* Fisher. in, Breeding pest-resistant trees. Proc. of a NATO and NSF Advanced Study Institute. Gerhold, H.D., E.J. Schreiner, R.E. McDermott, and J.A. Winineski (eds). Pergamon Press, London, 165-177.

127 Hardwick, R.C. 1987. The nitrogen content of plants and the self-thinning rule of plant ecology: A test of the core-skin hypothesis. Annals of Botany 60: 439-446.

128 Harlan, J.R. 1976. Diseases as a factor in plant evolution. Ann. Rev. Phytopath. 14: 31-57.

129 Harlow, W.M. 1941. Twig key to the deciduous woody plants of Eastern North America. Published by the author. Syracuse, New York. 56 p.

130 Harris, W.R. 1983. Arboriculture: Care of trees, shrubs, and vines in the landscape. Prentice-Hall, Inc. Englewood Cliffs, New Jersey, 688 p.

131 Hart, J.H. 1968. Morphological and chemical differences between sapwood, discolored sapwood, and heartwood in black locust and osage orange. For. Sci. 14: 334-338.

132 Hart, J.H., W.E. Wallner, M.R. Caris, and G.K. Dennis. 1967. Increase in Dutch elm disease associated with summer trimming. Plant Disease Reporter 51: 476-479.

133 Hartig, R. 1874. Important diseases of forest trees. Translation by W. Merrill, D.H. Lambert, and W. Liese, 1975. The Amer. Phytopath. Soc., St. Paul, Minnesota. 120 p.

134 Hartig, R. 1878. Die Zersetzungerscheinungen des Holzes der Nadelholzbbäume und der Eiche in forstlicher, botanische und chemischer Richtung. Springer, Berlin. VI v. 151 p.

135 Hawksworth, F.G., and D. Wiens. 1972. Biology and classification of dwarf mistletoes (*Arceuthobium*). US Dept Agric. Forest Service Agric. Handbook No. 401: 234 p.

136 Head, G.C. 1973. Shedding of roots. 237-293. in Shedding of Plant Parts. T. Kozlowski (ed), Academic Press. New York. 560 p.

137 Hearon, S.S., J.L. Sherald, and S.J. Kostka. 1980. Association of xylem-limited bacteria with elm, sycamore, and oak leaf scorch. Can. J. Bot. 58: 1986-1993.

138 Heikkenen, J.H. 1977. Southern pine beetle: A hypothesis regarding its primary attractant. J. For. 75: 412-413.

139 Hejnowicz, Z. and J.A. Romberger. 1979. The common basis of wood grain figures is the systematically changing orientation of cambial fusiform cells. Wood Sci. and Technol. 13: 89-96.

140 Hepting, G.H. 1935. Decay following fire in young Mississippi delta hardwoods. US Dept. Agric. Tech. Bull. 494, 32 pgs.

141 Hepting, G.H. 1971. Diseases of forest and shade trees of the United States. US Dept. Agric. Forest Service, Agric. Handbook No. 386: 658 p.

142 Hepting, G.H. and D.J. Blaisdell. 1936. A protective zone in red gum fire scars. Phytopathology 26: 62-67.

143 Hepting, G.H. and E.B. Cowling. 1977. Forest pathology: Unique features and prospects. Ann. Rev. Phytopathol. 15: 431-450.

144 Heuerding, E. 1982. Baumpflege bei Baumschäden. Publikation der Stadtgärtnerei, Bern, Nr. 3. 105 p.

145 Hickens, N.E. 1971. Termites: a world problem. Hutchinson and Co. LTD, London, 232 p.

146 Hillis, W.E. 1977. Secondary changes in wood. Recent Advances in Phytochemistry 11: 247-309. F.A. Loewus and V.C. Runeckles (eds), Plenum Publ. Corp. New York.

147 Hiratsuka, Y. 1987. Forest tree diseases of the prairie provinces. Can. J. For. Ser. Northern For. Cen. Inf. Report NOR-X-286. 142 p.

148 Houston, D.R. 1971. Discoloration and decay in red maple and yellow birch: reduction through wound treatment. For. Sci. 17: 402-406.

149 Houston, D.R. 1979. Understanding the game of the environment. US Dept. Agric. Info. Bull. 426, 174 p.

150 Hoyle, M.C. 1979. Response of yellow birch (*Betula alleghaniensis* Britton) in acid subsoil to micronutrient additions. Plant and Soil 51: 453-455.

151 Hubbes, M. 1962. Inhibition of *Hypoxylon pruinatum* by pyrocatechol isolated from bark of aspen. Science 136: 156.

152 Hubbes, M. 1987. Influence of biotechnology on forest disease research and disease control. Can. J. of Plant Pathology 9: 343-348.

153 Hubbes, M. 1988. Pathogen virulence and host reaction in Dutch elm disease. Naturaliste Can. (Rev. Ecol. Syst.) 115: 157-161.

154 Hubert, M. and Courraud, R. 1987. L'élagage et taille de formation des arbres forestiers. Inst. pour le Développement Forestier, Paris, 292 p.

155 Hutchison, R.A. 1988. A tree hugger stirs villagers in India to save their forests. Smithsonian, February. 184-193.

156 Hydro-Quebec. 1988. The right tree in the right place. Hydro-Quebec, National Library of Canada. 12 p.

157 Hyland, F. 1974. Fiber analysis and distribution in the leaves, juvenile stems and roots of the Maine trees and shrubs. Univ. Maine, Tech. Bull. 71. 68 p.

158 Intini, M. 1987. Phytopathological aspects of cashew (*Anocardium occidentale* L.) in Tanzania. Int. J. Tropical Plant Diseases 5: 115-130.

159 Jeffries, T.W. 1987. Physical, chemical and biochemical considerations in the biological degradation of wood. in: Kennedy, J.F., G.O. Phillips, P.A. Williams, (eds). Wood and cellulose: Industrial utilization, biotechnology, structure and properties. Chichester, West Sussex, England: Ellis Horwood Limited; 1987. Chapter 24: 213-230.

160 Johnson, D.W. 1981. Tree hazards: Recognition and reduction in recreation sites. 1981. US Dept. Agric. Forest Service, Tech. Report RS-1, 17 p.

161 Jones, A.L. and H.S. Aldwinckle (eds). 1990. Compendium of apple and pear diseases. Amer. Phytopath. Soc. Press. St. Paul, Minnesota. 100 p.

162 Jones, R.K., C.J. Krass, and R.J. Sava. 1978. Isolation of *Ceratocystis ulmi* from 14-year-old annual rings of English elm in California. Plant Disease Reporter 62: 994-995.

163 Joos, K.A. 1988. Investigation of a possible direct influence of highway traffic on nearby woods. Proc. IUFRO Congress, Interlaken, Switzerland, 3 p.

164 Joos, K.A. 1988. Investigation of any possible influence of high frequency electromagnetic fields on wood. Proc. IUFRO Congress, Interlaken, Switzerland, 3 p.

165 Joos, K.A., S.A. Masumy, F.H. Schweingruber, and C. Stäger. 1988. Untersuchung über mögliche Einflüsse hochfrequenter elektromagnetischer Wellen auf den Wald. Sonderdruck aus "Technische MitteilungenPTT" Nr. 1, 1988. Herausgegeben von den Schweizerischen PTT-Betrieben, Bern. 24 p.

166 Jorgensen, E. 1962. Observations on the formation of protection wood. Forestry Chronicle 38: 292-294.

167 Jost, L. 1901. Ueber einige Eigentümlichkeiten des Cambiums der Bäume. Botanische Zeitung, Berlin 59: 1-24.

168 Juzwik, J. and D.W. French. 1986. Relationship between nitidulids and *Ceratocystis fagacearum* during late summer and autumn in Minnesota. Plant Disease 70: 424-426.

169 Juzwik, J., D.W. French, and J. Jeresek. 1985. Overland spread of the oak-wilt fungus in Minnesota. J. Arboric. 11: 323-327.

170 Kandler, O. 1985. Immission-versus Epidemie-Hyposthesen. R. Oldenbourg Verlag Munchen, Wien. 59 p.

171 Kavaler, L. 1965. Mushrooms, molds, and miracles. The John Day Co. New York, 318 p.

172 Kienast, F., F.H. Schweingruber, O.U. Bräker, and E. Schär. 1987. Tree-ring studies on conifers along ecological gradients and the potential of single-year analyses. Can. J. For. Res. 17: 683-696.

173 Kile, G.A., J.D. Kellas, and R.G. Jarrett. 1982. Electrical resistance in relation to crown dieback symptoms, *Armillaria* infection and growth in *Eucalyptus obliqua* and *E. globulus* subsp. *bicostata*. Aust. For. Res. 12: 139-149.

174 Kile, G.A., J.D. Kellas, and R.G. Jarrett. 1982. Factors influencing resistance in stems of *Eucalyptus obliqua, E. globulus* subsp. *bicostata* and *E. viminalis*. Aust. For. Res. 12: 129-138.

175 Knowles, H. 1989. Woody ornamentals for the prairies. Univ. of Alberta, Edmonton, Canada. 279 p.

176 Kourik, R. 1986. Designing and maintaining your edible landscape naturally. Metamorphic Press, Santa Rosa, California, 370 p.

177 Kribs, D.A. 1968. Commercial foreign woods on the American market. Dover Publ., Inc., New York. 241 p.

178 Krommenhoek, W., J. Sebus, and G.J. va Esch. 1986. Atlas de Histologia Vegetal. Editorial Marban, Madrid. printed by L.C.G. Maimberg B.V., S-Hertogenbosch, the Netherlands, 1986.

179 Kucera, L.J., H.P. Buchner, and L.B. Strotz. 1988. Der Vitamat 4. Eidgenössishe Technische Hochschule, Zürich. 16 p.

180 Küster, E. 1925. Pathologische Pflanzenanatomie, 3. Aufl. Verlag G. Fisher, Jena. 558 p. (English translation in Library of Univ. Wisconsin, and Forest Insect and Disease lab. Hamden, Connecticut).

181 Kyle, N.E., J.L. Jakobek, R.A. Backhaus, J.C. Stutz, and T.L. Righetti. 1986. Micrografting between N-fixing and non-N-fixing genera of the Rosaceae. Bot. Gaz. 147: 243-246.

182 Lai, P.Y., M. Tamashiro, J.R. Yates, N.Y. Su, J.K. Fujii, and R.H. Ebesu. 1983. Living plants in Hawaii attacked by *Ceptotermes formosanus*. Hawaii Inst. Trop. Agric. and Human Resources, Journal Series, No. 2767, 24: 283-286, Univ. Hawaii, Hilo.

183 Laithwaite, E.R. 1960. A radiation theory of the assembling of moths. The Entomologist 93: 112-137.

184 Laithwaite, E.R. 1961. The assembling of moths: does radiation play a part? J. Inst. Elec. Eng. 7: 500-503.

185 Lambert, M.J. and J. Turner. 1977. Dieback in high site quality *Pinus radiata* stands—The role of sulphur and boron deficiencies. New Zealand J. For. Sci. 7: 333-348.

186 Lambert, M.J. and J. Turner. 1978. Interaction of nitrogen with phosphorus, sulphur and boron in N.S.W. *Pinus radiata* plantations. in Plant Nutrition 1978. Proc. of the 8th Inter. Colloquium on plant analysis and fertilizer problems, Auckland, New Zealand. Ferguson, A.R., R.L. Bieleski and I.B. Ferguson (eds). N.Z. DSIR Info Series 134, Wellington, New Zealand.

187 Landwehr, V.R., W.J. Phillipsen, M.E. Ascerno, and R. Hatch. 1981. Attraction of the native elm bark beetle to American elm after the pruning of branches. J. Econ. Entomol. 74: 577-580.

188 Langmuir, L. 1953. Pathological Science. General Electric Research and Development Center, Schenectady, N.Y., Report No. 68-C-035, Transcribed and edited by R.N. Hall, April 1968.

189 Leben, C. 1989. Effect of bark removal above and below wounds in red maple on bark dieback and discolored wood columns. Plant Disease 73: 565-566.

190 Ledig, F.T. and T.O. Perry. 1965. Physiological genetics of the shoot-root ratio. Proc., Soc. Amer. Foresters, Div. Silviculture, Detroit, Michigan.

191 Liese, W. and D. Dujesiefken. 1988. Reactionen von Bäumen auf Verletzungen. Das Gartenamt 37: 436-440.

192 Liese, W. and D. Dujesiefken. 1989. Aspekte und Befund zur Sanierungszeit in der Baumpflege. Das Gartenamt 38: 356-360.

193 Liese, W., D. Dujesiefken, and J. Bremer. 1988. Wundreaktionen bei linde nach astung in der baumpflege. Forstw. Cbl., 107: 184-196.

194 Lin, D., M.T. Dumas, and M. Hubbes. 1988. Isozyme and general protein patterns of *Armillaria* spp. collected from the boreal mixedwood forest of Ontario. Can. J. Bot. 67: 1143-1147.

195 Lorenz, R.C. 1944. Discoloration and decay resulting from increment borings in hardwoods. J. Forestry 42: 37-43.

196 Lowerts, G.A. and R.C. Kellison. 1981. Genetically controlled resistance to discoloration and decay in wounded trees of yellow-poplar. Silvae Genetica 30: 98-101.

197 Lundquist, K. 1983. Fromtidens Trädvärd. En dokumentation fron Trädvårdskonferensen i Alnap, Sweden. STAFs Förlag. Malmö. 43 p.

198 Lundquist, K. 1983. Radikal omvärdering av trädvård. Utemiljö 6: 4-5.

199 MacDougal, D.T. and G.M. Smith. 1927. Long-lived cells of the redwood. Science 66: 456-457.

200 Madar, Z., Z. Solel, and M. Kimchi. 1989. Effect of water stress in Cypress on the development of cankers caused by *Diplodia pinea* f. sp. *cupressi* and *Seiridium cardinale*. Plant Disease 73: 484-486.

201 Mahoney, R.J. 1990. Time to unshackle U.S. competitive strengths. Scientific American, May. 136.

202 Maramorosch, K. 1986. Lethal decline of coconut palms in Mauritius. Vistas in plant pathology. Varma A. and J.D. Verma (eds). Malhotra Publ. House, New Delhi. 185-190.

203 Marchand, P.J. 1983. Dendrochronology of a fir wave. Can. J. For. Res. 14: 51-56.

204 Margolis, H.A. and R.H. Waring. 1986. Carbon and nitrogen allocation patterns of Douglas-fir seedlings fertilized with nitrogen in autumn. I. Overwinter metabolism. Can. J. For. Res. 16: 897-902.

205 Margolis, H.A. and R.H. Waring. 1986. Carbon and nitrogen allocation patterns of Douglas-fir seedlings fertilized with nitrogen in autumn. II. Field performance. Can J. For. Res. 16: 903-909.

206 Marshall, K.C. 1975. Clay mineralogy in relation to survival of soil bacteria. Ann. Rev. Phytopath. 13: 357-373.

207 Marx, D.H. 1971. Ectomycorrhizae as biological deterrents to pathogenic root infections. in Mycorrhizae, E. Hacskaylo (ed). US Dept. Agric. Forest Service Misc. Publ. 1189: 81-96.

208 Mattheck, C. 1988. Warum sie wachsen, wie sie wachsen. Die Mechanik der Bäume. Kernforschungszentrum Karlsruhe GMBH, Karlsruhe. KFK 4486. 64 p.

209 Mattheck, C., F. Walther, and K. Keilen. 1989. Hirnrisse in Laubbäumen. Ihre Entstehung und Wege zu ihrer Vermeidung. Kernforschungszentrum Karlsruhe GMBH, Karlssruhe. KFK 4557. 40 p.

210 Mattheck, C., H. Huber-Betzer, and K. Keilen. 1989. Die Anpassung eines Baume san die Kontaktbelastung durch einen Stein. Kernforschungszentrum Karlsruhe GMBH, Karlsruhe. KFK 4526. 51 p.

211 Matthee, F.N. and A.C. Thomas. 1977. Wood-rotting fungi of fruit trees and vines. I. Diagnosing the main pathogens. The Deciduous Fruit Grower, Part 7, 27: 210-215.

212 Matthee, F.N. and A.C. Thomas. 1977. Wood-rotting fungi of fruit trees and vines. II. Importance of wound protectants. The Deciduous Fruit Grower, Part 7, 27: 216-223.

213 Maul, S.B. (no date) Production of ectomycorrhizal fungus inoculum by Sylvan spawn laboratory. Report by Sylvan Spawn laboratory, Butler Co. Mushroom Farm, Butler, Pennsylvania. 2 p.

214 Mayer-Wegelin, H. 1936. Ästung. Verlag M.V.H. Schaper, Hannover.

215 Mazzone, H.M. 1985. The fungus of Dutch elm disease and antibiotics. Develop. in Industrial Microbio. 26: 471-477.

216 McCartney, S.D. 1987. Timber decay meters: problems in practice. Scottish Forestry 41: 297-303.

217 McCoy, R.E. (ed). 1983. Lethal yellowing of palms. Univ. Florida Agric. Exp. Sta. Bull. 834. 100 p.

398

218 McCracken, F.I. 1988. Microorganisms associated with canker rots and heart rot of oaks. Eur. J. For. Path. 18: 391-396.

219 McCracken, F.I. and S.R. Vann. 1983. Sound can detect decay in standing hardwood trees. US Dept. Agric. Forest Service Res. Paper 50-195, 6p.

220 McCullen, J. and R. Webb. 1982. A manual on urban trees. St. Martin's House, Dublin. 139 p.

221 McCurrach, J.C. 1960. Palms of the world. 1980 reprint by Horticultural Books, Inc. Stuart, Florida.

222 McGinnes, E.A. Jr., P.J-Y. Lieu, and J.E. Phelps. 1976. Analyses of wood formation associated with tree injury — loose heart in a white oak, and radial seams and cracks in two black oaks. Appl. Polymer Symposium 28: 1261-1282. John Wiley & Sons, Inc.

223 McIntyre, G. 1987. The role of water in the regulation of plant development. Can. J. Bot. 65: 1287-1298.

224 McIntyre, G. and E. Damson. 1988. Apical dominance in *Phaseolus vulgaris*. The triggering effect of shoot decapitation and leaf excision on growth of the lateral buds. Physiologia Plantarum 74: 607-614.

225 Merrill, W. and E.B. Cowling. 1966. Role of nitrogen in wood deterioration: Amount and distribution of nitrogen in fungi. Phytopathology 56: 1083-1090.

226 Merrill, W. and E.B. Cowling. 1966. Role of nitrogen in wood deterioration: Amounts and distribution of nitrogen in tree stems. Can. J. Bot. 44: 1555-1580.

227 Meyer-Spasche, H. 1987. Entscheidungshilfen für die Baumsanierung (1). Das Gartenamt 36: 158-163.

228 Meyer-Spasche, H. 1987. Entscheidungshilfen für die Baumsanierung. 2. pH-Werte städtiische Böden und deren Beurteilung. Das Gartenamt 36: 378-384.

229 Michau, E. 1985. L'élagage la taille des arbres d'ornement. Inst. pour le Developpement Forestier, Paris, 302 p.

230 Millar, J.G. Zhao, C-H., G.N. Lanier, D.P. O'Callaghan, M. Griggs, J.R. West, and R.M. Silverstein. 1986. Components of moribund American elm trees as attractants to elm bark beetles, *Hylurgopinus rufipes* and *Scolytus multistriatus*. Journal of Chemical Ecology 12: 583-608.

231 Miller, R.W. 1988. Urban Forestry. Prentice Hall, Englewood Cliff, New Jersey, 404 p.

232 Miller-Jones, D.N., D.R. Houston, and T.F. Preece. 1977. The use of electrical resistance measurements to detect watermark disease of cricket bat willow. Plant Disease Reporter 61: 68-272.

233 Mill, L.J. and K. Russell. 1980. Detection and correction of hazard trees in Washington's recreation areas. A how-to guide for recreation site managers. State of Washington, DNR Report No. 42: 33 p.

234 Molina, R. and J.M. Trappe. 1984. Mycorrhiza management in bareroot nurseries. 211-223. in Duryea, M.L. and T.D. Landis (eds). Forest Nursery Manual: Production of Bareroot Seedlings. Martinus Nijhof/Dr. W. Junk Publishers. The Hague/Boston/Lancaster.

235 Moll, G. and S. Ebenreck (eds). 1989. Shading our cities. American Forestry Association. Island Press, Washington, D.C. 333 p.

236 Mooney, H.A. and C. Chu. 1974. Seasonal carbon allocation in *Heteromules arbutifolia*, a California evergreen shrub. Oecologia (Berl.) 14: 295-306.

237 Mulhern, J.E. Jr., B.M. Stavish, S.L. Witkowski, W.C. Shortle, and A.L. Shigo. 1981. Voltage changes along geranium petioles after leaf blade excision. J. Expt. Bot. 32: 573-579.

238 Mullick, D.B. 1977. The non-specific nature of defense in bark and wood during wounding, insect and pathogen attack. Recent Advances in Phytochemistry 11: 395-441. in F.A. Loewus and V.C. Runeckle (ed). Plenum Publishing Corp. New York.

239 Murdoch, C.W. and R.J. Campana. 1983. Bacterial species associated with wetwood in elm. Phytopathology 73: 1270-1273.

240 Necesany, V., M. Galádová, M. Tokosová, and A. Oberländerová. 1987. Makroskopické znaky dreva odumierajúcich dubov. Drevársky Vyskum 113: 19-37.

241 Neely, D. 1970. Healing of wounds on trees. J. Amer. Soc. Hort. Sci. 95: 536-540.

242 Neely, D. 1988. Closure of branch pruning wounds with conventional and "Shigo" cuts. J. Arboric. 14: 261-264.

243 Neumann, B. 1984. Das Verpflanzen grosser Bäume. Verlag Paul Parey, Berlin und Hamburg. 110 p.

244 Newbanks, D. and T.A. Tattar. 1982. Electrical resistance and stem water relations in Verticillium-infected red maple. European J. For. Path. 12: 113-123.

245 Newhouse, J.R. 1990. Chestnut blight. Scientific American 263: 106-111.

246 Ng, F.S.P. 1986. Tropical sapwood trees. Naturalia monspeliensia, Colloque international surl'Arbre. 61-67. For. Res. Inst. of Malaysia Kepong, Selangor.

247 Niemelä, T. and R. Erkkilä. 1988. Puita ja sieniä. Helsingin Kaupungin Rakennusuirasto Puisto-Osasto. T.A. Sahalan Kirjapaino Oy. 16 p.

248 O'Callaghan, D.P., E.M. Gallagher, and G.N. Lanier. 1980. Field evaluation of pheromon-baited trap trees to control elm bark beetles, vectors of Dutch elm disease. Environ. Entomol. 9: 181-185.

249 O'Callaghan, D.P., P.M. Atkins, and C.P. Fairhurst. 1984. Behavioral responses of elm bark beetles to baited and unbaited elms killed by cacodylic acid. Journal of Chemical Ecology. 10: 1623-1634.

250 Oberländerová, A. and V. Necesany. 1987. Sekundárne znaky smerekového dreva poskodeného priemyslovymi exhalátmi. Drevársky Vyskum 114: 3-15.

251 Old, K.M. and T. Kobayashi. 1988. Eucalypts are susceptible to the chestnut blight fungus, *Cryphonectria parasitica*. Aust. J. Bot. 36: 599-603.

252 Old, K.M., G.A. Kile, and C.P. Ohmart. (eds). 1980. Eucalypt dieback in forests and woodlands. Proc. Conf. CSIRO Div. of Forest Research, Canberra, 285 p.

253 Olesen, P.O. 1978. On cyclophysis and topophysis. Silvae Genetica 227: 173-178.

254 Olesen, P.O. 1982. Forest tree improvement 15. The effect of cyclophysis on tracheid width and basic density in Norway spruce. Arboretet Horscholm Akademisk Forlag, København, 80 p.

255 Onoe, M., J.W. Tsao, H. Yamada, H. Nakamura, J. Kogure, and H. Kawamura. 1984. Computed tomography for measuring the annual rings of a living tree. Nuclear Instruments and Methods in Physics Research 221: 213-220, North-Holland, Amsterdam.

256 Ossenbruggen, H.S. 1989. Tree energy systems. J. Arboric. 15: 53-58.

257 Paine, L.A. 1971. Accident hazard evaluation and control decisions on forested recreation sites. US Dept. Agric. Forest Service Res. Paper PSW-68, 10 p.

258 Parameswaran, N. and W. Liese. 1984. Über das Vorkommen von Rickettsien - ähnlichen Bacterien und Mycoplasma - ähnlichen Organismen in Buchen aus Waldschadensgebieten. Eur. J. For. Path. 14: 373-377.

259 Parker, C.A., A.D. Rovira, K.J. Moore, P.T.W. Wong, and J.F. Kollmorgen (eds). 1985. Ecology and management of soilborne plant pathogens. The Amer. Phytopath. Soc., St. Paul, Minnesota. 358 p.

260 Pawsey, R.G. 1983. Ash dieback survey. Commonwealth Forestry Institute, Univ. Oxford, Occasional paper No. 22. 22 p.

261 Pearce, R.B. 1988. Antimicrobial defences in secondary tissues of woody plants. In Fungal Infection of plants, G.F. Pegg and P.G. Ayres (eds). 219-238. Cambridge Univ. Press.

262 Pearce, R.B. 1986. Chlorantine fast green BLL as a stain for callose in oak phloem. Stain Technology 61: 41-50.

263 Pearce, R.B. and P.J. Holloway. 1984. Suberin in the sapwood of oak *(Quercus rubur L.)*: its composition from a compartmentalization barrier and its occurrence in tyloses in undecayed wood. Physiological Plant Pathology 24: 71-81.

264 Pearce, R.B. and J. Rutherford. 1981. A wound-associated suberized barrier to the spread of decay in the sapwood of oak *(Quercus rubur L.)* Physiological Plant Pathology 19: 359-369.

265 Pearce, R.B. and S. Woodward. 1986. Compartmentalization and reaction zone barriers at the margin of decayed sapwood in *Acer saccharum L.* Physiological and Molecular Plant Pathology 29: 197-216.

266 Penning de Vries, F.W.T. 1975. The cost of maintenance processes in plant cells. Annals of Botany 39: 77-92.

267 Perry, T.O. 1962. Racial variation in the day and night temperature requirements of red maple and loblolly pine. For. Sci. 8: 337-344.

268 Perry, T.O. 1971. Dormancy of trees in winter. Science 171: 29-36.

269 Perry, T.O. 1971. Seasonal and genetic differences in fats, phenols, isoenzymes, and pigments of red maple. Forest Sci. 17: 209-212.

270 Perry, T.O. 1971. Winter-season photosynthesis and respiration by twigs and seedlings of deciduous and evergreen trees. Forest Sci. 17: 41-43.

271 Perry, T.O. 1982. The ecology of tree roots and the practical significance thereof. J. Arboric. 8: 197-211.

272 Perry, T.O. 1989. Tree roots: Facts and fallacies. Arnoldia 49: 3-21.

273 Perry, T.O. and G.W. Baldwin. 1966. Winter breakdown of the photosynthetic apparatus of evergreen species. For. Sci. 12: 298-300.

274 Perry, T.O. and W.C. Wu. 1960. Genetic variation in the winter chilling requirement for date of dormancy break for *Acer rubrum*. Ecology 41: 785-790.

275 Persson, H. 1979. Fine-root production, mortality and decomposition in forest ecosystems. Vegetatio 41:L 101-109.

276 Persson, H. 1980. Death and replacement of fine roots in a mature Scots pine stand. Ecol. Bull. (Stockholm), 32: 251-260, in, T. Persson (ed). 1980. Structure and Function of Northern Coniferous Forests — An Ecosystem Study. Uppsala, Sweden.

277 Peterson, C.A. 1989. Significance of the exodermis in root function. in, B.C. Loughman et al. (eds). Structural and functional aspects of transport in roots, 35-40 (Kluwer Academic Publ.).

278 Pharis, R.P. and S.D. Ross. 1976. Gibberellins: their potential uses in forestry. Outlook on Agriculture 9: 82-87.

279 Phelps, J.E., E.A. McGinnes, Jr., and P.J-Y. Lieu. 1975. Anatomy of xylem tissue formation associated with radial seams and cracks in black oak. Wood Science 8: 397-405.

280 Piene, H., R.G. Thompson, J.E. McIsaac, and D.S. Fensom. 1983. Electrical resistance measurements on young balsam fir trees in relation to specific volume increment foliar biomass, and ion content of bark and wood. Can. J. For. Res. 14: 177-180.

281 Piirto, D.D. and W.W. Wilcox. 1978. Critical evaluation of the pulsed-current resistance meter for detection of decay in wood. For. Prod. Journal 28: 52-57.

282 Pirone, P.P. 1978. Tree maintenance. Oxford Univ. Press, New York, 587 p.

283 Poelker, R.H.J. and H.D. Hartwell. 1973. Black bear of Washington. Washington State Game Dept. Biol. Bull. No. 14: 180 p.

284 Polozhentsev, P.A. and L.A. Zolotov. 1970. Dynamics of electrical resistance of bast tissues in pine trees as an indicator of changes in their physiological condition. Sov. Plant Physiology 17: 694-698. (Translated from Fiziologiya Rastenii, 17: 830-835, Consultants Bureau, Div. of Plenum Pub. Corp. New York).

285 Pomerleau, R. 1980. Flore des champignons au Quebec et régions limitrophes. Les Éditions La Presse, Ltee. 653 p.

286 Powers, H.R., D. Lin, and M. Hubbes. 1989. Interspecific and intraspecific differentiation within the genus *Cronartium* by isozyme and protein pattern analysis. Plant Disease 73: 691-694.

287 Preston, J.F. and F.J. Phillips. 1911. Seasonal variation in the food reserves of trees. Forestry Quarterly 9: 232-245.

288 Priestly, C.A. 1970. Carbohydrate storage and utilization, in Physiology of Tree Crops, Proceeding of a symposium held at Long Ashton Research Station, Univ. Bristol, March 1969. Academic Press, London; New York. 113-127.

289 Puritch, G.S. 1973. Effect of water stress on photosynthesis, respiration, and transpiration of four *Abies* species. Can. J. For. Res. 3: 293-298.

290 Puritch, G.S. and D.B. Mullick. 1975. Effect of water stress on the rate of non-suberized impervious tissue formation following wounding in *Abies grandis*. J. Exp. Botany 26: 903-310.

291 Ramo, S. 1989. How we can regain our competitive edge. Scientific American, May, Essay, 148.

292 Raven, P.H., R.F. Evert, and S.E. Eichhorn. 1986. Biology of Plants. Worth Publ., Inc. New York. 775 p.

293 Rayner, A. 1988. Life in a collective: lessons from the fungi. New Scientist, 19 November: 49-53.

294 Reganold, J.P., R.I. Pependick, and J.F. Parr. 1990. Sustainable agriculture. Scientific American 262: 112-120.

295 Regner, K.M. and D.A. Johnson. 1990. Etiology of canker and dieback of sweet cherry trees in Washington state. Plant Disease 74: 430-433.

296 Rexrode, C.O. and J.E. Baumgras. 1980. Gum spots caused by cambium miner in black cherry in West Virginia. US Dept. Agric. Forest Service Res. Paper NE-463, 9 p.

297 Righetti, T.L., C.H. Chard, and R.A. Backhaus. 1986. Soil and environmental factors related to nodulation in Cowania and Purshia. Plant and Soil 91: 147-160.

298 Robbins, K. 1986. How to recognize and reduce tree hazards in recreation sites. US Dept Agric. Forest Service, NA-FR-31: 28 p.

299 Russell, B. 1989. Wisdom of the West. Cresent Books, New York, 320 p.

300 Santamour, F.S. Jr. 1979. Inheritance of wound compartmentalization in soft maples. J. Arboric. 5: 220-225.

301 Santamour, F.S. Jr. 1982. Seasonal variation in cambial electrical resistance in juvenile green ash from difference provenances. J. Arboric. 8: 100-103.

302 Santamour, F.S. Jr. 1984. Early selection for wound compartmentalization potential in woody plants. J. Environ. Hort. 2: 126-128.

303 Santamour, F.S. Jr. 1984. Wound compartmentalization in cultivars of Acer, Gleditsia, and other ᵃera. J. Environ. Hort. 2: 123-125.

304 Santamour, F.S. Jr., A.J. McArdle, and P.V. Strider. 1989. Susceptibility of flowering dogwood of various provenances to dogwood anthracnose. Plant Disease 73: 590-591.

305 Sarton, G. 1962. Sarton on the history of science. D. Stimson ed. Harvard Univ. Press. Cambridge, Massachusetts. 383 p.

306 Schink, B., J.C. Ward, and J.G. Zeikus. 1981. Microbiology of wetwood: Importance of pectin degradation in living trees. Apl. and Environmental Microbil. 42: 526-532.

307 Schink, B., J.C. Ward, and J.G. Zeikus. 1981. Microbiology of wetwood: Role of anaerobic bacterial populations in living trees. J. Gen. Microbiology 123: 313-322.

308 Schneider, R.W. (ed). 1989. Suppressive soils and plant disease. Amer. Phytopathological Soc. Press, St. Paul, Minnesota. 88 p.

309 Schoeneweiss, D.F. 1975. Predisposition, stress, and plant disease. Ann. Rev. Phytopath. 13: 193-211.

310 Schouten, H.J. 1989. A possible role in pathogenesis for the swelling of extracellular slime of Erwina amylovora at increasing water potential. Neth. J. Pl. Path. 95 Supplement 1: 169-174.

311 Schulz, H. 1984. Immissionen—Waldschäden und Holzqualität. Holz-Zentrolblatt 103, 6 p.

312 Schulz, H. 1985. Härtprofile als Hinweis auf verschiedene Festigkeitssysteme in Holz. Holz als Roh-und-Werkstoff 43: 215-222.

313 Schulz, H. 1985. Mögliche Einflüsse eines Waldsterbens auf Holzversorgung, Holzwirtschaft, in Holzqualität. Forstw. Cbl. 104: 243-255.

314 Schulze, E.D. 1989. Air pollution and forest decline in a spruce (Picea abies) forest. Science 244: 776-783.

315 Schweingruber, F.H. 1982. Microscopic wood anatomy. F. Flück-Wirth, Switzerland, 226 p.

316 Schwenke, W. 1966. Climatic and edophic dependence of insect nutrition and its importance for the problem of insect resistance in forest trees. in, Breeding pest-resistant trees. Proc. of a NATO and NSF Advanced Study Institute. Gerhold, H.D., E.J. Schreiner, R.E. McDermott, and J.A. Winineski (eds). Pergamon Press, London, 251-252.

317 Seattle City Light. 1988. The right tree book. Seattle City Light, Seattle, 17 p.

318 Seidler, R.J., P.E. Aho, P.N. Raju, and H.J. Evans. 1972. Nitrogen fixation by bacterial isolates from decay in living white fir trees [Abies concolor (Gord. and Glend.) Lindl.]. J. Gen. Microbiology 73: 413-416.

319 Shain, L. 1967. Resistance of sapwood in stems of loblolly pine to infection by Fomes annosus. Phytopathology 57: 1034-1045.

320 Shain, L. 1971. The response of sapwood of Norway spruce to infection by Fomes annosus. Phytopathology 61: 301-307.

321 Shain, L. 1979. Dynamic responses of differentiated sapwood in injury and infection. Phytopathology 69: 1143-1147.

322 Shain, L. and J.F. Graham Mackay. 1973. Seasonal fluctuation in respiration of aging xylem in relation to heartwood formation in Pinus radiata. 51: 737-741.

323 Shain, L. and J.B. Miller. 1988. Ethylene production by excised sapwood of clonal Eastern cottonwood and the compartmentalization and closure of seasonal wounds. Phytopathology 78: 1261-1265.

324 Sharon, E.M. 1973. Some histological features of Acer saccharum wood formed after wounding. Can. J. For. Res. 3: 83-89.

325 Sharon, E.M. 1974. An altered pattern of enzyme activity in tissues associated with wounds in Acer saccharum. Physiological Plant Pathology 4: 307-312.

326 Sharon, E.M. 1989. Tree failures, risk and reasonableness. A commonsense approach. Arboricultural Journal 13: 193-209.

327 Shortle, W. 1984. Biochemical mechanisms of discolouration, decay, and compartmentalization of decay in trees. IAWA Bulletin n.s. 5: 100-104.

328 Shortle, W.C. 1979. Compartmentalization of decay in red maple and hybrid poplar trees. Phytopathology 69: 410-413.

329 Shortle, W.C. 1979. Detection of decay in trees. J. Arboric. 5: 226-232.

330 Shortle, W.C. 1979. Mechanisms of compartmentalization of decay in living trees. Phytopathology 69: 1147-1151.

331 Shortle, W.C. 1982. Decaying Douglas-fir wood: Ionization associated with resistance to a pulsed electric current. Wood Science 15: 29-32.

332 Shortle, W.C. and E.B. Cowling. 1978. Interaction of live sapwood and fungi commonly found in discolored and decayed wood. Phytopathology 68: 617-623.

333 Shortle, W.C. and J.L. Hill. 1987. Ionized oak heartwood associated with checking during kiln drying. Holzforschung 41: 133-136.

334 Shortle, W.C. and K.T. Smith. 1988. Aluminum-induced calcium deficiency syndrome in declining red spruce. Science 240: 1017-1018.

335 Shortle, W.C. and K.T. Smith. 1990. Decay column boundary layer formation in maple. Biodeterioration 3: 377-389. Plenum Press, New York.

336 Siewniak, M. and D. Kusche. 1988. Baumpflege Heute. Patzer Verlag, Berlin, Hannover. 314 p.

337 Sinclair, W.A., H.H. Lyon, and W.T. Johnson. 1987. Diseases of trees and shrubs. Comstock Publ. Assoc., Div. of Cornell Univ. Press, Ithaca and London, 574 p.

338 Sinclair, W.A., J.P. Zahand, and J.B. Melching. 1974. Localization of infection in American elms resistant to *Ceratocystis ulmi*. Phytopathology 65: 129-133.

339 Sinclair, W.A., K.L. Smith, and A.O. Larsen. 1980. Verticillium wilt of maples: Symptoms related to movement of the pathogen in stems. Phytopathology 71; 340-345.

340 Sinn, G. and L. Wessolly. 1989. A contribution to the proper assessment of the strength and stability of trees. Arboricultural Journal 13: 45-65.

341 Sinnott, E.W. 1918. Factors determining character and distribution of food reserves in woody plants. Botanical Gazette 66: 161-175.

342 Siau, J.F. 1984. Transport processes in wood. Springer-Verlag, Berlin, Heidelberg, New York, Tokyo. 245 p.

343 Slankis, V. 1971. Formation of ectomycorrhizae of forest trees in relation to light carbohydrates, and auxins. in Mycorrhizae, E. Hacskaylo (ed). US Dept. Agric. Forest Service Misc. Publ. 1189: 151-167.

344 Smalley, E.B. 1963. Seasonal fluctuations in susceptibility of young elm seedlings to Dutch elm disease. Phytopathology 53: 846-853.

345 Smalley, E.B. and A.G. Kais. 1966. Seasonal variations in the resistance of various elm species to Dutch elm disease. in, Breeding pest-reisitant trees. Proc. of a NATO and NSF Advanced Study Institute. Gerhard, H.D., E.J. Schreiner, R.E. McDermott, and J.A. Winieski (eds). Pergamon Press, London, 279-287.

346 Smiely, E.T., G.W. Watson, B.R. Fraedrich, and D.C. Booth. 1990. Evaluation of soil aeration equipment. J. Arboric. 16: 118-123.

347 Smith, K.T. 1990. Sapstreak disease and biodeterioration of sugar maple. Biodeterioration 3: 303-310, Plenum Press, New York.

348 Smith, K.T., R.O. Blanchard, and W.C. Shortle. 1984. Cambial electrical resistance related to the number of vascular cambial cells in balsam fir. Can. J. For. Res. 14: 950-952.

349 Srivastava, L.M. 1964. Anatomy, chemistry, and physiology of bark. Inter. Rev. For. Res. 1: 203-277. Academic Press, New York.

350 Stipes, R.J. and R.J. Campana (eds). 1981. Elm diseases. Amer. Phytopathol. Soc. Press. St. Paul, Minnesota. 96 p.

351 Stolk, T. 1987. Afgrendelingslagen tomen aantastingen door schimmels in. Tuin and Landschap 10: 22-24.

352 Stone, E.L. 1974. The communal root system of red pine: growth of girdled trees. Forest Sci. 20: 294-305.

353 Stryer, L. 1988. Biochemistry. W.H. Freeman and Co. New York. 1089 p.

354 Stumpf, S.E. 1988. Socrates to Sartre: A history of philosophy. McGraw-Hill Book Co., New York. 558 p.

355 Sudds, R.H. and R.S. March. 1945. Pruning fruit trees. Ext. Circular 341, 38 p. West Virginia Univ., Morgantown, West Virginia.

356 Sutherland, J.R., T. Miller, and R.S. Quinard (eds). 1987. Cone and seed diseases of North American conifers. North American Forestry Commission Publ. No. 1. 77 p. Victoria, B.C. Canada.

357 Tattar, T.A. 1978. Diseases of Shade Trees. Academic Press, New York, 361 p.

358 Taylor, W.R. 1919. On the production of new cell formations in plants. Contribution Univ. Pennsylvania Bot. Lab. 4: 271-299.

359 Thimann, K.V. (ed). 1957. The Physiology of Forest Trees. The Ronald Press Co., New York, 678 p.

360 Thomas, A.C., F.N. Matthee, and J. Hadlow. 1978. Wood-rotting fungi in fruit trees and vines. III. Orchard evaluation of a number of chemical bases as wood protectants. The Deciduous Fruit Grower, Part 3, 28: 92-98.

361 Thomas, D.L., F.W. Howard, and H.M. Donselman (eds). 1979. Proc. Fourth meeting of the international council on lethal yellowing. Univ. Florida Agric. Res. Center, FL-80-1, 22 p.

362 Thompson, T. and R. Jagels. 1983. Intervascular pit plugs in the transition zone between sapwood and wetwood of Ulmus americana L. IAWA Bull. n.s. 4: 27-31.

403

363 Thornton, J.D. 1979. Detection of decay in wood using a pulsed-current resistance meter (Shigometer). 1. Laboratory tests of progression of decay of *Pinus radiata* D. Don sapwood by *Poria monticola* Murr. and *Fomes lividus* (Kolch.) Socc. Material and Organismen 14: 15-26.

364 Tippett, J.T. 1982. Shedding of ephemeral roots in gymnosperms. Can. J. Bot. 60: 2295-2302.

365 Tippett, J.T. 1986. Formation and fate of kino veins in Eucalyptus L'Hérit. IAWA Bull. n.s. 7: 137-143.

366 Tomlinson, P.B. 1984. Development of the stem conducting tissues in monocotyledons. in Contemporary problems in plant pathology. R.A. White and W.C. Dickinson, (eds). 1-51. Academic Press, Inc. New York, 598 p.

367 Trappe, J.M. 1977. Selection of fungi for ectomycorrhizal inoculation in nurseries. Ann. Rev. Phytopathol. 15: 203-222.

368 Trewavas, A. 1980. How do plant growth substances work? Plant, Cell and Environment 4: 203-228.

369 Turner, J., M.J. Lambert, and D.W. Edwards. 1979. A guide to identifying nutritional and pathological disorders of Pinus radiata. Forestry Comm. of N.S.W. Res. Note 36: 16 p.

370 Vagelos, P.R. 1989. The sorry state of science education. Scientific American, October, Essay, 148.

371 Van der Zwet, T. 1979. Fire blight. A bacterial disease of rosaceous plants. US Dept. Agric. Handbook No. 510. 200 p.

372 Van der Zwet, T., B.G. Zoller, S.V. Thomson. 1988. Controlling fire blight of pear and apple by accurate prediction of the blossom blight phase. Plant Disease 72: 464-472.

373 Vollbrecht, K.E.F. 1989. Träd, deras biologi och vård. Arbor Scandia, Åkarp, Sweden. 135 p.

374 von Aufsess, H. 1975. The formation of a protective zone at the base of branches of broadleafed and coniferous trees and its effectiveness in preventing fungi from penetrating into the heartwood of living trees. Forstwiss. Cbl. 94: 14-152.

375 von Aufsess, H. 1984. Some examples of wood discolourations related to mechanisms for potential protection of living trees against fungal attack. IAWA Bull. 5: 133-138.

376 Wagener, W.W. 1963. Judging hazard from native trees in California recreational areas: —a guide for professional foresters. US Dept. Agric. Forest Service Res. Paper PSW-P1, 21 p.

377 Wallis, G.W., D.J. Morrison, and D.W. Ross. 1980. Tree hazards in recreation sites in British Columbia. Can. For. Service, and British Columbia Ministry of Lands, Parks and Housing, Joint Report No. 13: 52 p.

378 Walters, R.S. 1982. Sugarbush management. in Sugar maple research: Sap production, processing, and marketing of maple syrup. US Dept. Agric. Forest Service, Gen. Tech. Report NE-72: 25-37.

379 Walters, R.S. and H.W. Yawney. 1982. Sugar maple tapholes. in Sugar maple research: Sap production, processing, and marketing of maple syrup. US Dept. Agric. Forest Service, Gen. Tech. Report NE-72: 8-15.

380 Ward, J.C. and D. Shedd. 1979. California black oak drying problems and the bacterial factor. US Dept. Agric. Forest Service Res. Paper FPL 344, 14 p.

381 Wargo, P.M. 1972. Defoliation-induced chemical changes in sugar maple roots stimulate growth of *Armillaria mellea*. Phytopathology 62: 1278-1283.

382 Wargo, P.M. 1975. Estimating starch content in roots of deciduous trees—a visual technique. US Dept. Agric. Forest Service Res. Paper NE-313, 9 p.

383 Wargo, P.M. 1976. Variation on starch content among and within roots of red and white oak trees. Forest Sci. 22: 468-471.

384 Wargo, P.M. 1977. Wound closure in sugar maple: adverse effects of defoliation. Can. J. For. Res. 7: 410-414.

385 Wargo, P.M. 1978. Judging vigor of deciduous hardwoods. Gypsy Moth Handbook. U.S. Dept. Agric. Info. Bull. 418, 15 p.

386 Wargo, P.M. 1978. Starch storage and radial growth in woody roots of sugar maple. Can. J. For. Res. 9: 49-56.

387 Wargo, P.W. 1971. Seasonal changes in carbohydrate levels in roots of sugar maple. US Dept. Agric. Forest Service Res. Paper NE-213, 8 p.

388 Wegelius, The. 1939. The presence and properties of knots in Finnish spruce. Acta Forestalia Fennica 48. Helsinki. 191 p.

389 Whitcomb, C.E. 1986. Landscape plant production, establishment, and maintenance. Lacebark Publ. Stillwater, Oklahoma, 680 p.

390 Wickson, E.J. 1919. The California fruits and how to grow them. Pacific Rural Press, San Francisco, California.

391 Wilson, C.L., S.S. Miller, B.E. Otto, and B.J. Eldridge. 1984. Pruning technique affects dieback and *Cytospora* infection in peach trees. Hort. Science, 19: 251-253.

392 Wisniewski, M. and C. Wilson. 1984. Host response to *Cytospora* canker and the possible role of carbohydrate reserves in the peach decline syndrome. in, 1984 Stone fruit tree decline workshop proceedings. US Dept. Agric. Agric. Res. Service, Kearneysville, West Virginia: 3-21.

393 Woodward, S. and R.B. Pearce. 1988. Responses of sitka spruce callus to challenge with wood decay fungi. Eur. J. For. Path. 18: 217-229.

394 Woodward, S. and R.B. Pearce. 1988. The role of stilbenes in resistance of Sitka spruce (*Picea sitchensis* (bong.) (arr.) to entry of fungal pathogens. Physiological and Molecular Plant Pathology 33: 127-149.

395 Woodward, S. and R.B. Pearce. 1988. Wound-associated responses in Sitka spruce root bark challenged with *Phaeolus schweinitzii*. Physiological and Molecular Plant Pathology 33: 151-162.

396 Woodwell, G.M. 1970. The energy cycle of the biosphere. Scientific American, September, 64-74. (Issue, The Biosphere).

397 Worral, J.J. and J.R. Parmeter. 1983. Inhibition of wood decay fungi by wetwood of white fir. Phytopathology 73: 1140-1145.

398 Wright, E. 1964. Mycorrhizae and survival of Douglas-fir seedlings. Oregon State Univ. Res. Note 50, 12 p.

399 Yang, D., R.S. Jenig, and M. Hubbes. 1989. Mansonone accumulation in elm callus induced by elicitors of *Ophiostoma ulmi*, and general properties of elicitors. Can. J. Bot. 67: 3490-3497.

400 Youngquist, W.G. and H.O. Fleischer. 1977. Wood in American Life. Forest Products Research Society, Madison, Wisconsin. 192 p.

401 Youvan, D.C. and B.L. Marrs. 1987. Molecular mechanisms of photosynthesis. Scientific American 256: 42-48.

402 Zanzi, D. 1987. L'albero: nuove acquisizioni pratiche. IL Giardino Fiorito 4: 50-56.

403 Zanzi, D. 1989. Potatura e chirurgia degli alberi in città. L'Italia Agricola 126: 231-248.

404 Ziller, W.G. 1974. The tree rusts of Western Canada. Can. For. Ser. Publ. No. 1329, 272 p.

405 Zimmerman, M.H. 1963. How sap moves in trees. Scientific American, March, 2-10.

406 Zimmerman, M.H. 1982. Piping water to the treetops. Natural History 91: 6-13.

407 Zimmerman, M.H. 1983. Xylem structure and the ascent of sap. Springer-Verlag, Berlin, Heidelberg, New York, and Tokyo.

408 Zimmerman, M.H. and C.L. Brown. 1980. Tree structure and function. Springer-Verlag, New York, Heidelberg, and Berlin.

409 Zycha, H. 1948. Uber die kernbildung und verwandte Vorgange im Holz der Rotbusche. fostwiss. Cbl. 67: 80-109.

405

PUBLICATIONS
by
ALEX L. SHIGO
and
COLLEAGUES

1. Shigo, A.L. 1959. Fungi isolated from oak wilt trees and their effects on Ceratocystis fagacearum. Mycologia 50: 757-769.
2. Shigo, A.L. 1960. Parasitism of Gonatobotryum fuscum on species of Ceratocystis. Mycologia 53: 584-598.
3. Shigo, A.L. 1960. Mycoparasitism of Gonatobotryum fuscum and Piptocephalis xenophila. Trans. New York Academy of Science. 22: 365-372.
4. Shigo, A.L. and G. Yelenosky. 1960. Nematodes inhabit soils of forest and clear cut areas. USDA For. Serv. Res. Note 101. NE For. Expt. Stn. 4 p.
5. Shigo, A.L., C.D. Anderson, and H.L. Barnett. 1961. Effects of concentration of host nutrients on parasitism of Piptocephalis xenophila and P. virginiana. Phytopathology 51: 616-620.
6. Shigo, A.L. 1962. Observations on the succession of fungi on hardwood pulpwood bolts. Plant Disease Reporter 46: 379-380.
7. Shigo, A.L. 1962. Another scale insect on beech. USDA For. Serv. Res. Pap. 168. NE For. Expt. Station. 13 p.
8. Shigo, A.L. 1963. Fungi associated with the discoloration around rot columns caused by Fomes igniarius. Plant Disease Reporter 47: 820-823.
9. Shigo, A.L. 1963. Ring shake associated with sapsucker injury. USDA For. Serv. Res. Pap. NE-8. NE For. Expt. Stn. 10 P.
10. Shigo, A.L. and G. Yelenosky. 1963. Fungus and insect injury to yellow birch seeds and seedlings. USDA For. Serv. Res. Pap. NE-11. NE For. Expt. Stn. 11 P.
11. Shigo, A.L. 1963. Beech bark disease. USDA For. Serv. Pest Leaflet 75. 8 p.
12. Shigo, A.L. 1964. The chainsaw: a valuable tool for research. Chain Saw Age 12: 8-9.
13. Shigo, A.L. 1964. Organism interactions in the beech bark disease. Phytopathology 54: 263-269.
14. Shigo, A.L. 1964. Collar crack of birch. USDA For. Serv. Res. Note. NE For. Expt. Stn. 4 p.
15. Shigo, A.L. 1964. A canker on red maple caused by fungi infecting wounds made by the red squirrel. Plant Disease Reporter 48: 794-796.
16. Shigo, A.L. 1965. The pattern of decay and discoloration in northern hardwoods. Phytopathology 55: 648-652.
17. Shigo, A.L. 1965. Decay and discoloration in sprout red maple. Phytopathology 55: 957-962.
18. Shigo, A.L. 1965. Patterns of defects associated with stem stubs of northern hardwoods. USDA For. Serv. Res. Pap. NE-34. NE For. Expt. Stn. 4 p.
19. Shigo, A.L. 1966. Organism interactions in decay and discoloration in beech, birch, and maple. USDA For. Serv. Res. Pap. NE-43. NE For. Expt. Stn. 43 p.

20. Shigo, A.L. 1966. Decay and discoloration following logging wounds on northern hardwoods. USDA For. Serv. Res. Pap. NE-47. NE For. Expt. Stn. 43 p.

21. Shigo, A.L. 1966. Decay and discoloration in northern hardwoods. A consideration of microorganisms and external signs. Proc. IUFRO Congress, Melbourne, Australia. 15 p.

22. Shigo, A.L. 1966. Organism interaction to decay and discoloration in beech, birch, and maple. Mat. und Org., Duncker and Humbolt, Berlin. 309-324.

23. Shigo, A.L. 1966. Defects in birch associated with injuries made by Xyloterinus politus Say. USDA For. Serv. Res. Note NE-49. NE For. Expt. Stn. 7 p.

24. Shigo, A.L. 1967. Successions of organisms in discoloration and decay of wood. Inter. Rev. For. Res. 2. Academic Press. 65 p.

25. Shigo, A.L. 1976. The early stages of discoloration and decay in living hardwoods in northeastern United States. A consideration of wound-initiated discoloration and heartwood. Proc. IUFRO Congress, Munich, West Germany. 17 p.

26. Shigo, A. L. and L. Kilham. 1968. Sapsuckers and Fomes ingiarius var. populinus. USDA For. Serv. Res. Note NE-84. NE For. Expt. Stn. 2 p.

27. Shigo, A. L. and E. M. Sharon. 1968. Discoloration and decay in hardwoods following inoculations with Hymenomycetes. Phytopathology 58: 1493-1498.

28. Shigo, A. L. 1969. The death and decay of trees. Natural History 78: 42-47.

29. Shigo, A. L. and E. vH. Larson. 1969. A photo guide to the patterns of discoloration and decay in northern hardwood trees. USDA For. Serv. Res. Pap. NE 127. NE For. Expt. Stn. 100 p.

30. Shigo, A. L. 1969. Diseases of birch. Birch Symposium Proc. 147-150. USDA For. Serv., NE For. Expt. Stn. 185 p.

31. Shigo, A. L. 1969. How the canker rot fungi, Poria obliqua and Polyporus glomeratus incite cankers. Phytopathology 59: 1164-1165.

32. Shigo, A. L. and E. M. Sharon. 1970. Mapping columns of discolored and decayed tissues in sugar maple, Acer saccharum Marsh. Phytopathology 60: 232-237.

33. Shigo, A. L. 1970. Growth of Polyporus glomeratus, Poria obliqua. Fomes igniarius, and Pholiota squarrose-adiposa in media amended with manganese, calcium, zinc, and iron. Mycologia 62: 604-607.

34. Shigo, A. L. 1970. An expanded concept of decay in living trees. In: Interaction of organisms in the process of decay of forest trees. Symp. under the chairmanship of Dr. A. L. Shigo, University of Laval, Quebec, Canada. Bull 13: 43 p.

35. Shigo, A. L. and F. M. Laing. 1970. Some effects of paraformaldehyde on wood surrounding tapholes in sugar maple trees. USDA For. Serv. Res. Pap. NE-161. NE For. Expt. Stn. 11 p.

36. Cosenza, B. J., M. McCreary, J. D. Buck, and A. L. Shigo. 1970. Bacteria associated with discolored and decayed tissues in beech, birch, and maple. Phytopathology 60: 1547-1551.

37. Shigo, A. L., J. Stankewich, and B. J. Cosenza. 1971. Clostridium sp. associated with discolored tissues in living oaks. Phytopathology 61: 122-123.

38. Friedrich, J. H., A. E. Rich, and A. L. Shigo. 1971. Diseases of fruits and seeds of northern hardwoods. Rhodora 73: 306-308.

39. Stankewich, J. P., B. J. Cosenza, and A. L. Shigo. 1971. Clostridium quercicolum sp. n., isolated from discolored tissues in living oak trees. Antonie van Leeuwenhoek 37: 299-302.

40. Shigo, A. L. 1971. The beech bark disease in northeastern United States. Proc. IUFRO Congress, Gainesville, Fl. 8 p.

41. Shigo, A. L. 1971. Shakes associated with wounds in trees. Proc. IUFRO Congress, Gainesvills, Fl. 5 p.

42. Shigo, A. L. 1971. Discoloration and decay in oaks. Oak Symp. Proc. USDA For. Serv., NE Forest Expt. Stn. 135-141.

43. Shigo, A. L. and C. L. Wilson. 1971. Are tree wound dressings beneficial? Arborist's News 36: 85-88.

44. Shigo, A. L. 1971. Successions of microorganisms and patterns of discoloration and decay following wounding in deciduous hardwoods. Second International Symposium on Plant Pathology Proceedings. Indian Agricultural Research Institute, New Delhi. 12 p. 175.

45. Shigo, A. L. 1972. Successions of microorganisms and patterns of discoloration and decay after wounding in red oak and white oak. Phytopathology 62: 256-259.

46. Shigo, A. L. 1972. Ring and ray shakes associated with wounds in trees. Holzforschung 26: 60-62.

407

47. Shigo, A. L. 1972. The beech bark disease today in Northeastern United States. J. Forestry 70: 286-289.
48. Skutt, H. R., A. L. Shigo, and R. A. Lessard. 1972. Detection of discolored and decayed wood in living trees using a pulsed electric current. Can. J. For. Res. 2: 54-56.
49. Hepting, G. H. and A. L. Shigo. 1972. Difference in decay rate following fire between oaks in North Carolina and Maine. Plant Disease Reporter. 56: 406-407.
50. Shigo, A. L. and C. L. Wilson. 1972. Discoloration associated with wounds one year after application of wound dressings. Arborist's News 37: 121-124.
51. Tatter, T. A., A. L. Shigo, and T. Chase. 1972. Relationship between degree of resistance to pulsed electric current and wood in progressive stages of discoloration and decay in living trees. Can. J. For. Res. 2: 236-243.
52. Rier, J. P. and A. L. Shigo. 1972. Some changes in red maple, Acer rubrum, tissues within 34 days after wounding in July. Can. J. Bot. 50: 1783-1784.
53. Shigo, A. L. 1973. Insect and disease control; forest fertilization relations. Proc. For. Symposium. USDA Tech. Rept. NE-3. 117-121.
54. Shigo, A. L. and W. E. Hillis. 1973. Heartwood, discolored wood, and microorganisms in living trees. Ann. Rev. Phytopathology 11: 197-222.
55. Shortle, W. C. and A. L. Shigo. 1973. Concentrations of manganese and microorganisms in discolored and decayed wood in sugar maple. Can. J. For. Res. 3: 354-358.
56. Filip, G. M., A. L. Shigo, M. C. Hoyle, and A. E. Rich. 1973. Effect of fertilizer salt accumulation and low relative humidity on development of stem lesions on yellow birch seedlings. Plant Disease Reporter. 57: 499.
57. Wilson, C. L. and A. L. Shigo. 1973. Dispelling myths in arboriculture today. Amer. Nurseryman 127: 24-28.
58. Shigo, A. L., W. B. Leak, and S. Filip. 1973. Sugar maple borer injury in four hardwood stands in New Hampshire. Can. J. For. Res. 3: 512-515.
59. Shigo, A. L. 1973. A tree hurts too. USDA For. Serv. NE-Inf. 16. 28 p.
60. Shigo, A. L. 1974. Effects of manganese, calcium, zinc, and iron on growth and pigmentation of Trichocladium canadense, Phialophora melinii, Hypoxylon rubiginosum, Daldinia concentrica, and Cystopora decipiens. Mycologia 66: 339-341.
61. Shigo, A. L. 1974. Relative abilities of Phialophora melinii, Fomes connatus, and F. igniarius to invade freshly wounded tissues of Acer rubrum. Phytopathology 64: 708-710.
62. Safford, L. O., A. L. Shigo, and M. Ashley. 1974. Concentrations of cations in discolored and decayed wood in red maple. Can. J. For. Res. 4: 435-440.
63. Sharon, E. M. and A. L. Shigo. 1974. A method for studying the relationship of wounding and microorganisms to the discoloration process in sugar maple. Can. J. For. Res. 4: 146-148.
64. Shigo, A. L. and A. Shigo. 1974. Detection of discoloration and decay in living trees and utility poles. USDA Res. Paper NE-294. 11 p.
65. Shigo, A. L. 1974. A new look at decay. Northern Logger 23: 10-11.
66. Shigo, A. L. 1974. Biology of decay and wood quality. In Biological Transformation of Wood by Microorganisms. Walter Liese, Ed., Proc. Symposium. Wood Products Pathology. Springer-Verlag Co., Berlin, Heidelberg, New York 1975. 1-15.
67. McGinnes, E. A. and A. L. Shigo. 1975. Use of an electronic technique for detection of discoloration and decay and injury associated with ring shake in black walnut. For. Prod. Journal 25: 30-32.
68. McGinnes, E. A. and A. L. Shigo. 1975. Effects of wounds on heartwood formation in white oak. Wood and Fiber 5: 327-331.
69. Pottle, H. W. and A. L. Shigo. 1975. Treatment of wounds on Acer rubrum with Trichoderma viride. Eur. J. For. Pathol. 5: 274-279.
70. Shigo, A. L. 1975. Wounds: Number one problem of city trees. J. For. Proc. 1974 SAF Meeting in New York. 4 p.
71. Shigo, A. L. and P. Berry. 1975. A new tool for detection of decay associated with Fomes annosus in Pinus resinosa. Plant Disease Reporter. 59: 739-742.
72. Shigo, A. L. 1975. Compartmentalization of decay associated with Fomes annosus in trunks of Pinus resinosa. Phytopathology 65: 1038-1039.

73. Shigo, A. L. 1975. Microorganisms associated with wounds inflicted during winter, summer, and fall in Acer rubrum, Betula papyrifera, Fagus grandifolia, and Quercus rubra. Phytopathology 66: 559-563.

74. Shigo, A. L. 1975. Heartwood and discolored wood. Northern Logger 24: 28-29.

75. Shigo, A. L. 1975. Wood decay. McGraw-Hill Book Co. Yearbook of Science and Technology. 417-419.

76. Shigo, A. L. and D. M. Carroll. 1975. Common tree families. Reader's Digest September issue. 8 p.

77. Shigo, A. L. 1975. A new look at decay in trees. New Horizons Hortic. Res. Instit. 10-12.

78. Shigo. A. L. and E. vH. Larson. 1975. Anatomy of a wound: How city trees react — how they can be helped. Weeds, Trees, and Turf 14: 20-22.

79. Shigo, A. L. 1975. New ideas in tree care. J. Arboric. 1: 234-237.

80. Shigo, A. L. 1975. Compartmentalization of discolored and decayed wood in trees. Mat. und Org. Berlin, Belheft 3: 221-226.

81. Shigo, A. L., E. Kerr, G. Lloyd, J. Riddle, and H. Marx. 1975. A guide to help package research for application. USDA For. Serv. 12 p.

82. Shigo, A. L. and R. J. Campana. 1976. Forest disease priorities in the Northeast. NE For. Comm. NE For. Expt. Stn. Upper Darby, PA 37 p.

83. Shigo, A. L. 1976. Decay: A problem in young and old trees. Amer. Nurseryman 144: 24-25.

84. Shigo, A. L. 1976. Rx for wounded trees. USDA For. Serv. Agric. Inf. Bull. 387. 37 p.

85. Shigo, A. L. 1976. Mineral stain. Northern Logger 24: 18-19.

86. Garrett, P. W., A. L. Shigo, and J. Carter. 1976. Variation in diameter of central columns of discoloration in six hybrid poplar clones. Can. J. For. Res. 6: 475-477.

87. Smith, D. E., A. L. Shigo, L. O. Safford, and R. Blanchard. 1976. Resistances to a pulsed electric current reveal differences between nonreleased, released, and released-fertilized paper birch trees. For. Sci. 22: 471-472.

88. Solomon, D. and A. L. Shigo. 1976. Discoloration and decay associated with pruning wounds on yellow birch. For. Sci. 22: 391-392.

89. Shigo, A. L. 1976. Communication of knowledge and needs between researcher and arboriculturist. J. Arboric. 2: 206-208.

90. Shigo, A. L. and C. L. Wilson. 1977. Wound dressings on red maple and American elm: Effectiveness after 5 years. J. Arboric. 3: 81-87.

91. Shigo, A. L. 1977. Injection wounds in elm. National Arborist Assoc. Symposium No. 1. The Current State of the Art of Dutch elm disease control. Washington, DC November 9-10. 1977.

92. Shigo, A. L., W. C. Shortle, and P. W. Garrett. 1977. Compartmentalization of discolored wood and decayed wood associated with injection-type wounds in hybrid poplar. J. Arboric. 3: 114-118.

93. Shigo, A. L., W. C. Shortle, and P. W. Garrett. 1977. Genetic control suggested in compartmentalization of discolored wood associated with tree wounds. For. Sci. 23: 179-182.

94. Shortle, W. C., A. L. Shigo, P. Berry, and J. Abusamra. 1977. Electrical resistance in tree cambium zone: Relationship to rates of growth and wound closure. For Sci. 23: 326-329.

95. Pottle, H. W., A. L. Shigo, and R. O. Blanchard. 1977. Biological control of wound hymenomycetes by Trichoderma harzianum. Plant Disease Reporter. 61: 687-690.

96. Shigo, A. L. 1977. Phialophora melinii: Effects of inoculations in wounded red maple. Phytopathology 67: 1333-1337.

97. Shigo, A. L. 1977. Superior tree production fights tree wound fatalities. Amer. Nurseryman 12: 10-11.

98. Shigo, A. L. 1977. A new look at tree care. Arboric. Jrnl. 3: 157-164.

99. Shigo, A. L., W. C. Shortle, and J. Ochrymowych. 1977. Shigometer method for detection of active decay at groundline in utility poles. Manual For. Serv. Gen. Tech. Rept. NE-35.

100. Shigo, A. L., N. Rogers, E. A. McGinnes, and D. Funk. 1978. Black walnut strip mine spoils: Some observations 25 years after pruning. USDA For. Serv. Res. Pap. NE-393. 14 p.

101. Shigo, A. L. and H. Marx. 1977. CODIT (Compartmentalization of decay in trees). Agric. Inf. Bull. 405. 73 p.

102. Shigo, A. L. 1977. Communication of knowledge and needs between forest researchers and practicing foresters. Northern Logger and Timber Processor 25: 7-8.

409

103. Shigo, A. L. and R. Campana. 1977. Discolored and decayed wood associated with injection wounds in American elm. J. Arboric. 3: 230-235.

104. Shigo, A. L. and W. C. Shortle. 1977. "New" ideas in tree care. J. Arboric. 3: 1-6.

105. Shigo, A. L., W. E. Money, and D. Dodds. 1977. Some internal effects of Mauget tree injections. J. Arboric. 3: 213-220.

106. Felix, R. and A. L. Shigo. 1977. Rots and rods. J. Arboric. 3: 187-190.

107. McGinnes, E. A., J. E. Phelps. P. S. Szopa, and A. L. Shigo. 1977. Wood anatomy after tree injury -A pictorial study. University of Missouri, Columbia Res. Bull. 1025. 35 p.

108. Blanchard, R., D. Smith, A. Shigo, and L. Safford. 1978. Effects of soil applied potassium on cation distribution around wounds in red maple. Can: J. For. Res. 8: 228-231.

109. Shigo, A. L. 1978. Tree decay: Time to expand the concept. IUFRO Proc. Kassell, Germany. 298-305.

110. Shortle, W. C., A. L. Shigo, and J. Ochrymowych. 1978. Patterns of resistance to a pulsed electric current in sound and decayed utility poles. For. Prod. Jrnl. 28: 48-51.

111. Walters, R. and A. L. Shigo. 1978. Discoloration and decay associated with paraformaldehyde treated tapholes in sugar maple. Can. J. For. Res. 8: 54-60.

112. Garrett, P. W. and A. L. Shigo. 1978. Selecting trees for their response to wounding. METRIA 1: 69-72.

113. Shortle, W. C. and A. L. Shigo. 1978. Effect of plastic wrap on wound closure and internal compartmentalization of discolored and decayed wood in red maple. Plant Disease Reporter. 62: 999-1002.

114. Collins, W. M., A. L. Shigo, and T. P. McGrail. 1978. RSV-induced tumors in chickens: resistance to a pulsed current in terminal and non-terminal types. Poultry Sci. 57: 1478-1481.

115. Shigo, A. L. 1978. Dealing with decay factors in our urban forests. Weeds, Trees, and Turf 17: 14-18.

116. Schmitt, D., P. Garrett, and A. Shigo. 1978. Decay resistant hardwoods? You bet! Northern Logger and Timber Processor 27: 20-21, 30-31.

117. Walters, R. S., and A. L. Shigo. 1978. Tapholes in sugar maples. What happens in a tree. For. Serv. Gen. Tech. Rept. NE-47. 12 p. illus.

118. Shigo, A. L., A. E. McGinnes, D. Funk, and N. Rogers. 1979. Internal defects associated with pruned and nonpruned branch stubs in black walnut. For. Serv. Res. Pap. NE-440. 27 p.

119. Shigo, A. L. 1979. Tree decay: An expanded concept. Agric. Bull. 419. 73 p.

120. Shigo, A. L. 1979. How to minimize the injury caused by injection wounds in trees. Proc. of Symp. on Systemic Chemical Treatments in tree culture. October 9-11, 1978. Michigan State Univ., East Lansing, MI.

121. Mulhern, J., W. Shortle, and A. L. Shigo. 1979. Barrier zones in red maple: An optical and scanning microscope examination. For. Sci. 25: 311-316.

122. Shigo, A. L. 1979. Decay resistant trees. Proc. of the 26th Northeastern Tree Improvement Conf. 64-72.

123. Garrett, P. W., W. K. Randall, A. L. Shigo, and W. C. Shortle. 1979. Inheritance of compartmentalization of wounds in sweetgum (Liquidambar styraciflua L.) and Eastern cottonwood (Populus deltoides Bartr.). For. Serv. Res. Pap. NE-443. 4 p.

124. Eckstein, D., W. Liese, and A. L. Shigo. 1979. Relationship of wood structure to compartmentalization of discolored wood in hybrid poplar. Can. J. For. Res. 9: 205-210.

125. Davis, W., A. L. Shigo, and R. Weyrick. 1979. Seasonal changes in electrical resistance of inner bark in red oak, red maple, and eastern white pine. For. Sci. 25: 282-286.

126. Shigo, A. L. and Walter C. Shortle. 1979. Compartmentalization of discolored wood in heartwood of red oak. Phytopathology 69: 710-711.

127. Shigo, A. L. 1979. Compartmentalization of decay associated with Heterobasidion annosum in roots of Pinus resinosa. Eur. J. For. Pathol. 9: 341-347.

128. Shigo, A. L. 1979. Science communication: Process and problems. Proc. Nat'l. Agric. Sci. Information Conf. Ames, IA October 22-26, 1979. 4-11.

129. Merrill, W. and A. L. Shigo. 1979. An expanded concept of tree decay. Phytopathology 69. 1158-1161.

130. Shigo, A. L. 1979. Patterns of discolored and decayed wood in black walnut. USDA For. Serv. Gen. Tech. Rept. NC-52. 88-93. Walnut insect and diseases. Workshop Proc.

410

131. Tippett, J. and A. L. Shigo. 1980. Barrier zone anatomy in red pine roots invaded by Heterobasidion annosum. Can. J. For. Res. 10: 224-232.

132. Shigo, A. L., R. Campana, F. Hyland, and J. Andersen. 1980. Anatomy of injected elms to control Dutch elm disease. J. Arboric. 6: 96-100.

133. Shigo, A. L. and F. G. Hawksworth. 1980. A dwarf mistletoe on red spruce in New Hampshire. For. Notes. Fall 1980.

134. Hawksworth, F. and A. L. Shigo. 1980. Dwarf mistletoe on red spruce in the White Mountains of New Hampshire. Plant Disease Reporter. 64: 880-882.

135. Shigo, A. L. 1980. Branches. J. Arboric. 6: 300-304.

136. Shigo, A. L. and R. Felix. 1980. Cabling and bracing. J. Arboric. 6: 5-9.

137. Bauch, J., A. L. Shigo, and M. Starck. 1980. Wound effects in the xylem of Acer and Betula species. Holzforschung 34: 153-160.

138. Owens, C. W., W. C. Shortle, and A. L. Shigo. 1980. Preliminary evaluation of Silicon Tetrachloride as a wood preservative. Holzforschung 34: 223-225.

139. Davis, W., W. C. Shortle, and A. L. Shigo. 1980. A potential hazard rating system for fir stands infested with budworm using cambial electrical resistance. Can. J. For. Res. 10: 541-544.

140. Shigo, A. L. 1981. To paint or not to paint. In: Handbook on Pruning. Brooklyn Botanical Gardens Plants and Gardens. Vol. 37: 20-22.

141. Shigo, A. L. 1981. Proper pruning of tree branches. In: The Garden. Vol. 106: 471-473.

142. Tippett, J. T. and A. L. Shigo. 1981. Barriers to decay in conifer roots. Eur. J. For. Pathol. 11: 51-59.

143. Mulhern, J. E., B. M. Stavish, S. L. Witkowski, W. C. Shortle, and A. L. Shigo. 1981. Voltage changes along geranium petioles after leaf blade excision. J. Experimental Bot. 22: 573-579.

144. Green, D., W. C. Shortle, and A. L. Shigo. 1981. Compartmentalization of discolored and decayed wood in red maple branch stubs. For. Sci. 27: 519-522.

145. Armstrong, J. E., A. L. Shigo, D. T. Funk, E. A. McGinnes, and D. E. Smith. 1981. A macroscopic and microscopic study of compartmentalization and wound closure after mechanical wounding of black walnut trees. Wood and Fiber 13: 275-291.

146. Shigo, A. L. and J. T. Tippett. 1981. Compartmemtalization of decayed wood associated with Armillaria mellea in several tree species. For. Serv. Res. Pap. NE-488. 20 p.

147. Ostrofsky, A. and A. L. Shigo. 1981. A myxomycete isolated from discolored wood of living red maple. Mycologia 73: 997-1000.

148. Butin, H. and A. L. Shigo. 1981. Radial shakes and "frost cracks" in living oak trees. For. Serv. Res. Pap. NE-478. 21 p.

149. Tippett, J. T. and A. L. Shigo. 1981. Barrier zone formation: A mechanism of tree defense against vascular pathogens. IAWA Bull. Vol.2: 163-168.

150. Leben, C., A. L. Shigo, and T. H. Hall. 1982. A method for evaluating tree wound treatment. Can. J. For. Res.12: 115-117.

151. Shigo, A. L. 1982. Tree health. J. Arboric. 8: 311-316.

152. Shigo, A. L. 1982. A pictorial primer for proper pruning. For. Notes. Spring issue. 18-21.

153. Shigo, A. L. 1982. Trees: How they build up and break down. In: Trees. 57-69. Published by Men of the Trees, Crawley, Sussex, England.

154. Shigo, A. L. Wood decay: In: Encyclopedia of Science and Technology. 5th Ed. New York. McGraw-Hill. 680-683.

155. Shigo, A. L. 1980. Trees resistant to spread of decay associated with wounds. In: Proc. of Third International Workshop on the Genetics of Host Parasite Interactions in Forestry; Wageningen, The Netherlands. September 14-21, 1980.

156. Shigo, A. L. and K. Dudzik. 1982. Chestnut blight: Defense reactions. Proc. of the USDA For. Serv. Am. Chestnut Cooperators Meeting. January 5-7, 1982. Morgantown, West Virginia.

157. Shigo, A. L. 1982. Tree decay in our urban forests: What can be done about it? Plant Disease 66: 763-768.

158. Shigo, A. L. and C. L. Wilson. 1982. Wounds in peach trees. Plant Disease 66: 895-897.

159. Shigo, A. L. 1982. Dutch elm disease: A CODIT perspective. Proc. Dutch elm disease Symp. and Workshop. October 5-9, 1981. Winnipeg, Manitoba, Canada. 151-168.

160. Shigo, A. L. 1982. Injections and injury. Proc. Dutch elm disease Symp. and Workshop. October 5-9, 1981. Winnipeg, Manitoba, Canada. 483-485.

411

161. Tippett, J. T., A. L. Bogle, and A. L. Shigo. 1983. Response to balsam fir and hemlock roots to injuries. Eur. J. For. Pathol. 2: 357-364.

162. Shigo, A. L. 1983. Targets for proper tree care. J. Arboric. 9: 285-294.

163. Shigo, A. L. and W. C. Shortle. 1983. Wound dressings: Results of studies over 13 years. J. Arboric. 9: 317-329.

164. Shigo, A. L. 1982. Tree decay. Proc. of Korea-USA Joint Seminar on Forest Diseases and Insect Pests. September 22-30, 1982. 188-203.

165. Shigo, A. L., D. Dorn, and H. C. Lee. 1983. Selections of maple and birch trees with high resistance to spread of decay associated with wounds. Proc. of NE Forest Tree Improvement Conf. July 7-9, 1983. University of New Hampshire. 110-117.

166. Shigo, A. L. and K. Roy. 1983. Violin woods: A new look. University of New Hampshire, Durham, NH. 67 p.

167. Shigo, A. L. 1983. The relationship between better trees and better wood products from spruce and fir. Proc. of Conference on utilization technology. August 17-19, 1983. Orono, Maine.

168. Shigo, A. L. 1983. Tree defects: A photo guide. USDA For. Service Gen. Tech. Report. NE-82. 167 p.

169. Shigo, A. L. 1984. Tree decay and pruning. Arboric. Jrnl. 8: 1-12.

170. Shigo, A. L. 1984. The right treatments for troubled trees. Amer. Forests, February issue. 13-16.

171. Rademacher, P., J. Bauch, and A. L. Shigo. 1984. Characteristics of xylem formed after wounding in Acer, Betula, and Fagus. IAWA Bull. n.s. 5(2): 141-151.

172. Ostrofsky, A. and A. L. Shigo. 1984. Relationship between canker size and wood starch in American chestnut. Eur. J. For. Pathol. 14: 65-68.

173. Shigo, A. L. 1984. Trees and discolored wood. In: Development and characteristics of discolored wood. Reprinted from IAWA Bull. 5(2):99. Edited by J. Bauch and P. Baas.

174. Shigo, A. L. 1984. Compartmentalization: A conceptual framework for understanding how trees grow and defend themselves. Ann. Rev. Phytopathology 22: 189-214.

175. Shigo, A. L. 1984. How to assess the defect status of a stand. Northern Journal of Applied Forestry 1(3): 41-49.

176. Peters, M., P. Ossenbruggen, and A. L. Shigo. 1984. Cracking and failure behavior models of defective balsam fir trees. Holzforschung 39: 125-135.

177. Shigo, A. L. 1984. Tree defects: Cluster effect. Northern Journal of Applied Forestry 1(3): 41-49.

178. Shigo, A. L. 1984. Tree survival after injury and infection. Eighth North American Forest Biology Workshop. July 30 - August 1, 1984. Utah State University, Logan, UT 11-24.

179. Shigo, A. L. 1984. Wood problems start in the living tree. Forest Notes, Fall: No. 158: 20-22.

180. Shigo, A. L. 1984. Root rots in trees. Proc. of the Sixth International Conf. on Root and Butt Rots of Forest Trees. G. A. Kile, ed. IUFRO Working Party, CSIRO, Melbourne, Australia. 305-312.

181. Andersen, J. L., R. J. Campana, A. L. Shigo, and W. C. Shortle. 1985. Wound response of Ulmus americana L. Results of chemical injection in attempts to control Dutch elm disease. J. Arboric. 11(5): 137-142.

182. DeGraaf, R. M. and A. L. Shigo. 1985. Managing cavity trees for wildlife in the Northeast. USDA For. Serv. Gen. Tech. Rep. NE-101. 21 p.

183. Ossenbruggen, P. J., M. Peters, and A. L. Shigo. 1985. Potential failure of a decayed tree under wind loading. Wood and Fiber 18 (1): 39-48.

184. Shigo, A. L. 1985. Stress and death of trees. Society of American Foresters Region VI Technical Conference. USDA For. Serv. Gen. Tech. Rep. NE-99: 31-38.

185. Shigo, A. L. 1985. Compartmentalization of decay in trees. Scientific American 252(4): 96-103.

186. Shigo, A. L. 1985. How tree branches are attached to trunks. Can. J. Bot. 63: 1391-1401.

187. Shigo, A. L. 1985. How trees survive after injury and infection. Proc. of the 1984 Stone Fruit Tree Decline Workshop. Appalachian Fruit Research Station, Kearneysville, WV.

188. Shigo, A. L. and K. R. Dudzik. 1985. Response of uninjured cambium to xylem injury. Wood Science and Technology 19: 6 p.

189. Shigo, A. L. and Walter C. Shortle. 1985. Shigometry — A Reference Guide. USDA, For. Serv. Agric. Handbook No. 646, 48 p.

190. Tower, L., A. L. Shigo, and E. Brennan. 1985. The short-term effect of simulated acidic rainfall on the formation of discolored wood in Acer rubrum. J. Arboric. 11(7): 197-199.

191. Shigo, A. L. 1985. Wounded forests, starving trees. J. Forestry 83: 668-673.

192. Shigo, A. L. 1986. Tree decay. Int. J. Tropical Plant diseases 4: 95-121.

193. Shigo, A. L. 1986. Journey to the center of a tree. American Forests 92: 18-22, 46-47.

194. Shigo, A., G. F. Gregory, R. J. Campana, K. R. Dudzik, and D. M. Zimel. 1986. Patterns of starch reserves in healthy and diseased American elms. Can. J. For. Res. 16: 204-210.

195. Shigo, A. L. 1986. A New Tree Biology. Shigo and Trees, Associates, Durham, New Hampshire. 595 p.

196. Shigo, A. L. 1986. A New Tree Biology Dictionary. Shigo and Trees, Associates, Durham, New Hampshire. 132 p.

197. Shigo, A. L., K. Vollbrecht, and N. Hvass. 1987. Tree Biology and Tree Care. SITAS - Skovvej 56, Ballerup, Denmark, (published also in German, Swedish, Danish, Dutch, French, and Italian).

198. Shigo, A. L. 1987. New tree health. Shigo and Trees, Associates, Durham, New Hampshire. 10 p. (Published in French, Italian, Dutch, and Spanish).

199. Shigo, A. L. 1988. A new tree biology. Annual Journal, Royal New Zealand Institute of Horticulture 15: 51-57.

200. Shigo, A. L. 1988. Branch failures: a closer look at crack drying. J. Arboric. 14: (in press).

413

INDEX

414

416

Microelements, 173, 216, 218, 244, 384, 386
Microorganisms, 70, 245, 268
Migratory birds, 152
Mind, muscle, money, 346
Misfits, 270
Mistletoe, 340
Mites, 156
Mobile battery, 200
Modern Arboriculture, 23, 28, 258
Modesto ash, 175
Mold, black sooty, 177
Mole, 246
Molecular biology, 19, 198
Monocots, 314
Montmorillinite clays, 242
Moss, 150, 172, 340
"Mother Nature", 270
Motion or exercise, 31
Motor, 229
Move, 26
Mulching, 283, 310, 329
Multiple plant, 72, 262
Mushrooms, 251, 255
Musical instrument, 28
Mycoplasma-like organism, 315
Mycorrhizae, 40, 195, 222, 236, 241, 251, 252,
    253, 254, 262, 263, 271, 283, 289, 299, 313,
    329
NAA-naphthalene acetic acid, 34, 230
Natural forest, 43, 46, 266
Natural systems, 22, 24, 27, 59, 74
Natural target pruning, 92
Nectararies, 85
Needles, 219
    diseases, 179
Negligence, 359
Nematodes, 157
New plantings, 307
Newsletter, 358
Niche, 70, 250
Nickel, 244
Nitrate, 252
    anion, 234, 236
Nitrogen, 232, 239, 244, 272, 295
    -based substances, 385
    pathway, 236
    reserves, 266
No absolutes, 33
Nodes, alternate, opposite, whorled, branch, 39
Nodules, 252
Noise, 354
Non-biodegradeable strings, 308
Nonresinous wood, 52
Nonspecific dynamic process, 384
Nutrient, 243
Nutrition, proper, 31
Nuts, 118
Oak, 34, 174
    wilt, 159
"off site", 42

Ohmmeter, 274
Oils, 228
Old arboriculture, 18, 292, 346
Old branch core, 64
    "old age pension", 46
    trees, 46
    trees, dignity, 10
Olives, 34
Onset of growth, 268
Orchids, 340
Order, maintain, 256
Organic matter, 255
    molecules, 234, 244, 245
Organs, 262
Oscillating seesaw system, 298
Osmotic pressure, 220, 226, 247
Ovary, 34
Overpruning, 115
    palms, 316
Overfertilization, 254
Overtapping, 58
Ovule, 34
Oxygen, 243
    bonds, 242
Palisade layer, 219
Palms, 314
Paraformaldehyde pills, 58, 65
Parasites, 206
    obligate, 136
    plants, 340
Parenchyma, 50, 273
    cells, 47, 49
Parenchyma, axial, 51, 54, 57, 60, 61, 224
    contact, 58
    marginal axial, 50
Parenchyma, radial, 51, 55, 58, 61, 224
Park design, 304
    manager, 355
Particles, 191
Pathogens, 139, 206, 252, 260, 265, 268, 299
    wetwood, 184
Patterns, boundary, 82
    phenological, 269
People touching trees, 12
Peptides, 234
Perfect machine, 258, 261
Perfect system, 261
Periclinal plane, 62
Periderm, 53
Perpetual motion machine, 257
Pesticides, 215
Petals, 34
Petiole, 35
pH, 384
    scale, 246
    soils, 291
Phellinus tremulae, 176
Phelloderm, 53
Phellogen, 53, 54, 56, 60
Phellum, 53

419

Phenol-based substances, 90, 388
Phenological periods, 271
Phenology, 268
Philosophy, 20, 350
Phloem, 49, 50, 51, 52, 180
    companion cells, 224
    fibers, 224
    rays, 54
    transport, 224, 226
Phosphorus, 195, 244, 251
Photons, 191, 192, 200, 231
Photosynthate, 87, 224, 226
Photosynthesis, 193, 196, 219, 231, 243
    and light, 198
Photosynthetic period, 268
Physics, 30
Physiology, 387
Pin oak, 43
Pinaceae, 341
Pine, 34
Pinning, 280
Pioneer invaders, 387
Pioneer species, 40
Pioneers, 70, 388
Pistil, 34
Pith, 35, 52, 300
Pits, 56
Plane tree, 351
    canker *(Ceratocystis fimbriata),* 125
    problems, 117
Plantations, 372
Planting on a mound, 284
    problems, 308
    site, 282
Plasmodesmata, 54
Plasmolysis, 248, 249
Plastic wrap, 150
Platanus, 326
Plots, permanent inventory, 372
Plugs, 58
Points of meristematic tissue, 89
Polar molecule, 221
    organic urea, 236
Pollarding, 116
Pollen, 34
Polyene, 238
Polypeptides, 234
Polysaccharide, 53, 147
Poplar, 34, 174
Populus, 40, 386
    tremuloides, 83, 143, 176
Porcupines, 152
Porous, diffuse, 50
Potassium, 220, 244
Potential energy, 230, 231, 264, 265, 271
Power lines, 302
    rights-of-way, 345
Presentations, 356
Priestly, 271
Professional, 24, 32

Progress, 29
Projects, 364
    individual, 360
    long term, 362
Protection, 230
    wood, 64, 384, 386
    wood summary, 189
    wood, age-altered, 47
    zone, 90, 91, 257
    zone, branch, 185, 189
Protective guards, 152
Proteins, 259
    -based molecules, 216
Protoplasm, 49, 248
Pruning, 114, 116
    codominant stem, 108, 109
    correct, 230
    dose, 131
    first order, 120
    natural directional, 122
    natural target, 92, 94
    near electric utility lines, 119
    palms, 316
    root, 290
    second order, 121
    shrubs, 138
    third order, 124
    wounds, 173
Pull out, branch, 325
Pumps, 206, 224
Quercus alba, 275
Quercus robur, 275
Quercus rubra, 275
Radial, 47
    connections, 60
    parenchyma, 51, 58
    view, 48, 53, 55
Radio waves, 194
Ram's horn, 137, 185
Ray, 50, 51, 56, 58, 59
    initials, 60
    medullary, 59
    phloem, 54
Rays, wood, 54, 59
Reaction wood, 63, 388
    zone, 181, 189
Reactions, chemical, 191
    from heat, 191
Receptacle, 34
Recipes, 346
Recognition, 67
Records, 345, 346
Recycle, 255, 263, 264, 266, 295, 298
Red heart, 386
Removal, 351
    dead branch, 102
    older trees, 307
Removing, 332
Reproduction, 196, 230
Reproductive parts, 228, 262, 263

421

Kicking and Screaming
they resisted being
dragged from the shadows of the cave
out into the light of
understanding.

Plato — Cave Allegory

MODERN ARBORICULTURE IN PRACTICE

Phoenix Park, Dublin, Ireland is one of the largest and oldest parks in Europe. Park Director John McCullen and assistant Noel O'Shea have developed a tree maintenance program based on the concepts given in this book.